FOCUS ON SICKLE CELL RESEARCH

FOCUS ON SICKLE CELL RESEARCH

RALPH L. PLASMAR
EDITOR

Nova Biomedical Books
New York

Production Coordinator: Donna Dennis
Coordinating Editor: Tatiana Shohov
Senior Production Editors: Susan Boriotti and Donna Dennis
Production Editors: Marius Andronie and Rusudan Razmadze
Office Manager: Annette Hellinger
Graphics: Levani Chlaidze
Editorial Production: Maya Columbus, Aloysha Klestov, Vladimir Klestov,
Matthew Kozlowski and Lorna Loperfido
Circulation: Ave Maria Gonzalez, Vera Popovic, Luis Aviles, Jonathan Boriotti, Alexandra Columbus,
Raymond Davis, Cathy DeGregory, Melissa Diaz, Magdalena Nuñez, Marlene Nuñez,
Jeannie Pappas and Frankie Punger
Communications and Acquisitions: Serge P. Shohov

Library of Congress Cataloging-in-Publication Data
Focus on sickle cell research / Ralph L. Plasmar, editor.
p. cm.
Includes index.
ISBN 1-59033-920-7 (hardcover)
1. Sickle cell anemia.
[DNLM: 1. Anemia, Sickle Cell. WH 170 F652 2003] I. Plasmar, Ralph L.
RC641.7.S5F63 2003
616.1'527--dc22 2003028116

An imprint of Nova Science Publishers, Inc.
400 Oser Ave, Suite 1600
Hauppauge, New York 11788-3619
Tele. 631-231-7269Fax 631-231-8175
e-mail: Novascience@earthlink.net
Web Site: http://www.novapublishers.com

Printed in the United States of America

CONTENT

PREFACE

Sickle cell anemia is an inherited blood disorder, characterized primarily by chronic anemia and periodic episodes of pain and occurring in approximately 1 in every 400 African-American infants born in the United States each year. Individuals of Mediterranean, Arabian, Caribbean, South and Central American, and East Indian ancestry can also be affected. The underlying problem involves hemoglobin, a component of the red cells in the blood. The hemoglobin molecules in each red blood cell carry oxygen from the lungs to the body organs and tissues and bring back carbon dioxide to the lungs. In sickle cell anemia, the hemoglobin is defective. After the hemoglobin molecules give up their oxygen, some of them may cluster together and form long, rod-like structures. These structures cause the red blood cells to become stiff and to assume a sickle shape. Unlike normal red cells, which are usually smooth and donut-shaped, the sickled red cells cannot squeeze through small blood vessels. Instead, they stack up and cause blockages that deprive the organs and tissue of oxygen-carrying blood. This process produces the periodic episodes of pain and ultimately can damage the tissues and vital organs and lead to other serious medical problems. Unlike normal red blood cells, which last about 120 days in the bloodstream, sickled red cells die after only about 10 to 20 days. Because they cannot be replaced fast enough, the blood is chronically short of red blood cells, a condition called anemia. Sickle cell anemia is caused by an error in the gene that tells the body how to make hemoglobin. The defective gene tells the body to make the abnormal hemoglobin that results in deformed red blood cells. This book gathers the latest research in this important field.

In: Focus on Sickle Cell Research
Editor: Ralph L. Plasmar, pp. 1-17
ISBN 1-59033-920-7

Chapter I

ENERGY AND PROTEIN METABOLISM IN SICKLE CELL DISEASE: EVIDENCE OF ABERRATIONS

Andrea C. Buchholz and Maciej S. Buchowski
Department of Medicine, Division of Gastroenterology, Hepatology and Nutrition, Vanderbilt University Medical Center and Department of Family and Community Medicine, Meharry Medical College
Nashville, TN

ABBREVIATIONS

kcal	kilocalorie
RBC	Red blood cell
REE	Resting energy expenditure
SCA	Sickle cell anemia
SCD	Sickle cell disease

SICKLE CELL DISEASE: BACKGROUND

Sickle cell disease is a collective term describing a group of conditions in which pathology is attributed to the presence of sickle hemoglobin. Sickle hemoglobin is the result of a glutamic acid-to-valine mutation at amino acid position six in the β globin chain [63]. The term *sickle cell disease* (SCD) applies to all individuals with at least one sickle hemoglobin chain and one other abnormal β globin chain. The most common form is *sickle cell anemia* (SCA), which accounts for 60% to 70% of SCD in the U.S. [38] and affects more than 50,000 Americans, primarily those of African origin. SCA results from inheritance of the sickle hemoglobin gene from both parents and is characterized by the production of more than 90% sickle hemoglobin. Other abnormal hemoglobin genes inherited with sickle hemoglobin may also cause SCD. These include hemoglobin C (common in West Africa), β^+

thalassemia and β° thalassemia, the clinical severity of which vary, in part, with the amount of normal hemoglobin produced and the degree of anemia. However, SCA has the most severe clinical manifestations of any of the SCD variants.

The hallmark of SCD is the sickling of red blood cells (RBCs), the latter of which are normal in appearance when oxygenated in the lung but which become sickled when deoxygenated in peripheral capillary beds. Sickling occurs due to the polymerization and aggregation of the four globin chains of sickle hemoglobin, with the resulting rigid polymer causing the RBC to become elongated and misshapen. This structural change damages the RBC membrane and drastically reduces the lifespan of the RBC [63], leading to a normocytic, normochromic hemolytic anemia. It also compromises the ability of the RBCs to flow through fine capillaries, causing vasoocclusion. Eventually, vasoocclusion leads to tissue hypoxia resulting in bone, tissue and organ damage, as well as accelerated whole-body atrophy similar to that occurring during the normal aging process [26]. Common clinical manifestations associated with SCD are infection, inflammation, painful vasoocclusive crises, acute chest syndrome, stroke, splenic sequestrations and functional asplenia, and aplastic crises, all of which are important causes of morbidity and mortality throughout the lifespan. Therefore, life expectancy of males and females with SCA in the U.S. is significantly reduced, averaging 42 and 48 years, respectively [20].

At a more fundamental level, SCD is also associated with increased energy metabolism. Energy is constantly expended by the body to perform physical work, maintain concentration gradients, fuel biochemical cycles and transport, synthesize, degrade and replace cell constituents. Indirect evidence of hypermetabolism early in life is provided by the widely reported delays in growth and development seen in children with SCD. Weight-for-age, height-for-age, weight-for-height and/or tricep z scores as well as fat-free mass and fat mass are lower in children with SCA than race- and sex-matched healthy controls [7]. The impaired growth and development are most likely caused by the diversion of energy and/or protein from normal uses towards supporting disease-specific processes. This chapter will review the current state of knowledge of disturbances in energy and protein metabolism in the sickle cell population. These disturbances and their known and proposed mechanisms are summarized in **Figure 1**.

EVIDENCE OF HYPERMETABOLISM IN SICKLE CELL DISEASE

Resting energy expenditure (REE) is the minimum level of energy expended by the body to sustain basic physiologic functions such as heartbeat, respiration, and muscle contraction and function [31]. It accounts for approximately 60% to 65% of total daily energy expenditure. REE can be determined using indirect calorimetry, which measures respiratory gas exchange (oxygen consumption and carbon dioxide production), and is typically expressed in kilocalories (kcals) per day.

Figure 1. Sickle cell disease is a model of chronically elevated protein turnover and resting energy expenditure. Dotted lines represent hypothetical associations. See text for details of model.

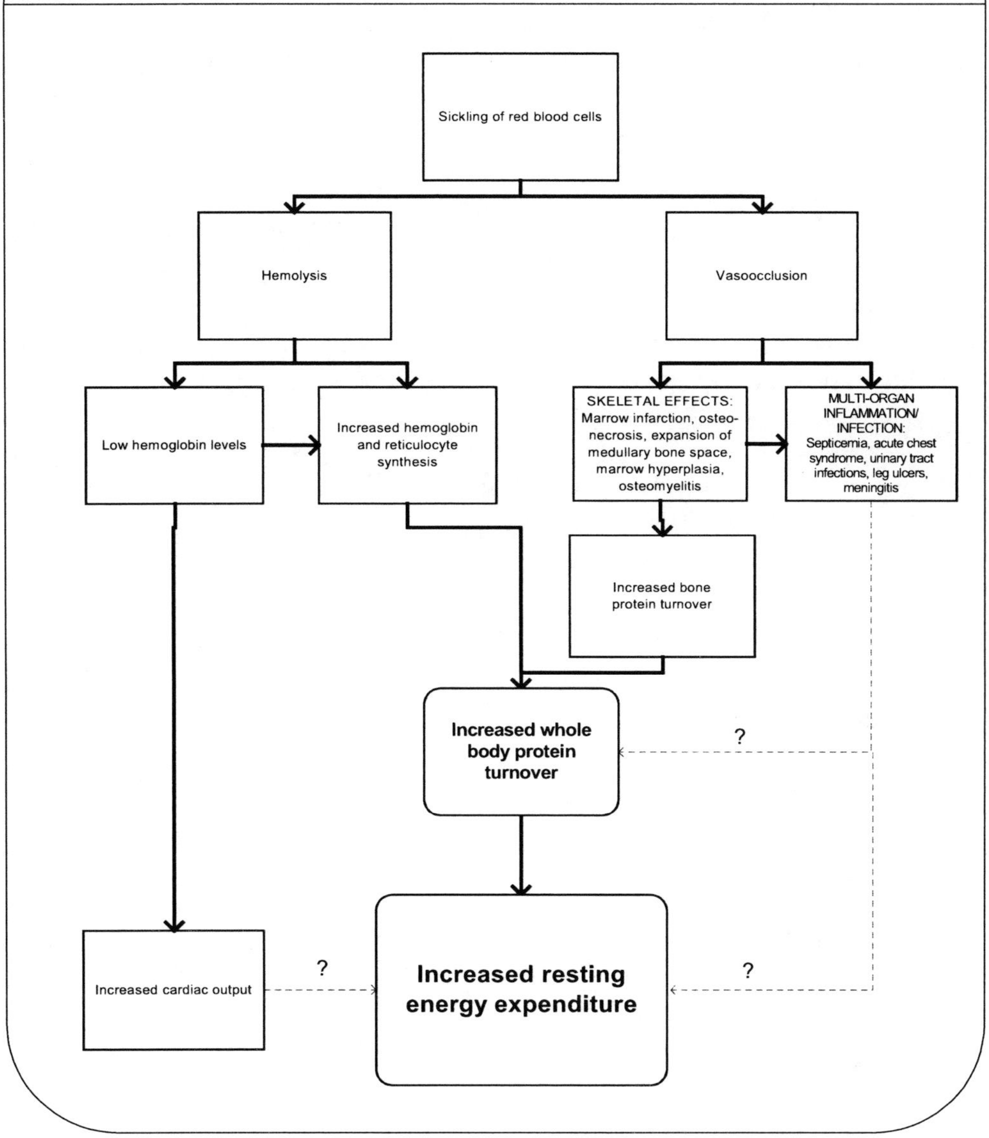

Elevated REE has been associated with depressed growth in such pediatric populations as cystic fibrosis [68, 76] and hepatic disease [72], likely due to the diversion of energy to disease-specific processes. SCD appears to follow a similar hypermetabolic pattern. Measured REE is 3.4% to 17% higher in subjects with SCA vs. controls [3, 7, 50, 57, 58]. When adjusted for differences in fat-free mass between groups, the difference in REE between subjects with SCD and controls increases to 7.4% to 46.4% [7, 17, 19, 50, 57, 58]. The reason for the greater difference in REE after adjustment for fat-free mass is known. The fat-free mass of the body, which includes skeletal muscle, organs and extracellular mass (skeleton, cartilage, connective tissue, lymph and plasma), has been found to explain 70 to

85% of the variance in REE in healthy males and females [1, 15, 23]. The high energy expenditure of fat-free mass is due to the numerous high-energy processes which occur in skeletal muscle and organs, especially the liver, brain and kidney. These processes include ion pumps, synthesis and degradation of cell constituents, biochemical cycles (eg. glucose phosphorylation in the liver), and leakage of protons across mitochondrial membranes. Because subjects with SCD have less fat-free mass than healthy controls [6], adjusting energy expenditure per unit of fat-free mass provides a more accurate estimate of energy expenditure than does unadjusted REE. The fact that REE is elevated, *even after adjustment for fat-free mass and irrespective of age*, indicates that persons with SCD may be in a chronic state of hypermetabolism. Data from these studies are summarized in **Table 1**. Only studies on free-living subjects in steady state, in which energy expenditure was adjusted for differences in body composition between groups, are included in the table.

Table 1. Summary of Evidence of Hypermetabolism in Sickle Cell Disease[a]

Authors	Population[b]	Results	P value
Buchowski et al., 2002 [19]	28 adolescents with steady-state SCA (15.6±1.5 years) and 22 control adolescents (15.9±1.6 years)	FFM- and sex-adjusted REE 214 kcal/d >in SCA	<0.0001
Barden et al., 2000 [7]	36 children with SCA (11.3±3.8 years) and 30 control children (11.2±3.2 years)	FFM-and sex-adjusted REE 11.2% > in SCA	0.001
Buchowski et al., 2000 [17]	37 subjects with SCD (12 boys 15.4±1.6 years; 10 men 30.6±7.0 years; 8 girls 15.4±1.5 years; 7 women 25.6±4.7 years) compared with 37 control subjects (11 boys 14.9±1.3 years; 11 men 25.0±4.7 years; 9 girls 15.4±1.4 years; 6 women 23.5±1.1 years)	REE/kg FFM was 9.0% > in SCA boys than control boys 7.4% > in SCA men than control men 46.4% > in SCA girls than control girls 23.0% > in SCA women than control women	All <0.05
Singhal et al., 1997 [58]	16 male adolescents with SCA (18.3±0.9 years) and 16 male control adolescents (18.0±1.1 years)	Lean-body-mass adjusted REE 335 kcal/day >in SCA	NS
Salman et al., 1996 [50]	8 children with steady-state SCA (11.2±0.4 years 4M, 4F) and 7 control children (11.3±0.4 years; 5M, 2F).	FFM-adjusted REE 16.7% >in SCA	<0.01
Singhal et al., 1993 [57]	20 adolescents with SCA (median age=16.2 years, range 15.0-17.3 years; 8M, 12F) and 20 control adolescents (median age=16.2 years, range 15.0-17.4 years; 8M, 12 F)	Median REE/kg lean body mass 14.3%>in SCA	0.002

[a]only studies on free-living subjects in steady state, for which energy expenditure was adjusted for differences in fat-free mass between groups, are included in the table

[b]age reported as mean ± SD unless otherwise noted

In the absence of indirect calorimetry, REE can be predicted using well-recognized equations developed by Harris and Benedict [34], Schofield [52] and the World Health Organization [75] in healthy males and females. The equations probably most commonly used in the clinical setting are those of Harris and Benedict. Prediction of REE, in kcals per day, is based on weight (in kilograms), height (in centimeters) and age (in years), as follows:

$$\text{Males} = 66 + (13.7 \times \text{weight}) + (5 \times \text{height}) - (6.8 \times \text{age})$$
$$\text{Females} = 655 + (9.6 \times \text{weight}) + (1.7 \times \text{height}) - (4.7 \times \text{age})$$

However, such equations significantly underestimate REE in SCD by 9% to 17% [18, 29, 74]. For example, Buchowski et al. [18] showed that the Harris and Benedict equations significantly underestimated measured REE by a mean 222±124 kcals per day in adolescents with SCA. The reason for the poor predictive ability of such equations is due, in part, to the fact that body composition of many clinical populations differs from that of the individuals in which the equations were originally validated. As well, underlying disease processes that may affect energy metabolism are not accounted for in equations validated in healthy subjects with normal energy metabolism. The result is a significant over or underprediction of energy expenditure, as has been demonstrated in clinical populations including cirrhosis [40], central nervous system impairment [5], anorexia nervosa [2], chronic spinal cord injury [14], and HIV [53]. This phenomenon points to the importance of using population-specific prediction equations when possible, as the ability to more accurately predict energy expenditure may help clinicians better meet nutritional requirements of their patients with SCA.

To address this issue, two studies in the literature developed equations specific to the sickle cell population [18, 74]. Williams et al. [74] studied 18 boys and girls with SCA, ranging in age from six to 11 years. Buchowski et al. [18] studied 37 male and female adolescents with SCA, ranging in age from 14 to 18 years. In both studies, REE was measured using indirect calorimetry. The resulting sex-specific equations, shown in **Table 2**, include weight and/or height and/or age, and all include hemoglobin as a negative predictor variable. When Williams et al. applied their modified equations to an independent group of 20 children with SCA, the mean difference between measured and predicted REE was less than 1% ($P \geq 0.6$). Although Buchowski et al. did not prospectively test their new equations in an independent group of adolescents with SCA, the new equations explained a significant amount of the variance in measured REE (r^2 ranged from 0.76 to 0.86, $P \leq 0.0001$).

Table 2. Equations for predicting resting energy expenditure in the pediatric sickle cell population

Study	Prediction equations[a] (kcals/day)	Performance of equations
Williams et al., 2002 [74]	Modified Harris-Benedict equation Girls: [655+(9.56×weight)+(1.85×height)-(4.68×age)]×(1.3595-0.0242×hemoglobin) Boys: [66.5+(13.75×weight)+(5×height)-(6.76×age)]×(1.3278-0.0242×hemoglobin)	Mean difference between measured and modified $REE_{Harris-Benedict}$=14 kcals/day (P=0.9273)
	Modified WHO equations Girls 3 to 10 years: (499+22.5×weight)×(1.4775-0.0309×hemoglobin) Girls 10 to 18 years: (746+12.2×weight)×(1.4775-0.0309×hemoglobin) Boys 3 to 10 years: (495+22.7×weight)×(1.3074-0.0309×hemoglobin) Boys 10 to 18 years: (651+17.5×weight)×(1.3074-0.0309×hemoglobin)	Mean difference between measured and modified REE_{WHO}=-13 kcals/day (P=0.6215)
Buchowski et al., 2002 [18]	Adolescent females: 1100 + 13.3×weight – 30.2×hemoglobin	R^2 between measured and predicted REE=0.86, $p \leq 0.0001$
	Adolescent males: 1305+18.6×weight-55.7×hemoglobin	R^2 between measured and predicted REE=0.76, $p \leq 0.0001$

[a]Where weight is in kilograms, height is in centimeters, age is in years and hemoglobin is in g/dL

Alterations in Protein Homeostasis as a Cause of Hypermetabolism

Fat-free mass is not the only factor that explains variance in REE. There are a number of disease-specific processes unique to SCD that may contribute to the hypermetabolism commonly seen in this population. One of the most influential of these may be altered protein homeostasis. It has been estimated that approximately 50% of the increase in REE in SCD is accounted for by the enhanced energy cost of protein synthesis [12]. This is due to the fact that considerable energy is expended for peptide bond formation, amino acid transport, protein degradation, urea formation, and excretion of degradation waste products.

Early studies established that serious abnormalities in protein homeostasis exist in SCD. Using three different levels of nitrogen intake, Odonkor et al. [44] demonstrated that daily urinary and fecal nitrogen losses were 8% to 20% and 35% to 216% greater, respectively, in adolescents with SCD compared to age- and sex-matched controls. Daily nitrogen balance was negative in the SCD patients at all levels of nitrogen intake but was positive in the controls. In an effort to define the events leading to impaired protein homeostasis, Waterlow [73] found that whole-body protein turnover was twofold greater in two male subjects with SCD than in a male control subject. Recent research efforts have extended Waterlow's findings. Salman et al. [50] studied eight children with SCA who were free of infection or vasoocclusive disease, and seven control children, both in the postabsorptive state. Each child received a continuous four hour infusion of L-[1-^{13}C]leucine to determine the rate of leucine oxidation and appearance and nonoxidative leucine disposal, and subsequently, whole body protein breakdown and synthesis. Infusion of L-[2-^{15}N]glutamine was used to assess rate of glutamine utilization. This amino acid is a preferred substrate for tissues with rapid rates of cell replication such as reticulocytes and is an important source of nitrogen for synthesis of purines and pyrimidines required in rapidly dividing cells; its turnover has been found to be elevated in adults with SCA [43]. Compared with control subjects, children with SCA had a 58% higher leucine rate of appearance (indicative of increased rates of protein breakdown) and 65% higher nonoxidative leucine disposal (indicative of increased whole body protein synthesis). They also had 47% higher rates of whole body glutamine utilization and 19% higher REE (all $P<0.05$). Further, REE was significantly correlated with rates of leucine appearance, nonoxidative leucine disposal, glutamine rate of appearance and glutamine *de novo* synthesis ($r^2=0.44\text{-}0.55$, all $P<0.01$).

These findings are not unique to the pediatric SCD population. Badaloo et al. [3] found that whole-body protein synthesis was 88% and protein degradation 100% greater (both $P<0.001$) in six adults with SCA compared with six adult control subjects of similar age. Similarly, in our studies of adolescents and adults aged 14 to 50 years, SCD increased rates of whole body protein synthesis by 38% to 49% and breakdown by 32% to 45% (all $P\leq0.05$) [12, 16]. Taken together, these findings indicate that protein turnover is significantly higher in those with SCA, irrespective of age, and that it is associated with increased energy expenditure.

Hematologically-Related Causes of Increased Protein Turnover

Protein turnover is increased in part because of hematological aberrations. The sickling of RBCs results in increased hemolysis, necessitating an increase in reticulocyte and hemoglobin synthesis. Salman et al. [50], as part of the previously mentioned study, found that reticulocyte count was positively related to both glutamine rate of appearance and REE (r^2=0.57 and r^2=0.54, respectively, both P<0.01). And calculations from various studies estimate that hemoglobin synthesis contributes 12% to total protein synthesis in individuals with SCA compared with only 2% to 4% in control subjects [3, 7, 12]. Given the relationship between hemoglobin and protein synthesis, and the relationship between protein turnover and REE, it is not surprising that hemoglobin has been found to be negatively correlated with REE [18, 50, 74].

The effects of such hematological aberrations on protein turnover and REE were further investigated by Badaloo et al. [4] in their study of children with SCD and hypersplenism. Hypersplenism, defined as chronic red cell sequestration with marked splenomegaly [56], is characterized by elevated reticulocyte count, extreme erythropoietic activity in bone marrow and progressive lowering of hemoglobin below steady state levels (usually to 3-5g/dL) [55]. Protein turnover was measured using ^{15}N-glycine and REE by indirect calorimetry before preoperative transfusion and at least eight weeks after splenectomy in six prepubertal children with SCD, aged 5.7 to 10.5 years. Following splenectomy, mean reticulocyte count fell by 61% and hemoglobin levels increased by 94% (both P<0.008). There was a concomitant decrease in protein turnover of 33% and in REE of 15% (both P<0.03), equivalent to an energy saving of 8.1 kcals per kg per day. Further, weight velocity, which was below normal before surgery (z=-2.3), improved significantly after surgery (z=0.7). The authors of this important study concluded that hypersplenism in children with SCA places a substantial demand on protein metabolism and that post splenectomy, energy savings accompany the fall in protein turnover, increasing the likelihood of meeting total requirements for growth and development.

Bone Turnover and Protein Turnover

The skeletal system of the patient with SCD is a frequent target of the consequences of sickling. The most dramatic skeletal effects are marrow infarction [21, 41], osteonecrosis [25, 41], expansion of the medullary bone space [41] and marrow hyperplasia [3], all of which may increase bone turnover and subsequently, protein turnover. Markers of bone turnover include bone-specific alkaline phosphatase (BAP, synthesized by osteoblasts), plasma type I procollagen carboxy-terminal propeptide (PICP, the major collagen produced by osteoblasts during bone formation) and urinary pyridinoline cross-links (PYD, formed from type I collagen during bone resorption). BAP has been found to be 61% higher (P<0.05) in 20 adults with SCD vs. 20 age-matched adult controls [11]. PICP and PYD have been found to be 184% and 133% higher (both P<0.0001), respectively, in 28 adolescents with SCA vs. 26 control subjects [16]. Further, there was a positive linear relationship in the latter study between PICP and whole body protein synthesis after adjustment for FFM and age (r^2=0.92, P<0.0001), as well as between PYD and whole body protein breakdown (r^2=0.91, P<0.0001). Thus, bone turnover and protein turnover appear to be inextricably linked.

Whether the synthesis of other body proteins in SCD is increased has not been reported. However, the multi-organ effects of SCD and magnitude of increase in whole body protein turnover suggest that other, non-RBC proteins, such as skeletal muscle, cardiac muscle, hepatic or gastrointestinal proteins may also be increased. There are currently no data to support or refute this hypothesis.

Does Increased Cardiac Output Contribute to Hypermetabolism?

Beyond its effect on protein turnover, depressed hemoglobin may also increase REE by increasing cardiac output. Cardiac output, the product of stroke volume (in mL) and heart rate (in beats per minute), is increased in SCD because of the low oxygen-carrying capacity of the blood [8, 51, 69]. The effect of anemia on cardiac output and capacity has received considerable attention in the SCD literature. An early review paper on this topic reported that cardiac output at rest in patients with SCA with hemoglobin levels between 6-8g/dL was 50% above normal [39]. Despite this, only one study in the literature has reported the relationship between energy expenditure and cardiac function. In their study of eight children with SCA and seven control children, Salman et al. [50] found REE to be significantly and positively correlated with cardiac index ($L/min/m^2$, $r^2=0.45$, $P<0.01$). Given this preliminary finding and the recognized changes in cardiac capacity in SCD, future research may investigate the relationship between these changes and energy expenditure as another possible mechanism of hypermetabolism in this population. Whether a relationship would still exist after adjusting for the effect of low hemoglobin merits further investigation.

Do Inflammation and Infection Contribute to Hypermetabolism?

Infection may cause hypermetabolism due to the release of a number of hormonal and nonhormonal mediators that induce metabolic changes such as protein and fat catabolism, negative nitrogen balance, hyperglycemia and insulin resistance. Significant associations between infection and REE have been reported in clinical populations such as amyotrophic lateral sclerosis [24], cystic fibrosis [10, 45], chronic obstructive pulmonary disease [42] and HIV [30, 49]. In the latter study, C-reactive protein – a marker of systemic inflammation - was an independent predictor of fat-free-mass-adjusted REE, explaining 25% of the variance in REE. Given that C-reactive protein has been found to be significantly increased in sickle serum vs. normal serum [9], even in subjects in steady-state [59], it would be reasonable to infer that inflammation and infection contribute to REE in this population as well. However, no study in the SCD literature has reported any such association. This is disturbing as one of the main causes of mortality throughout the life span of persons with SCA is bacterial infection, especially from encapsulated organisms, the most common being *Streptococcus pneumoniae*. The increased risk of infection may be due to a combination of asplenia [38] and increased circulating levels of type 2 cytokines [46, 65], the latter which result in possible suppression of both humoral and cell-mediated immunity. The lung is a particularly common site of infection in the SCD population. The term *acute chest syndrome* is used to describe any acute illness with the appearance of new pulmonary infiltrate on chest x-ray, and is usually accompanied by fever, cough, tachypnea, pleuritic chest pain, and/or hypoxemia [38]. It is the second leading cause of hospitalization in patients with SCA, after painful crises, with 50% of all children experiencing at least one episode [70]. SCD also increases susceptibility to urinary tract infections, septicemia, meningitis and osteomyelitis. The frequency of infection in persons with SCA and the fact that even when free of complications, subclinical vasoocclusion and thus inflammation may occur, suggests that the term "steady state" may be a misnomer. SCD may in fact be considered a chronic inflammatory disease. The association between infection, inflammation and energy expenditure merits further research.

Can Hypermetabolism Be Decreased?

Preliminary evidence indicates that decreases in REE may be achieved with hydroxyurea. Hydroxyurea is an orally administered antineoplastic agent found to result in a 40% reduction in mortality in 233 adults with SCA followed for nine years [62]. Hydroxyurea therapy has been associated with decreased rates of painful events and acute chest syndrome, length of hospital stay, and need for transfusion in a large, placebo-controlled, clinical trial of adults with SCD [22]. Smaller studies conducted in children have produced similar results [27, 28, 36, 37, 54]. Further, there is evidence that mean REE in children with SCD treated with hydroxyurea for 6.9±3.5 months was reduced by 16.6% ($P<0.001$) [29]. Mechanisms proposed by the authors included decreased sickling and enhanced survival of RBCs as well as increased hemoglobin concentrations, which together may reduce protein turnover, cell destruction, painful events and inflammation [29]. The authors concluded that, over time, the reduction in REE could result in improved energy balance and therefore growth in children with SCD. Despite concerns that the drug may impair growth in children, there was no adverse effect on height or weight gain or pubertal development in school-aged children with SCA treated with hydroxyurea for one year [71]. As well, hydroxyurea has been associated with weight gain in adults with SCD [32].

Given the effects of hematological aberrations on protein turnover and cardiac output, and consequently REE, it may be reasonable to assume that chronic transfusion may decrease REE in this population. In fact, Vaisman et al. [67] found that hemoglobin concentrations increased significantly post transfusion in seven adults with β-thalassemia, while REE decreased from 112±11% to 103±8% of predicted (using equations of the World Health Organization). Interestingly, this finding has not been replicated in those with SCA. Most recently, Harmatz et al. [33] found that REE in five adolescents with SCA was 124% above predicted and increased further to 134% above predicted (using equations of Schofield) post RBC transfusion ($P<0.05$ from pre- to post-transfusion levels). The effect of transfusion therapy on energy expenditure and protein turnover merits further research.

PHYSICAL ACTIVITY

Physical activity includes the daily energy cost of all physical movement including spontaneous activity (ie. fidgeting), and accounts for 25% to 30% of total daily energy expenditure. In their review of the literature, Raunikar and Sabio [48] noted that irrespective of etiology, anemia can decrease physical performance by decreasing maximum oxygen consumption and work capacity, lowering endurance, and increasing fatigue. Despite this, only three studies have addressed physical activity in the SCD population. Singhal et al. [58] compared total daily energy expenditure and physical activity level in 16 postpubertal boys with SCA with those of 16 control boys matched for age and pubertal stage. As might be expected, physical activity level was 46%, and total daily energy expenditure 31.4%, lower in subjects with SCA (both $P<0.04$), supporting the hypothesis that a reduction in physical activity is a compensatory mechanism for elevated REE. Similar findings regarding physical activity have since been reported. Barden et al. [7] measured total daily energy expenditure and activity-related energy expenditure in 36 children with SCA compared with 30 control children. Total daily energy expenditure was 12.4% (NS) lower in the subjects with SCA, a difference that remained non-significant when adjusted for FFM and sex. Activity-related energy expenditure was 58.9% ($P=0.03$) lower in the group with SCA, a tendency that remained after adjusting for FFM and sex (42.3% lower in SCD, $P=0.08$). Similarly, Buchowski et al. found total daily energy expenditure to be 5.4% (NS) and physical activity level 12.1% ($P=0.001$) lower in 28 adolescents with SCA relative to 22 age-matched controls [19]. These differences remained after adjustment for FFM and sex. In the latter study, physical activity was separated into categories according to estimated energy expenditure expressed as metabolic equivalents (METs), the ratio of the energy expenditure for a specific activity to measured REE. Category 1 consisted of activities equal to 1 MET (equivalent to REE), Category 2 of sedentary activities requiring 1.1 to 3 METs, and Category 3 of moderate and vigorous intensity activities requiring >3 METs. There were no significant differences between subjects with SCA and control participants in time spent in Categories 1 or 2. Subjects with SCA spent 62.2% less time in Category 3 activities than control participants (18.3 ± 21.7 vs. 48.4 ± 31.2 minutes per day, $P<0.001$). It is therefore not surprising that a positive linear relationship has been reported between physical activity and hemoglobin concentration in subjects with SCA [19].

Taken together, these findings indicate that total daily energy expenditure may be similar to, or lower, in subjects with SCA vs. controls because of opposing effects of elevated REE and reduced physical activity in SCA.

THERMIC EFFECT OF FOOD

The thermic effect of food is the increase in REE after ingestion of a meal, and accounts for approximately 5% to 10% of total daily energy expenditure. More specifically, the thermic effect of food relates to the energy expended during digestion, absorption and processing of nutrients [64]. To the best of our knowledge, no study in the literature has reported the thermic effect of food in SCD. One preliminary study did report that dietary fat absorption was normal in four out of five pediatric subjects with SCA and that intestinal mucosal morphology was normal in all five subjects [35]. Similarly, Rahbar et al. [47] found that 16 children and adolescents with SCA exhibited normal macronutrient (xylose, fat and/or protein) absorption and/or normal jejunal biopsies. However, the sample sizes of these studies were small, and neither study investigated energy expenditure associated with digestion and absorption. Even though it accounts for only a small portion of total daily energy expenditure, if thermic effect of food is found to be higher in SCD than in healthy controls, this may provide further evidence of a hypermetabolic state in this population.

Summary and Future Directions

The effects of sickle cell disease on total daily energy expenditure and its components are summarized in **Table 3**. Sickle cell disease is a model of chronically and significantly elevated protein turnover and resting energy expenditure. The most likely reason for hypermetabolism is the enhanced energy cost of protein turnover, caused by energy-costly hematological aberrations. The concomitant reduction in physical activity may allow energy balance to be maintained in the short term, but a persistent energy deficit and compromised protein balance may contribute to growth retardation [58], as appears to be the case in children with sickle cell disease.

Table 3. Alterations in energy expenditure in sickle cell disease

Component	Alterations in sickle cell population
Resting energy expenditure (adjusted for fat-free mass)	Increased by 7.4% to 46.4%
Physical activity	Decreased by 12.1% to 51.0%
Thermic effect of food	Not known
Total daily energy expenditure	Decreased by 5.1% to 31.5%

A number of research questions pertaining to energy and protein homeostasis have yet to be answered in sickle cell population. Some of these are listed below.

1. To date, studies on energy and protein homeostasis have included only subjects with SCA, have mixed genotypes into one group, or have not specified genotype. Other forms of SCD include SC sickle cell disease, β^{+} thalassemia, and β° thalassemia, each of which is associated with varying degrees of anemia. Given that REE appears to be inversely related to hemoglobin and directly related to reticulocyte count, it is likely to vary by genotype. This requires confirmation.
2. What are the energy and protein requirements of persons with SCA? Many studies have demonstrated negative energy and protein balance, at least in the short-term, but none have developed dietary guidelines to correct these deficits.
3. Related to this, recently developed prediction equations for resting energy expenditure require further prospective testing. If shown to be valid in independent samples of individuals with SCA, they may be used to determine energy needs, allowing for tailoring of dietary recommendations.
4. The relationship between cardiac output and energy expenditure merits further research. This relationship would require adjustment for the effect of hemoglobin, as there is a well-recognized inverse association between low hemoglobin and cardiac output.

5. The contribution of inflammation and infection (in both steady state and acute crises) to energy metabolism requires further investigation.
6. What is the turnover of non-RBC proteins, such as skeletal muscle, cardiac muscle, hepatic or gastrointestinal proteins, and how does this affect overall protein homeostasis and resting energy expenditure?
7. The effects of chronic transfusion and/or hydroxyurea on energy metabolism and possible reversal of growth retardation require further study.
8. Even if aberrations in resting energy metabolism could be corrected earlier in childhood, the benefits on improved growth rate have yet to be demonstrated. To date, no evidence links body composition to health outcomes in this population.
9. Despite the well-recognized delays in growth and development, children with SCD do exhibit catch-up growth in both weight and height in later adolescence [61, 66]. This indicates that the scales of energy balance tip in favor of growth and development in later adolescence. The exact timing, and perhaps more importantly, mechanisms of this correction in energy balance, require further study.

ACKNOWLEDGEMENTS

Supported in part by grants G12RRO3032, KO1HL6777, 5SO6GM008037 and 5M01RR000095 from the National Institues of Health.

REFERENCES

[1] Arciero PJ, Goran MI, Poehlman ET. Resting metabolic rate is lower in women than in men. *J Appl Physiol.* 1993;75:2514-20.

[2] Azcue MP, Zello GA, Levy LD, Pencharz PB. Energy expenditure and body composition in children with spastic quadriplegic cerebral palsy. *J Pediatr.* 1996;129:870-6.

[3] Badaloo A, Jackson AA, Jahoor F. Whole body protein turnover and resting metabolic rate in homozygous sickle cell disease. *Clin Sci (Lond).* 1989;77:93-97.

[4] Badaloo AV, Singhal A, Forrester TE, Serjeant GR, Jackson AA. The effect of splenectomy for hypersplenism on whole body protein turnover, resting metabolic rate and growth in sickle cell disease. *Eur J Clin Nutr.* 1996;50:672-675.

[5] Bandini LG, Puelzl-Quinn H, Morelli JA, Fukagawa NK. Estimation of energy requirements in persons with severe central nervous system impairment. *J Pediatr.* 1995;126:828-32.

[6] Barden EM, Kawchak DA, Ohene-Frempong K, Stallings VA, Zemel BS. Body composition in children with sickle cell disease. *Am J Clin Nutr.* 2002;76:218-225.

[7] Barden EM, Zemel BS, Kawchak DA, Goran MI, Obene-Frempong K, Stallings VA. Total and resting energy expenditure in children with sickle cell disease. *J Pediatr.* 2000;136:73-79.

[8] Batra AS, Acherman RJ, Wong WY, et al. Cardiac abnormalities in children with sickle cell anemia. *Am J Hematol.* 2002;70:306-12.

[9] Belcher JD, Marker PH, Weber JP, Hebbel RP, Vercellotti GM. Activated monocytes in sickle cell disease: potential role in the activation of vascular endothelium and vaso-occlusion. *Blood.* 2000;96:2451-9.

[10] Bell SC, Bowerman AM, Nixon LE, Macdonald IA, Elborn JS, Shale DJ. Metabolic and inflammatory responses to pulmonary exacerbation in adults with cystic fibrosis. *Eur J Clin Invest.* 2000;30:553-9.

[11] Bolarin DM. Bone-specific alkaline phosphatase protein, total alkaline phosphatase activity and lactate dehydrogenase in sera of patients with sickle cell disease. *Haematologia.* 2001;31:51-56.

[12] Borel MJ, Buchowski MS, Turner EA, Goldstein RE, Flakoll PJ. Protein turnover and energy expenditure increase during exogenous nutrient availability in sickle cell disease. *Am J Clin Nutr.* 1998;68:607-614.

[13] Borel MJ, Buchowski MS, Turner EA, Peeler BB, Goldstein RE, Flakoll PJ. Alterations in basal nutrient metabolism increase resting energy expenditure in sickle cell disease. *Am J Physiol (Endocrinol. Metab. 37).* 1998;274:E357-E364.

[14] Buchholz AC, McGillivray CF, Pencharz PB. Differences in resting metabolic rate between paraplegic and able-bodied subjects are explained by differences in body composition. *Am J Clin Nutr.* 2003;77:371-8.

[15] Buchholz AC, Rafii M, Pencharz PB. Is resting metabolic rate different between men and women? *Br J Nutr.* 2001;86:641-6.

[16] Buchowski MS, De La Fuente FA, Flakoll PJ, Chen KY, Turner EA. Increased bone turnover is associated with protein and energy metabolism in adolescents with sickle cell anemia. *Am J Physiol Endocrinol Metab.* 2001;280:E518-E527.

[17] Buchowski MS, Simmons LA, Chen KY, Flakoll PJ, Mellen BG, Turner EA. Plasma leptin association with body composition and energy expenditure in sickle cell disease. *J Am Coll Nutr.* 2000;19:228-236.

[18] Buchowski MS, Chen KY, Byrne D, Wang WC. Equation to estimate resting energy expenditure in adolescents with sickle cell anemia. *Am J Clin Nutr.* 2002;76:1335-1344.

[19] Buchowski MS, Townsend KM, Williams R, Chen KY. Patterns and energy expenditure of free-living physical activity in adolescents with sickle cell anemia. *J Pediatr.* 2002;140:86-92.

[20] Charache S. Natural History of Disease: Adults. *Sickle Cell Disease: Basic Principles and Clinical Practice.* Pennsylvania: Lippincott-Raven; 1996.

[21] Charache S, Page DL. Infarction of bone marrow in the sickle cell disorders. *Ann Intern Med.* 1967;67:1195-1200.

[22] Charache S, Terrin ML, Moore RD, et al. Effect of hydroxyurea on the frequency of painful crises in sickle cell anemia. Investigators of the Multicenter Study of Hydroxyurea in Sickle Cell Anemia. *N Engl J Med.* 1995;332:1317-1322.

[23] Cunningham JJ. A reanalysis of the factors influencing basal metabolic rate in normal adults. *Am J Clin Nutr.* 1980;33:2372-4.

[24] Desport JC, Preux PM, Magy L, et al. Factors correlated with hypermetabolism in patients with amyotrophic lateral sclerosis. *Am J Clin Nutr.* 2001;74:328-34.

[25] Diggs LW. Bone and joint lesions in sickle-cell disease. *Clin Orthop.* 1967;52:119-143.

[26] Embury SH, Hebbel RP, Steinberg MH, Mohandas N. Pathogenesis of vasoocclusion. *Sickle Cell Disease: Basic Principles and Clinical Practice*. Pennsylvania: Lippincott-Raven; 1996:311-326.

[27] Ferster A, Tahriri P, Vermylen C, et al. Five years of experience with hydroxyurea in children and young adults with sickle cell disease. *Blood.* 2001;97:3628-32.

[28] Ferster A, Vermylen C, Cornu G, et al. Hydroxyurea for treatment of severe sickle cell anemia: a pediatric clinical trial. *Blood.* 1996;88:1960-4.

[29] Fung EB, Barden EM, Kawchak DA, Zemel BS, Ohene-Frempong K, Stallings VA. Effect of hydroxyurea therapy on resting energy expenditure in children with sickle cell disease. *J Pediatr Hematol Oncol.* 2001;23(9):604-8.

[30] Garcia-Lorda P, Serrano P, Jimenez-Exposito MJ, et al. Cytokine-driven inflammatory response is associated with the hypermetabolism of AIDS patients with opportunistic infections. *J Parenter Enteral Nutr.* 2000;24:317-322.

[31] Goran MI. Energy metabolism and obesity. *Med Clin NA.* 2000;84:347-362.

[32] Hackney AC, Hezier W, Gulledge TP, et al. Effects of hydroxyurea administration on the body weight, body composition and exercise performance of patients with sickle-cell anaemia. *Clin Sci (Lond).* 1997;92:481-6.

[33] Harmatz P, Heyman MB, Cunningham J, et al. Effects of red blood cell transfusion on resting energy expenditure in adolescents with sickle cell anemia. *J Pediatr Gastroenterol Nutr.* 1999;29:127-31.

[34] Harris JA, Benedict FG; *Standard Basal Metabolism Constants for Physiologists and Clinicians: A Biometric Study of Basal Metabolism in Man.* Phildelphia: JB Lippincott; 1919.

[35] Heyman MB, Vichinsky E, Katz R, et al. Growth retardation in sickle-cell disease treated by nutritional support. *Lancet.* 1985;1:903-6.

[36] Jayabose S, Tugal O, Sandoval C, et al. Clinical and hematologic effects of hydroxyurea in children with sickle cell anemia. *J Pediatr.* 1996;129:559-65.

[37] Koren A, Segal-Kupershmit D, Zalman L, et al. Effect of hydroxyurea in sickle cell anemia: a clinical trial in children and teenagers with severe sickle cell anemia and sickle cell beta-thalassemia. *Pediatr Hematol Oncol.* 1999;16:221-32.

[38] Lane PA. Sickle cell disease. *Pediatr Clin North Am.* 1996;43:639-64.

[39] Lindsay J Jr, Meshel JC, Patterson RH. The cardiovascular manifestations of sickle cell disease. *Arch Intern Med.* 1974;133:643-51.

[40] Madden AM, Morgan MY. Resting energy expenditure should be measured in patients with cirrhosis, not predicted. *Hepatology.* 1999;30:655-64.

[41] Milner PF, Joe C, Burke GJ. Bone and joint disease. *Sickle Cell Disease: Basic Principles and Clinical Practice*. Philadelphia, PA: Lippincott-Raven; 1996:645-661.

[42] Nguyen LT, Bedu M, Caillaud D, et al. Increased resting energy expenditure is related to plasma TNF-alpha concentration in stable COPD patients. *Clin Nutr.* 1999;18:255-257.

[43] Niihara Y, Zerez CR, Akiyama DS, Tanaka KR. Increased red cell glutamine availability in sickle cell anemia: demonstration of increased active transport, affinity, and increased glutamate level in intact red cells. *J Lab Clin Med.* 1997;130:83-90.

[44] Odonkor PO, Addae SK, Yamamoto S, Apatu RS. Effect of dietary nitrogen on urinary excretion of non-protein nitrogen in adolescent sickle cell patients. *Hum Nutr Clin Nutr.* 1984;38:23-29.

[45] Pencharz PB, Durie PR. Pathogenesis of malnutrition in cystic fibrosis, and its treatment. *Clin Nutr.* 2000;19:387-394.

[46] Raghupathy R, Haider MZ, Azizieh F, Abdelsalam R, D'Souza TM, Adekile AD. Th1 and Th2 cytokine profiles in sickle cell disease. *Acta Haematol.* 2000;103:197-202.

[47] Rahbar F, Scott RB, Jilly P. Studies in sickle cell anemia: Preliminary observation on gastrointestinal digestion and absorption. *J Natl Med Assoc.* 1977;69:103-4.

[48] Raunikar RA, Sabio H. Anemia in the adolescent athlete. *Am J Dis Child.* 1992;146:1201-5.

[49] Roubenoff R, Grinspoon S, Skolnik PR, et al. Role of cytokines and testosterone in regulating lean body mass and resting energy expenditure in HIV-infected men. *Am J Physiol Endocrinol Metab.* 2002;283:E138-45.

[50] Salman EK, Haymond MW, Bayne E, et al. Protein and energy metabolism in prepubertal children with sickle cell anemia. *Pediatr Res.* 1996;40:34-40.

[51] San M, Demirta M, Burgut R, Birand A, Burgut R, Birand A. Left ventricular systolic and diastolic functions in patients with sickle cell anemia. *Int J Angiol.* 1998;7:185-7.

[52] Schofield WN. Predicting basal metabolic rate, new standards and review of previous work. *Human Nutr: Clin Nutr.* 1985;39C:5-41.

[53] Schwenk A, Hoffer-Belitz E, Jung B, et al. Resting energy expenditure, weight loss, and altered body composition in HIV infection. *Nutrition.* 1996;12:595-601.

[54] Scott JP, Hillery CA, Brown ER, Misiewicz V, Labotka RJ. Hydroxyurea therapy in children severely affected with sickle cell disease. *J Pediatr.* 1996;128:820-8.

[55] Serjeant GR. Chronic Hypersplenism. *A Guide to Sickle Cell Disease*. Kingston, Jamaica: Sickle Cell Trust; 2001, 23.

[56] Serjeant GR; *A Guide to Sickle Cell Disease*. Kingston, Jamaica: Sickle Cell Trust; 2001.

[57] Singhal A, Davies P, Sahota A, Thomas PW, Serjeant GR. Resting metabolic rate in homozygous sickle cell disease. *Am J Clin Nutr.* 1993;57:32-34.

[58] Singhal A, Davies P, Wierenga KJ, Thomas P, Serjeant G. Is there an energy deficiency in homozygous sickle cell disease? *Am J Clin Nutr.* 1997;66:386-90.

[59] Singhal A, Doherty JF, Raynes JG, et al. Is there an acute-phase response in steady-state sickle cell disease? *Lancet.* 1993;341:651-653.

[60] Singhal A, Parker S, Linsell L, Serjeant G. Energy intake and resting metabolic rate in preschool Jamaican children with homozygous sickle cell disease. *Am J Clin Nutr.* 2002;75(6):1093-1097.

[61] Singhal A, Thomas P, Cook R, Wierenga K, Serjeant G. Delayed adolescent growth in homozygous sickle cell disease. *Arch Dis Child.* 1994;71:404-408.

[62] Steinberg MH, Barton F, Castro O, et al. Effect of hydroxyurea on mortality and morbidity in adult sickle cell anemia: risks and benefits up to 9 years of treatment. *JAMA.* 2003;289:1645-51.

[63] Steinberg MH, Embury SH. Sickle Hemoglobin. Embury SH, Hebbel RP, Mohandas N, Steinberg MH. *Sickle Cell Disease: Basic Principles and Clinical Practice*. Philadelphia, PA: Lippincott-Raven; 1996:9-11.
[64] Tappy L. Thermic effect of food and sympathetic nervous system activity in humans. *Reprod Nutr Dev*. 1996;36:391-7.
[65] Taylor SC, Shacks SJ, Qu Z, Wiley P. Type 2 cytokine serum levels in healthy sickle cell disease patients. *J Natl Med Assoc*. 1997;89:753-7.
[66] Thomas PW, Singhal A, Hemmings-Kelly M, Serjeant GR. Height and weight reference curves for homozygous sickle cell disease. *Arch Dis Child*. 2000;82:204-208.
[67] Vaisman N, Akivis A, Sthoeger D, Barak Y, Matitau A, Wolach B. Resting energy expenditure in patients with thalassemia major. *Am J Clin Nutr*. 1995;61:582-4.
[68] Vaisman N, Pencharz PB, Corey M, Canny CJ, Hahn E. Energy expenditure of patients with cystic fibrosis. *J Pediatr*. 1987;111:496-500.
[69] Veille JC, Hanson R. Left ventricular systolic and diastolic function in pregnant patients with sickle cell disease. *Am J Obstet Gynecol*. 1994;170:107-10.
[70] Vichinsky EP, Styles LA, Colangelo LH, Wright EC, Castro O, Nickerson B. Acute chest syndrome in sickle cell disease: clinical presentation and course. Cooperative Study of Sickle Cell Disease. *Blood*. 1997;89:1787-92.
[71] Wang WC, Helms RW, Lynn HS, et al. Effect of hydroxyurea on growth in children with sickle cell anemia: results of the HUG-KIDS Study. *J Pediatr*. 2002;140:225-9.
[72] Wasserman D, Zemel BS, Mulberg AE, et al. Growth, nutritional status, body composition, and energy expenditure in prepubertal children with Alagille syndrome. *J Pediatr*. 1999;134:172-177.
[73] Waterlow JC. Lysine turnover in man measured by intravenous infusion of L-[U-^{14}C]lysine. *Clin Sci*. 1967;33:507-515.
[74] Williams R, Olivi S, MacKert P, Fletcher L, Tian G-L, Wang W. Comparison of energy prediction equations with measured resting energy expenditure in children with sickle cell anemia. *J Am Diet Assoc*. 2002;102:956-961.
[75] World Health Organization. Energy and protein requirements. Report of a Joint FAO/WHO/UNU Expert Consultation. 1985;724:1-206.
[76] Zemel BS, Kawchak DA, Cnaan A, Zhao H, Scanlin TF, Stallings VA. Prospective evaluation of resting energy expenditure, nutritional status, pulmonary function, and genotype in children with cystic fibrosis. *Pediatr Res*. 1996;40:578-586.

In: Focus on Sickle Cell Research
Editor: Ralph L. Plasmar, pp. 19-58
ISBN 1-59033-920-7

Chapter II

CEREBRAL VASCULOPATHY IN SICKLE CELL ANEMIA: DIAGNOSIS, THERAPEUTIC CLINICAL TRIALS AND THE POTENTIAL FOR PREVENTION

Darleen R. Powars*
Department of Pediatrics, Hematology
LAC+USC Medical Center
Los Angeles, CA 90033

ABSTRACT

Cerebral vasculopathy in children with sickle cell anemia (Hb SS) was originally thought to be relatively infrequent until several seminal natural history studies were reported during the decades of 1970 and 1980. At that time, overt clinical stroke was identified to occur in 7.8 to 10% of Hb SS children. Recent data based on marked refinements in neuroimaging technology demonstrate that nearly 50% of children with sickle cell anemia have both large and small vessel central nervous system infarctions. In 10 to 15% of children, completed infarctions are found in the regional distribution of the large cerebral blood vessels. They are overly symptomatic with hemiparesis. Incomplete (silent) infarctions are identified in one-third of children and are often microvascular in distribution marked by more subtle cognitive and neurofunctional disability. Over time, the circulating sickle red cell damages the endothelium of the vasculature. This is mediated by several adhesion molecules, intracellular red cell dehydration and a deleterious effect on nitric oxide (NO) synthesis. Decreased circulating levels of NO are thought to be caused by the constantly elevated levels of free intravascular hemoglobin resulting from the lifelong hemolytic anemia. The pathophysiology of sickle induced neurovasculopathy, clinical risk factors, rate of progression of dsabling manifestations and potential treatment modalities are presented in this chapter.

---

* Correspondence: Darleen R. Powars, M.D., Professor of Pediatrics, Women's and Children's Hospital, LAC+USC Medical Center, 1240 N. Mission Road, Rm L902, Los Angeles, CA 90033, (323)226-3853, (323)226-5049 FAX, powars@hsc.usc.edu: e-mail

INTRODUCTION

Cerebral infarction in young children with sickle cell anemia (SS) was first described in 1930 by Cook who reported one child with cerebral softening at autopsy [44]. This was followed by Arena in 1939 who reported several SS children with hemiparesis [13, 14]. One year later, Hughes and Diggs published a group of 6 children who had their first hemiparetic stroke before age 10 [83]. Prior to this early cluster of case reports, sickle cell anemia was not known to be a cause of cerebral vascular disease. Subsequent to that time, there have been extensive broad-spectrum publications such as case reports, cohort studies and clinical trials regarding cerebral vasculopathy; manifest as cerebral infarction or intracranial hemorrhage; now numbering more than 2000 reported subjects. The reported prevalence of clinical hemiparetic stroke in SS subjects is 0.76/100 patient's years [137], 7.8% between ages 1 to 14 years [21] and 11% by the age of 20 years [121]. Recurrent events in untreated subjects were reported as occurring in 67% with temporal clustering [137], 90% within the first 19 months post first overt clinical stroke [146] and in 43% in the Jamaican cohort study [21]. The prevalence of incomplete infarction, ie, 'silent' strokes is reported to be 17-25% based on neuroimaging modalities and clinically manifest as cognitive dysfunction [113, 129, 180, 186, 190].

Polymerization of sickle hemoglobin with the resultant intraerythrocytic cellular dehydration is the initial and primary process that leads to the pathophysiologic effect. Irreversible adhesion of the sickle erythrocyte is the deleterious link between intraerythrocytic Hb S polymerization and endothelial damage resulting in endothelial hyperplasia and the resultant tissue infarction [161].

At the current time, ischemic brain injury is the most severe disabling complication in children who have sickle cell anemia. Cerebral blood flows (CBF) is inversely related to hemoglobin concentration reaching maximal rates with anemia of 7gms/dl of hemoglobin or less [74, 84, 177, 150]. Maximal cerebral flow exposes the brain vascular endothelium to damage induced by increased numbers of hypoxic sickle red cells.

Transfusion replacing the sickle red cells with normal hemoglobin AA red cells has been the most effective therapy to date in the prevention of second strokes [3, 34, 146, 148, 151]. Transfusion is effective in preventing progression of the cerebral vasculopathy in those subjects with increased cerebral vessel velocity as measured by TCD associated with cMRI evidence of ischemic brain damage in neurologically asymptomatic children [6].

The ongoing focus of several investigational studies is aimed at elucidating the mode of interaction of the hypoxic sickle red cell and the vascular endothelium with the aim of interrupting this pathologic process thereby protecting the subject from irreversible neuronal damage. The overriding clinical issue is the identification of therapeutic approaches with the least adverse effects for children thought to be at risk for cerebral ischemia. Currently, preventive therapy options are relatively unsatisfactory.

PATHOPHYSIOLOGY OF CEREBRAL VASCULOPATHY IN SICKLE CELL ANEMIA

The predictability of a first overt clinical stroke is age-specific during the first decade of life [3, 64, 137]. The vascularity of the border-zone lesions of the high cerebral convexity is exquisitely responsive to cerebral oxygen needs, providing a regulatory mechanism for age-specific changes in the cerebral blood flow (CBF). Blood flow in the internal carotid artery (measured as mL/100 g brain tissue/min) is highest during early childhood and becomes higher in those who have chronic anemia. Cerebral blood flow slowly decreases after age 6, coincidental with the diminishing metabolic needs of the mature brain [150]. These factors taken together account for the high age-specificity of infarctive risk during the first decade of life and for the remarkable decrease in the appearance of first infarction as the SS child enters the second decade of life.

The cerebral infarction patterns in SS children are characterized by wedge-shaped lesions in the territorial regions of the larger cerebral blood vessels, particularly the anterior and middle cerebral vessels often sparing the territories of the posterior cerebral and basilar vessels [3, 96]. Borderzone infarctions in the watershed regions and small punctate lesions in the deep white matter are frequently seen. Subjects with clinical stroke usually have infarction in the cortex in continuation with deep white matter. In large vessel stenosis with overt stroke, the infarction is complete and irreversible with regional loss of neurons, glia, and microvessels. Incomplete (cystic) infarction represents selective neuronal loss with preservation of some neurons, glia and microvessels and is often not visible as a low attention region on computed tomography (CT) [61]. Unrecognized 'asymptomatic' subjects referred to as having 'silent' infarction have lesions more confined to the watershed and deep white matter [111, 113]. The gross structure of the cortex is preserved.

Pathological examination of the diseased vasculopathic segments demonstrate intimal proliferation with discontinuity of the internal elastic lamina. Endothelial cells may proliferate to resurface denuded areas, but they remain in a monolayer, whereas components of the hyperplastic intima underneath include fibroblasts, fibrous tissue, and scattered smooth muscle cells. The larger arteries show fragmentation and duplication of internal elastic lamina and extensive intimal hyperplasia [95, 123, 145, 201]. Concomitant thrombus formation in areas of endothelial damage may both perpetuate the vicious cycle of intimal changes and serve as the proximate source of artery-to-artery emboli occasionally responsible for some distal occlusions [3]. In the brain tissue, hyperplasia of both large vessel and micro vessel intima is present. More than half of the subjects with clinical stroke have been shown to have large vessel stenosis particularly in the supra clinoid internal carotid and the proximal middle and anterior cerebral arteries [145]. The cause of intimal hyperplasia, and why is occurs at specific sites in the anterior circulation is not known. Large vessel disease with regional infarction subsequently develops fragile small vascular collaterals which appears as a 'puff of smoke' on angiography-designated as the Moyamoya malformation [67, 105, 175, 182]. These fragile vessels rupture resulting in massive intracranial hemorrhage. Regional cerebral infarction is a manifestations of large vessel disease. Contrariwise, pathologic manifestations of cerebral microinfarctions, end stage chronic renal disease known as sickle renal failure

(SRF), chronic obstructive pulmonary disease, and retinopathy are manifestations of an obstructive vasculopathy of the small arteriolar vessels.

Various cytokines and adhesion molecules have been shown to induce endothelial damage resulting in intimal hyperplasia in subjects with sickle cell anemia. Data suggest that young deformable sickle red cell adhere to endothelium preferentially as compared to normal red cells [71, 87, 110, 156]. Vascular adhesion molecule (VCAM-1) adheres to the receptor $\bullet_{4}\bullet_{1}$ on the red cell membrane and promotes the preferential adhesion of sickle red cells to endothelial cells [62, 157]. VCAM-1 and a number of other plasma factors that enhance adhesion are elevated in blood samples in subjects with sickle cell anemia [168]. Thrombospondin binds to CD36 receptors on the red cell membrane and 'bridges the gap' between the endothelial cell and the sickle red cells. Other plasma factors that enhance adhesion are von Willebrands factor, Factor VIII, fibrinogen, fibronectin and activated micro particles. Taken together these factors combine to encourage binding of the sickle red cell to the endothelial cells [71, 77, 87, 170]. This initiates the movement of P-selectin, a glue like molecule to the outer surface of the endothelial cell which permanently binds with the sickle cells [26, 104]. Thus, initiating vaso-occlusion of both large and small vessels. Regional patterns of increased blood flow and oxygen utilization coupled with hypoxia, oxygen radicals (H_2O_2), and hyperosmolality decrease the time to tissue infarction. The membrane actin of the sickle red cell is the key target of protein nitration with increased rates of production of reactive oxygen and nitrogen species in tissues. The functional impairment of actin results in a defective erythrocytic cytoskeleton [17].

Nitric oxide (NO) is a physiologic vasodilator continuously synthesized in endothelial cells by the nitric oxide synthase enzyme systems [63]. NO down regulates endothelial adhesion molecules such as VCAM-1, ICAM-1, CD18 dependent adhesion and others. Subjects with sickle cell anemia (SS) during the steady state have been found to have impairment of the endothelial production of NO and L-arginine (substrate for NO synthase) lower than normal persons. These NO levels are further depressed during acute painful episodes and with acute chest syndrome [168]. Nitric oxide reduces neutrophile-endothelial adhesion and inhibits platelet aggregation. Taken together, the complex processes in which NO maintains the balance between adhesion molecule production and protects the blood vessel endothelial cells is compromised by lowered NO production in sickle cell anemia [63]. It is clear that this stabilizing process is at risk in fragile children who have increased cerebral blood flow and a high risk of hypoxic states with dehydration with fever. The cerebral blood vessels (and probably the splenic arterioles) are particularly vulnerable to the interaction of these factors.

NEUROIMAGING

Neuroimaging provides accurate visualization of brain structure and function. Computed tomography (CT), conventional magnetic resonance imaging (cMRI) are the readily available imaging modalities used to confirm a clinical diagnosis of cerebral infarction in nearly 100% of SS subjects with clinical strokes (Table 1) [64, 111]. Enhanced computed tomography and magnetic resonance imaging (cMRI and diffusion-weighted MRI) provide exquisite detail about brain structure [46, 62, 101, 112, 178]. The technology of neuroimaging is in a rapid phase of development and the choice of preferred methodology is institution dependent, based on the available radiologic, nuclear medicine, and ultrasonographic expertise [18, 94, 160, 163, 178]. Magnetic resonance angiography (MRA) permits non-invasive visualization of the vascular tree. The usefulness of the different modalities in sickle cell anemia are reviewed in Table 1 and Table 2. Duplex color doppler and transcranial doppler (TCD) ultrasonography provide directional measures of blood flow velocity. Stenosis or occlusion of the large intracranial vessels of the circle of Willis, particularly the middle cerebral artery, detected by transcranial Doppler, duplex Doppler, or magnetic resonance angiography can be used to predict an increased risk of clinical infarctive stroke [5].

Cerebral infarction lesions appear hyperintense on T_2 weighted cMRI and hypointense on T_1 weighted images. In SS, infarcts are frequently located in the high cerebral convexity, particularly in the gray matter in the vascular distribution of the MCA and ACA and in the white matter borderzones [138, 208]. White matter borderzone hyperintensities seen in T_2 weighted images are consistently associated with quantitative MRI (qMRI) contiguous cerebral lesions [163]. Steen et al., [162] report on further refinement of qMRI based on fluid-attentuated inversion recovery (FLAIR) and demonstrate that gray matter abnormalities were present in 35% of SS subjects without clinical stroke similar to findings using PET technology [135, 207]. Kirkham et al. (2001) compared T_2 weighted, diffusion and perfusion MRI (DWI) to cMRI [90]. Perfusion abnormalities were larger than the cMRI identified infarction regions identifying penumbral regions. MRI (DWI) abnormalities were associated with soft neurologic symptoms even in subjects with normal cMRI, MRA and normal TCD velocities [139]. These imaging findings document that CNS microvasculopathy contributes significantly to subject morbidity and cognitive dysfunction. Realignment of Hb S polymers has been demonstrated in vitro in the magnetic resonance equipment but no in vivo rheologic changes in blood flow while the subject is in the magnetic field or afterward has been found [29]. The ultimate aim is to rapidly perform anatomical studies including cMRI, qMRI, diffusion weighted MRI (DWI), and MRA at one time using the same equipment and programming. This would allow for rapid assessment of the state of the cerebral vasculopathy defining completed infarctions, incomplete infarctions ('silent'), early gray matter neuronal loss without infarction and the extent of the affected penumbral regions [139].

Several comparison studies have shown equivalent specificity of magnetic resonance angiography (MRA) for the diagnosis of cerebral arterial stenosis compare to conventional angiography or doppler [48, 88, 93, 179]. Using conventional angiography as the 'gold' standard, Kandeel et al., reported that MRA made the 'correct' diagnosis in 85% of the vessels with a sensitivity of 80.5% and a specificity of 94% [88]. However, Verlhac argues that digitized cerebral angiography should become the 'gold' standard for pretreatment confirmation of large vessel disease detected by ultrasonography or MRA [178, 179]. Aneurysms of the Circle of Willis and the narrow twisted fragile vessels characteristic of Moyamoya anomaly can be detected by MRA with less risk, less hospital preparation time and no prior transfusion required as compared to conventional angiography. Programming with thin flow T_1 weighted imaging can differentiate large vessel true endothelial roughening with early stenosis from turbulent blood flow. Turbulence disappears after the anemia is corrected, while stenosis of the major vessels remains evident.

Table 1: Brain Imaging Modalities* (Anatomic)

MODALITY	ACTIVITY	ADVANTAGES	DISADVANTAGES
Computed tomography (CT)	Low attention regions in completed infarctions Cerebral atrophy well defined	Short acquisition time Readily available Acute hemorrhage is hyperintense And identifiable within a few hours	Incomplete ('silent') borderzone infarctions are often not identified as hypodense regions
Conventional Magnetic Resonance Imaging (cMRI)	Acute infarction visible on T_1 weighted sequences (low attention) Hyperintense T_2 weighted sequence identifies borderzone incomplete infarction (silent infarction)	Widely available equipment allows high resolution anatomic visualization of gray and white matter cerebral infarction Requires modest technical experience	Confinement time in equipment is prolonged; use in unstable patients or during stroke in progression not recommended.
Quantitative Magnetic Resonance Imaging (qMRI)	T_1 (spin-lattice relaxation time) demonstrates subtle gray matter abnormalities in subjects with normal cMRI	Very high resolution using available equipment Good correlation with regional cognitive deficiencies	Requires special software and extensive radiologic expertise
Angiography (Conventional)	Injection of contrast agent into the carotid artery clearly demonstrates cerebral vascular patency of arteries	Clear definition of smaller collateral arteries Good definition of small aneurysms in multiple locations	Requires transfusion prior to study recent FDA approval of contrast agents with lower osmolality (non ionic) are safer
Magnetic Resonance Angiography (MRA)	High resolution visualization of stenotic carotid and intracerebral arteries	Good correlation to conventional angiography with less adverse risk. Uses available MRI equipment with slight increase in time of confinement	Endothelial roughening and irregular blood flow velocity mimics stenosis

*References: 88, 94, 96, 111, 113, 163, 178, 187

Table 2: Functional (Physiologic)

MODALITY	ACTIVITY	ADVANTAGES	DISADVANTAGES
Positron Emission Tomography (PET)	Measures neuronal and other tissue glucose Utilization (FDG). Cerebral blood flow (perfusion) ($[^{15}0]H_20$)	High spatial resolution in gray matter Wide versatility for total body use Direct measurement of active neuronal Function, microvascular blood flow, and Oxygen extraction fraction	Injection of intravenous radioligand tracers required Cyclotron to produce short half life radioisotopes available Non-mobile equipment Poor white matter definition
Single photon emission computed tomography (SPECT) ^{99m}Tc HMPAO or ^{99m}Tc ECD and other radiotracers	Measures functional neuronal receptors	Relatively inexpensive equipment	Injection of intravenous radioligand tracers Restricted spatial resolution Limited versatility Cannot measure regional cerebral metabolism
^{133}-Xenon-CT regional cerebral blood flow (XeCT)	Measures cerebral blood flow	Accurate	Inhalation of Xenon gas, requires highly trained operators, subject cooperation High radiation exposure
Near-infrared Spectroscopy (NIRS)	Absorption of near-infrared light by chromophores change with oxygenation state Hypoxia detected before permanent ischemic insult	Non-invasive portable equipment Rapid measurement of cerebral hemodynamics and oxygenation	Spatial resolution poor and pathlength measurement needs validation High movement artifact Equipment in development
Magnetic Resonance Spectroscopy (MRS)	Spectra measures brain lactate, glutamine, N-acetyl aspartate and other metabolites	Rapid onset but short lived elevation of lactate and glutamate with ischemia in gray matter before cMRI or CT abnormalities appear	Adult norms achieved by age 2 Difficult clinical monitoring during critical period of stroke in progression Subject immobility required

Table 2: Continued

MODALITY	ACTIVITY	ADVANTAGES	DISADVANTAGES
Diffusion and perfusion weighted Magnetic Resonance Imaging MRI (DWI)	Identifies molecular displacement of water	Early hyperdense detection of acute ischemia before cMRI or CT are sensitive Identifies penumbral areas surrounding infarcts Can be incorporated into routine MRI procedure by addiing 3 minutes to immobility time	Requires high speed echoplanar imaging (EPI) with absolute immobility of head(single shot requires 100 ms)
Functional Magnetic Resonance Imaging(fMRI)	Increase in deoxyhemoglobin decrease T_2 weighted signal Blood oxygen level dependent (BOLD) method preferred	Measures cerebral blood flow and tissue perfusion without using radioisotopes	Assumption is that blood flow reflects brain activity. Subject cooperation required. Improvements needed to negate motion artifact, scanner noise, quantification of accuracy, brain stem imaging artifact
Transcranial Doppler Ultrasonography (TCD)	Measures blood flow velocity in dICA, MCA ACA >170 cm/sec in anemic children is conditionally elevated	Portable Best used for screening of pre-symptomatic cerebrovascular disease	Non-duplex (no direct visualization of vessels) Cannot demonstrate small vessel disease Requires great technical expertise Velocity decreases to normal in SS transfused subjects
Modifications of color duplex doppler ultrasonography including high resolution B-mode ultrasonography	Measures cerebral blood vessel flow Measures cerebral vessel intima/media thickness	Direct duplex visualization of cerebral vessels Good visualization of bifurcation of distal internal carotid artery, posterior cerebral artery, basilar artery Best used for screening for cerebrovascular disease Widely available in tertiary medical centers	In transfused SS, velocities decrease to normal range Requires meticulous examination technique

* References:18, 24, 35, 46, 47, 51, 74, 81, 90, 93, 101, 116, 119, 120, 135, 139, 142, 153, 160, 187, 194

Positron emission tomography (PET) can gauge the functional activity of the cerebral tissues (Table 2) by using radioactive tracers to indicate glucose metabolism 2-deoxy-2 [^{18}F] fluoro-D-glucose and evaluate microvascular blood flow ([^{15}0]$H_2$0) (51). XeCT provides regional measures of blood flow. The relatively high XeCT radiation dose (150 mm SV) precludes repeat studies in younger children during the age of brain maturation [120]. Positron Emission Tomography (PET) identifies subtle loss of neuronal metabolism [24]. PET technology fails to show high convexity white matter borderzone lesions as seen on cMRI [160]. White matter hyperintensities on cMRI are frequently associated with decreased CBF on PET [135] or XeCT [120]. Four non-randomized published studies describing PET in highly selected subjects with sickle cell anemia show cerebral ischemia in 67% of the cases [74, 135, 142]. PET identifies gray matter hypointensities in subjects with normal cMRI and more extensive penumbral neuronal loss as compared to the abnormalities found on cMRI [24, 135, 142]. Quantification of • •amino butyric acid receptor loss using radioactive tracers identified by positron emission tomography (PET) measures the number of synapses, thus by inference, the intactness of the cortical neurons. Similar gray matter reductions are reported using T_1 qMRI technology [162]. Sensitivity and specificity comparisons between functional brain imaging (PET and SPECT) and T_1 maps of spin-lattice relaxation time (qMRI) are not reported [18]. For safety reasons, PET examinations in young subjects are performed non-quantitatively, ie, without arterial blood sampling or inhalation of radiopharmaceutical gases such as [^{15}O] [92]. This precludes the direct measurement of the oxygen extraction fraction, a powerful predictor of incipient ischemia and stroke [207]. Techniques are being developed to eliminate the need for timed breathing with arterial sampling that is required for inhalation [^{15}O] PET because of compliance difficulties in children or cognitively impaired adults [69].

The sensitivity of either cMRI or PET in confirming cerebral ischemia in neurologically abnormal subjects is 89%. It can be improved to 100% if both cMRI and PET are used [135] based on the clinical observation of neurologic events as the 'gold' standard. PET technology is now being combined with CT. Since white matter lesions are poorly visualized on PET and gray matter penumbral lesions are less apparent on CT, this should rapidly enhance anatomic accuracy and completeness of diagnosis at one sitting.

Magnetic Resonance Spectroscopy (MRS) in sickle cell anemia can demonstrate significant metabolic changes in areas of recent ischemia [47, 119, 193, 194]. Increases in the level of lactate and glutamate and deceases the level of N-acetyl aspartate can be measured within minutes of the insult and are present for 3-6 hours. These acute changes are valuable in the differentiation of old infarction from new ischemic lesions in penumbral regions. In old infarcts readily seen on PET, XeCT or qMRI, patients with stable neurologic deficits do not show specific spectral abnormalities.

Ultrasonography using Transcranial Doppler (TCD) or duplex color doppler (US) [5, 93, 103, 153, 154, 179] provides a safe and non-invasive measure of blood flow velocity in the carotid siphon (ICA), proximal middle cerebral artery (MCA), and proximal anterior cerebral artery (ACA). The velocity of the posterior cerebral artery (PCI) and basilar arteries is less well defined particularly using TCD [81, 116]. Bulas et al., report some technique variations between TCD and transcranial duplex imaging and report that velocities obtained by duplex were somewhat lower than TCD [35]. Velocity of blood flow in the internal carotid arteries

(ICA) is highest in early childhood and slowly decreases over time coincident with the diminishing metabolic needs of the mature brain [5, 35]. Both very high and very low velocities are manifestations of stenosis and/or incipient occlusions. An elevated blood flow velocity of 200 cm/second or greater in the carotid siphon, MCA, and ACA predicts a significant risk of subsequent stroke in SS children [5, 129, 154]. Sensitivity and specificity comparing ultrasonography to MRA vary with the maximum velocity cutoff values, the ultrasonography equipment used, and the hemoglobin concentration at the time of the study. Seibert et al., report a sensitivity of 78% and specificity of 87% at a maximum cutoff velocity of 170 cm/s based on multiple vessel duplex color doppler evaluation [154]. Kogutt et al., report a 91% sensitivity and 22% specificity [93]. Adams et al., report a TCD sensitivity of 90% and a specificity of 100% at a cutoff of 190 cm/s using conventional angiography as the 'gold' standard [5].

TCD velocity compared to abnormal conjunctival velocity based on computer assisted intravital microscopy (CAIM) found a correlation between MCA and conjunctival (small vessel) flow velocities. It is hypothesized that small vessel vasculopathy might be an 'indicator' of large vessel disease [39].

Ultrasonography is not helpful in long term followup of chronically transfused subjects because ICA and MCA velocities decrease markedly with increasing hemoglobin concentration even in the face of increasing vessel stenosis [84, 177]. Ultrasonography's greatest value is in the rapid non-invasive identification of high blood velocity states in the carotid MCA and ACA vessels in asymptomatic non-transfused SS subjects. In those with elevated velocity, subtle functional or structural abnormalities in the ipsilateral regions of the cerebrum can be identified using PET, XeCT, MRS or anatomically by a qMRI or MRI (DWI)

Clinical Presentation

Cerebral vasculopathy is manifest as cerebral infarction and intracranial hemorrhage. The type of stroke is age specific with distinct difference in outcome [126, 137, 138]. Cerebral infarction begins during childhood, rarely cases death immediately. As reported by Ohene-Frempong, no immediate mortality was observed in 62 cerebral infarctions but severe neurologic and cognitive deficits were frequent [121]. The association of incomplete ('silent') infarction on cMRI with the increased risk of clinical stroke and cognitive dysfunction observed in children with sickle cell anemia is analogous to that decline observed in 'healthy' elderly adults [11, 16, 70, 149, 180, 187, 191, 202]. Thalamic infarcts are associated with a decline in memory performance and nonthalamic lesions with poor psychomotor speed [16, 107, 172, 190, 203]. Contrariwise, acute intracranial hemorrhage has been associated with an immediate mortality of 24% [121]. This recent data compares to our older study published in 1978 with a high rate immediate of death secondary to massive intracranial hemorrhage [137]. The diagnosis of clinical stroke and unrecognized incomplete infarctions (silent stroke) is now accurate in nearly 100% of cases based on confirmation by neuroimaging (Table 1 and 2) [3, 111]. Asymptomatic subjects with vascular abnormalities found using transcranial doppler ultrasonography (TCD) combined with conventional magnetic resonance imaging (cMRI) have a significant risk of subsequent clinical stroke and increasing penumbral damage [5, 7, 108, 126, 127]

In our 4 decade natural history study of cerebrovascular accidents we observed 122 subjects with sickle cell anemia who had a clinically apparent stroke. Sixty three had cerebral infarction and 29 had intracranial hemorrhage (Figure 1). Twenty three subjects had an unspecified CVA usually occurring before modern neuroimaging capability was available. Six subjects had clinical cerebral infarctions followed at a later age by intracranial hemorrhage [133] (data not shown). Representative of this phenomena is one subject who had her first recognized CVA at age 25, an intracranial hemorrhage followed in a few months by a second lethal hemorrhage. At autopsy old infarctions with cerebral atrophy were found in the brain regions not obliterated by the recent hemorrhage. In our group, the median age of onset for recognized cerebral infarctions (CI) was 13.88 years (range 1.2 to 58.18) and for intracranial hemorrhage was 31.75 years (range 4.87 to 51.5 years). As time progresses and the subjects survive beyond the third decade, intracranial hemorrhage is the most common type of clinical CVA observed. We are now observing a few elderly subjects (55 years) with infarctive disease (n=3). There is a significant impact of chronic renal insufficiency with impaired platelet function on the prevalence of intracranial hemorrhage. After the third decade of life, as end stage renal disease and chronic lung disease with pulmonary hypertension increases in prevalence, this enhances the risk of rupture of small fragile collateral vessels in the brain (Moyamoya) which are often not recognized to be present [67, 175].

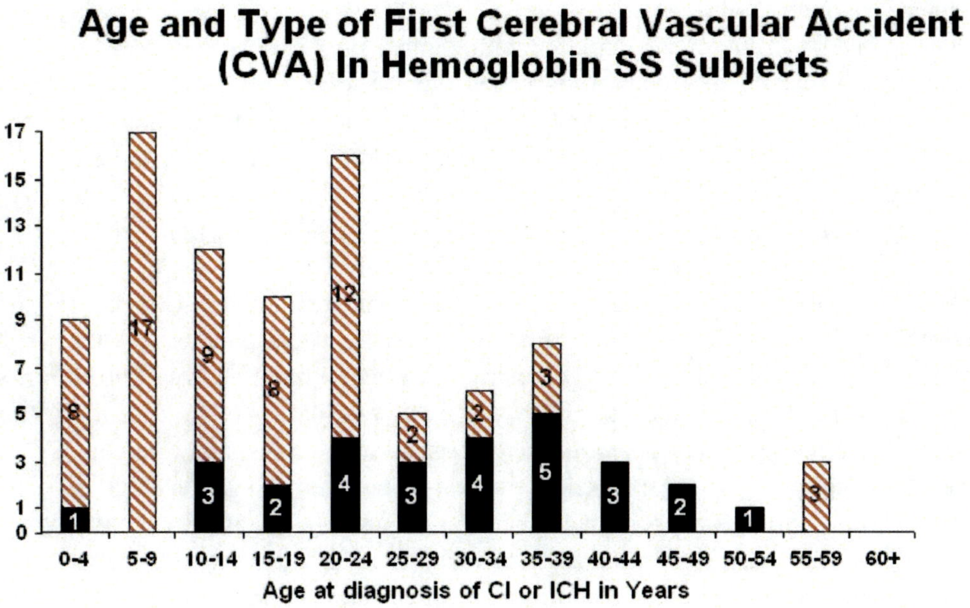

Figure 1. The specific type of clinical stroke was identified based on neuroimaging or autopsy in 91 subjects with sickle cell anemia. Intra cranial hemorrhage (ICH) was found in 28 subjects and cerebral infarction in 63.

PREDISPOSING RISK FACTORS FOR CEREBRAL VASCULOPATHY

Several prognostic models suggests that the combination of clinical, genetic and laboratory risk factors has strong predictive power for stroke in SS children (Table 3) [7, 21, 28, 52, 56, 99, 106, 108, 109, 121, 134, 136, 151, 190]. Most reported series that identified clinical risk factors are based on retrospective analysis of subjects who already had an overt hemiparetic stroke as confirmed by computer tomography (CT), conventional magnetic resonance imaging (cMRI), magnetic resonance angiography (MRA), ultrasonography, and positron emission tomography (PET). A prospective analysis of risk factors in a newborn cohort identified severe disease expression among 17% (67/392) of North American SS children by 2 years of age [3, 107, 127]. In those who were categorized as severe, with 3 or more risk factors, clinical apparent stroke subsequently occurred in 38.3% by age 8. This is significantly higher than that associated with ICA or MCA stenosis analyzed as a single entity at 26% (6 of 23) or at 15% (10 of 67) [3, 5, 129]. The risk factors were onset of splenic dysfunction by age 1, dactylitis by age 1, prior transient cerebral ischemia (TIA), increased numbers of pocked red cells, fetal hemoglobin (Hb F) less than 13% by age 2, low hemoglobin concentration (<7.5 g/dl) and persistently high neutrophil and platelet counts [107]. Repeated severe hypoxic episodes marked by seizures ($Pa0_2$ <60mmHg), severe acute chest syndrome (ACS), severe recurrent asthma, bacterial meningitis, systolic hypertension, aplastic crisis and exchange transfusion act as independent compounding factors that are associated with increased cerebral microvasculopathy (Table 3) [52, 73, 89, 151]. There is an unexplained association of priapism to cerebral ischemia [140]. Scothorn et al., document an important point in a group of 137 children with clinical stroke [151]. All were being treated with transfusion therapy of Hb A erythrocytes. Twenty-two percent (n=31) had a second stroke. The subjects who had their initial stroke in relationship to a concurrent medical problem, such as ACS, did not have recurrent strokes. Contrariwise, of the 101 subjects with no initiating medical illness, 1.9 per 100 patient years had recurrent strokes despite long term transfusion therapy. Thus, the absence of an initiating illness for the first stroke is a major risk factor for recurrent stroke even while on transfusion therapy.

The neurologically 'asymptomatic' high risk SS anemic child whose CBF is >150 ml/100 gm of brain tissue per minute (3 times the normal adult) who has carotid, MCA, or ACA stenosis, with increased ipsilateral oxygen extraction fraction has a highly significant risk for subsequent stroke. Stage II hemodynamic cerebral vascular failure, known as 'misery perfusion', has been repeatedly documented as the sentinel of impending infarction [92, 207]. An increased regional oxygen extraction fraction using PET inhalation [^{15}O] signals that ipsilateral regional blood flow is so inadequate that the brain must extract increasingly greater amounts of oxygen per ml of blood flow to maintain neuronal function. As the SS child becomes progressively more anemic during the first year of life, cerebral hyperemia is required to meet the high cerebral oxygen extraction demands of the maturing brain [138]. The vascularity of the borderzone regions of the high cerebral convexity is exquisitely responsive to cerebral oxygen needs providing a regulatory mechanism for changes in cerebral blood flow (CBF) [194]. Increased oxygen extraction fraction is thought to aggravate the deleterious effects of the Hb S red cell on the neurovascular endothelium. These factors taken together account for high specific infarctive stroke risk during the first decade.

Table 3: Cerebral Infarction: Factors Predictive of Risk⁺

CLINICAL FACTORS
- Age 2 thru 8 years (elevated cerebral blood flow)
- SS sibling with stroke
- Incomplete (silent) infarction
- Prior TIA
- Bacterial meningitis
- B19 infection induced aplastic crisis
- Repeat episodes of severe acute chest syndrome with hypoxia (Pa O_2) <60 mmHg)
- Nocternal hypoxemia with or without sleep apnea
- Acute anemic episode (Hb 2g/dl below normal level)
- Repeat seizure episodes
- Dactylitis before age 1
- Splenic dysfunction or infarction near age 1
- Priapism
- Systolic hypertension*
- Moyamoya (angiography)
- Decreasing academic school performance
- Decreasing fine motor skills (Zurick fine motor examination, Perdue non-dominant hand pegboard)
- Abnormal Test of Variables of Attention

LABORATORY RISK FACTORS
- Hemoglobin (steady state) concentration <7.5 g/dl with high reticulocyte count
- Leukocyte count $>15x10^9/1$ (absolute granulocyte count $>8x10^9/1$)
- Platelet count $>450x10^9/1$
- Pocked (pitted) RBC, $\geq$ 3.5% by 24 months of age
- Fetal hemoglobin $\leq$ 13% by age 24 months
- CAR haplotype on chromosome 11
- No alpha gene deletion
- HLA subtypes (DPBI*0401), (HLA-A*0102), (HLA-A*2612)**

+Observations in young children during steady state, not recently transfused and not on chemotherapy (hydroxyurea). In a prospective natural history study, 17% of North American SS children who had 3 or more risk factors by age 2 demonstrated a 38.3% frequency of clinical stroke by age 8 years (ref 107)

*Frequently associated with adult onset uremia and intracranial hemorrhage

**Ref 79

The neuroradiologic diagnosis of incomplete cerebral infarction [61] in an "asymptomatic" child less than 8 years old is a major risk factor for clinical hemiparetic stroke [5, 108, 126, 127]. These incomplete infarctions are often referred to as 'silent' infarctions [113]. In those with incomplete infarctions there is an increased risk of substantial spread to the penumbral regions and cognitive impairment [129]. In North American and French SS children of mixed ethnic background, significant neuropsychologic impairments have been found in 21.5% in those with cMRI 'silent' infarction [16, 28, 113].

A family member with a stroke is a predictor of stroke in SS siblings [3, 56, 137, 146]. Specific HLA types appears to be related to an increased susceptibility to overt stroke [169]. Based on a study of 231 SS children, 71 of which had a cMRI confirmed cerebral infarction, cerebral infarctions were divided into 2 subgroups, large vessel infarctions and those with microvascular obstructions. HLA alleles HLA-A *0102 and HLA-A* 2612 were associated with a significant risk of large vessel occlusions and with clinical stroke [79]. The HLA-DRB1 loci including DRBI* 0401 were associated with incomplete infarctions identified on cMRI [79, 169]. Thus, the inherited HLA subtypes or other genetic factors may partially explain the high sibling risk of cerebral vasculopathy [174]. Among relatively stable non mixed African ethnic groups, there is significantly different risk of overt stroke. Haplotypes of the • •^{S} gene cluster and • •gene status are important correlates of severe disease expression and stroke risk [4, 59, 134]. The haplotypes are designated by convention according to their geographic African origin [134]. The prevalence of symptomatic infarction with paresis nears 8% in Jamaica and Nigeria (Benin haplotype), 8% in Turkey (Benin haplotype), 10 to 18% in Brazil (CAR haplotype) and 1% in Eastern Saudi Arabia (Saudi haplotype) [12, 21, 40, 59, 65, 121, 124]. The Sen/Saudi haplotypes were first described in Senegal and Eastern Saudi Arabia and are generally less severe in clinical expression [134]. Cerebral infarction is rare in Arab children with the Saudi Arab/Indian haplotypes when coupled with • •thalassemia-2 which is found in 52.4% of the population [8]. Alpha thalassemia-2 as a co-inherited genetic condition in 30% of African American subjects seems to confer some protection for clinical stroke [14, 50, 75, 82, 89, 121, 134].

At what age in high risk SS children should the initial neuroimaging workup begin? Cognitive problems are not frequently identified before three years of age [188]. Steen et al., has shown based on quantitative magnetic resonance imaging (qMRI), significant neuronal drop out by age 4 [163]. Thus, we recommend neuroimaging well before 4 years of age. The reported sensitivity or specificity of neurologic examination in young children for the identification of asymptomatic incomplete cerebral infarction is generally low. However, Mercuri et al. by means of an exquisitely detailed neurologic examination identified 70% (7/10) [106]. Siegel et al., report a 92% sensitivity and 83% specificity combining neurologic examination with ultrasonography elevated blood flow velocity confirmed using cMRI as the 'gold' standard [158]. In a prospective study, Glauser et al., observed the onset of the first neurologic event between 2.4 and 6.1 years [64]. He found that the SS child who has 'soft' neurologic signs, TIA, or evanescent neurologic symptoms usually had (71%, 12/17) 'silent' incomplete infarction on cMRI. Wang et al. was able to show that 7 of 39 very young neurologically asymptomatic children had significant neuroimaging abnormalities based on magnetic resonance technology [190]. In three very young children with elevated blood flow velocities, but normal cMRI, decreased glucose metabolism (FDG) and perfusion $[^{15}O]H_2O$ on PET has been observed in the ipsilateral brain region supplied by the stenotic blood vessel [135].

Defining the population according to predictive risk factors very early in life (Table 3), verified by the identification of neuroimaging abnormalities increases the subsequent infarction risk to greater than 50%, if untreated [96]. The identification of ICA and MCA stenosis, cMRI borderzone lesions and functional abnormalities on PET or loss of gray matter on qMRI is already well into the disease progression. Mild cognitive deficiency may be inevitable although overt stroke and severe cognitive disability should be preventable with adequate treatment [172, 197, 202, 203]. It follows that the basic requirement of successful management is the treatment of the SS child before neuronal loss has begun.

CURRENT CONVENTIONAL THERAPY

Transfusion Therapy

In untreated children, repeat clinical strokes occur in two-thirds of the subjects [137]. If maintained on Hb A red cell transfusion, the majority with hemiparetic strokes demonstrate fewer recurrent clinical episodes but may have new incomplete infarctions [52, 146, 148]. Most survive childhood [34, 43, 126, 151]. The goal is to maintain the hemoglobin concentration at 12g/dl and Hb S percentage at <30% [6]. In SS subjects with prior stroke, transfusion is associated with a 20% reduction in time averaged mean MCA blood flow velocities as measured by TCD [177]. These reductions occurred rapidly within the first 3 hours of transfusion and are directly correlated to the rise in hematocrit (29% to 34%). Because the remaining Hb S red cells and reticulocytes retain more oxygen, blood rheology immediately improves.

The cerebral vasculopathy during the first decade is not a static process; on transfusion some will show improvement in functional neuroimaging (PET) during the first year of therapy [135] whereas others develop new asymptomatic penumbral lesions [127, 191]. Conventional angiograms and MRA show absence of progression of vessel disease and occasional smoothing of previously roughened endothelium in some patients, but progression of large vessel disease in others [146]. However, completed infarction sites [61] do not improve and penumbral lesion progression occurs with continued loss of neuropsychologic function [16, 45]. Even in less severely involved subjects, based on the Zurick neuromotor 'soft' sign test or the ABC motor dysfunction test coupled with neuropsychologic testing, return of normal function is usually incomplete [45, 49, 196].

Despite the clear immediate hemodynamic benefits, the morbidity of long term transfusion therapy is formidable given the need for parenteral chelation [30, 42, 198] and the 30% frequency of alloimmunization, and technical problems of venous access [117, 144, 147, 155, 159]. Erythrocytapheresis can reduce iron overload but is more expensive [2, 118]. The risk of acute, delayed and bystander transfusion reactions increase with the cumulative number of transfusion administered.

Functional neurologic deficits persist and become more obvious as the child matures [28, 45, 191]. As young adults, they often die of massive intracranial hemorrhage, adult respiratory distress syndrome (ARDS), or complications of transfusion induced hemosiderosis [43, 66, 132, 133].

How long should a transfusion program continue after the first stroke? In young children with elevated CBF who are less than age 10, stroke frequently reoccurs when the transfusion program has been discontinued [204]. One subject had a repeat stroke as the hemoglobin concentration decreased to 7.5 g/dl even though the Hb S percentage remained <30%. Wang et al. reported valuable details regarding 10 subjects ages 10 to 21 years who had transfusion therapy discontinued after more than 5 years [189]. Three of the patients were 17 to 21 years of age when transfusion was discontinued and had no new infarctions or intracranial hemorrhage. Six of the younger subjects had major untoward CNS events within one year of discontinuance of transfusion. Thus, general consensus is that the transfusion program should continue until approximately age 18 years. Attempts to reduce the transfusion level after a number of years in adolescents and young adults has been shown to be relatively safe. The Hb S percentage is allowed to rise to approximately 50%. The reported subjects did not have recurrent infarctions [43] despite a rise in the CBF [84]. There is little evidence based data to support or refute this consensus opinion. Data are now becoming available to provide age specific guidelines for discontinuance of transfusion therapy near age 18 [141, 195]. In these young adults, chelation was continued and hydroxyurea therapy was given. Discontinuation as the subject nears the third decade of life appears to be relatively safe with rare recurrent clinical infarction. One American national study has been suggested to deal with this question based on intent to treat randomization protocols.

Prevention of First Stroke in Subjects at Risk

On what basis can treatment be initiated before the overt stroke occurs? And can transfusion ameliorate the progression of neuronal damage in those with incomplete ('silent') infarction? For the first time, an evidence based randomized clinical trial aimed at the prevention of clinical stroke has been published [6]. TCD was used as the initial screening neurophysiologic tool in neurologically asymptomatic children. In those with elevated ICA, MCA or ACA velocities, the subjects were randomized to receive transfusion support or observation and cMRI was performed. Adams et al. demonstrated the value of maintenance transfusion in the prevention of ischemic stroke (p=0.001) in those with ICA, MCA, or ACA stenosis. A 30% (7/25) risk for cerebral infarction within 3 years [6, 126, 129] was observed in neurologically asymptomatic children with elevated vessel velocities of >200 cm/sec and concurrent borderzone cMRI abnormalities who had been randomized to no transfusion [128]. These subjects were statistically analyzed without regard for the presence of other stroke predictive risk factors [129]. No data is reported on the rate of asymptomatic progression of the cerebral vasculopathy and cognitive decline in this cohort of subjects. In this study which was discontinued early within 3 years, no plan was developed regarding the continuation of transfusion therapy in those children with an elevated TCD velocity who had no clinical events and a normal cMRI. The individual centers involved have developed local algorithms for repeat cMRI and functional neuroimaging correlated to neuropsychologic evaluation aimed at developing a plan of discontinuing transfusion therapy safely. Initiating hydroxyurea or similar therapy in those with no neuroimaging abnormalities prior to discontinuing transfusion similar to that in adults but during late adolescence is erratically being implemented.

INVESTIGATIVE THERAPY (TABLE 4)

Hematopoietic Cell Transplantation (HCT) Bone marrow transplantation (BMT) or cord blood from a histocompatible HLA non SS donor is curative [117]. Stem cell or cord blood transplantation may successfully engraft even in the face of moderate HLA incompatibility. Young high risk children with minimal evidence of cerebrovasculopathy are encouraged to undergo BMT with the hope that the CNS disease will not progress. BMT requires a year of intensive invasive medical intervention as the trade-off for a life time cure [27, 181, 184, 185]. Initially, BMT was associated with an adverse risk of inducing progression of already existent cerebral vasculopathy [1]. One subject died of a massive intracranial hemorrhage 42 days after transplantation (186) while severely thrombocytopenic. Revision of protocol management guidelines and intake criteria has lessened the CNS complication rate. Overall survival is 93%, nearly 80% of the SS patients will successfully engraft the bone marrow transplant with an event free survival [27, 184]. No improvement has been demonstrated in completed infarcts in those transplanted after the onset of symptomatic cerebral vasculopathy. In those subjects, new ischemic lesions and increasing arterial stenosis have been occasionally reported after successful BMT [1, 86]. Return of splenic function has been reported associated with increased levels of Hb F [57]. The French and Belgian SS subjects have had fewer complications because the majority of these young subjects were transplanted before the cerebral vasculopathy had progressed or proliferative Moyamoya vasculopathy was present [27, 181]. Overall, children less than 10 years of age have better survival with less graft vs host disease (13%) compared to adolescents (28%) and adults (40%). Neuroimaging including cMRI and MRA immediately prior to BMT is essential to identify fragile vessel collaterals (Moyamoya) because of the potential for rupture of these vessels with uncontrolled thrombocytopenia, Cyclosporin A induced hypertension, or sudden changes in CBF and blood viscosity [186]. Only 18% of patients with sickle cell anemia in the United States have compatible donors whereas in France and Belgium, compatible donors approach the expected 25% of siblings tested. Chimeric BMT transplantation has the potential of a lower complication rate but moderate numbers of sickle cells may remain in the circulation potentially leading to further endothelial damage.

Cord blood transplantation has been shown to have a lower incidence of graft vs host disease of 11% with event free survival rates of 79% in • •thalassemia and 90% in sickle cell disease [100]. It seems possible that intra osseus bone marrow transplantation (IBMT) of hematopoietic stem cells may improve engraftment [206] because stem cells are delivered more efficiently. This procedure has the potential advantage of extending the use of cord blood to adults.

Gene Therapy for sickle cell disease has not been successful with low levels of hemoglobin produced in part because of difficulties in obtaining high-titer stable vectors [125]. There have been adverse chromatin rearrangements when segments and the • •globin locus control region are incorporated into retroviral vectors precluding functional translation downstream to the • •globin locus. There is a need to further understand the obstacles related to the presence of chromatin position effects and find better vectors. Baum et al., recently reviewed the therapeutic issues and potential limitations in human subjects undergoing gene therapy [25]. As stated, it is vital "to improve safety, efficiency and prognosis" for patients with genetic disorders.

Table 4: Classification of Potential Treatment Targets

- Medical Therapy
  - Induce fetal hemoglobin production
  - Prevent intraerythrocytic dehydration
  - Prevent endothelial dysfunction
  - Anti adhesion molecules
  - Regulate basal vascular tone
    - Nitric oxide (NO)
  - Regulate abnormal coagulation
- Curative Therapy
  - Hematopoietic cell transplantation
    - Bone marrow transplantation (BMT)
    - Stem cell transplantation
    - Chimeric BMT
  - Gene therapy

Aspirin to Prevent Stroke Platelet activation in the presence of 'diseased' erythrocytes induces a release reaction and generate biologically active products that recruit additional platelets into a developing thrombus. SS subjects at high risk for stroke usually have a moderate thrombocytosis. Insufficient blockade of this pro-aggregatory property of abnormal erythrocytes has led to development of additional ischemic complications [87, 176]. It is hypothesized that low-dose aspirin by shifting the balance away from thrombosis would inhibit platelet aggregation without impairing the generation of prostacycline by the vascular endothelium. No evidence based clinical trials of aspirin for stroke prevention in SS subjects are reported.

Fetal Hemoglobin Switch Therapy Pharmacologic induction of fetal hemoglobin (Hb F) has been under investigation for 2 decades initiated by the studies of 5-azacytidine in baboons by De Simone et al. [53, 54]. A number of agents have been investigated that can perturb erythropoiesis in such a way as to elevate the Hb F percentage in the peripheral blood. A listing of some of these agents is shown in Table 5. The butyrates have been shown to have mild histone deacetylase (HDAC) inhibition effects possibly accounting for the selective rise in • •globin production [19, 20, 130, 143]. Witt et al. studied the inhibition of HDAC by apicidin [205]. Apicidin is a novel HDAC inhibitor and induces Hb F synthesis activating the • •globin promoter in human K562 erythro-leukemia cells. Using this model, apicidin was compared to butyrate, phenyl butyrate, isobutyramide, hydroxyurea and 5-azycytidine, and a 10 fold greater stimulation of Hb F was observed [205]. Agents with similar molecular mechanisms are under development and phase I clinical trials are being initiated.

Hydroxyurea has undergone an evidence based randomized placebo controlled clinical trial in adult SS subjects [38]. Hydroxyurea is the single chemotherapeutic agent that is approved in the United States for treatment of sickle cell disease [199]. Observed was a significant reduction in adult onset painful crisis ($p<0.001$), fewer episodes of acute chest syndromes, a decreased transfusion requirement and a modest reduction in 9 year followup mortality (Table 6) [164]. The reduced adult death rate was positively correlated to the rise of Hb F levels. No difference in hepatic sequestration or the rate of cerebral vasculopathy (clinical stroke) was observed. Since sickle related cerebral vasculopathy begins during early childhood (age <6 years), and new strokes are rare after age 18, this study could not be expected to show beneficial effects preventing stroke in young adults. Hydroxyurea in subjects who have already developed multilobar cerebral infarction with overt stroke or proliferative arteriolar vasculopathy (Moyamoya) has shown no beneficial effect. It has been associated with intracranial hemorrhage [183] possibly because of hydroxyurea induced thrombocytopenia in subjects with Moyamoya.

Table 5: Agents that Induce Fetal Hemoglobin Switch in Sickle Cell Anemia*

Cell Cycle Specific Agents	Route of Administration
5-Azacytidine	IV
Cytosine arabinoside	IV
Hydroxyurea	IV or po
Hematopoietic Growth Factors	
Erythropoietin (rH_{μ} EPO)	IV or subcue
Colony-stimulating factor (GM-CSF)	IV or subcue
Interleukin-3 (IL-3)	IV or subcue
Butyrates	
Arginine butyrate	IV
Sodium phenylbutyrate	po
Isobutyamide	po
Apicidin	
Valproic acid	po

*Combinations of cell cycle specific agents, hematopoietic growth factors combined with agents that prevent intraerythrocytic dehydration are in clinical trials

Hydroxyurea is a cell-cycle specific cytotoxic agent that acts by inhibiting ribonucleotide reduction with no DNA demethylation activity. Physiologic stress induced switch to increased • •chain production has been recognized for decades when humans (or baboons) bleed and become anemic, or in subjects recovering from bone marrow transplantation, in infantile chronic juvenile myelomonocytic leukemia and during bone marrow recovery immediately following cytotoxic cancer chemotherapy. The perturbation of cellular kinetics and cytotoxicity recovery apparently recruits erythroblasts or primitive erythroid progenitors (BFU-E) and initiate a reactive reversal of the • •chain switch increasing the amount of Hb F in the reticulocytes [22, 36].

Table 6: Effects of Hydroxyurea (HU)

A. PATHOPHYSIOLOGIC EFFECTS OF HYDROXYUREA
   - Cell-cycle specific cytotoxic agent which inhibits ribonucleotide reductase
   - Increases red cell fetal hemoglobin (Hb F) by 2 fold in 50% of SS subjects
   - Decreases production of sickle reticulocyte
   - Decreases sickle adhesion to endothelial cells with decreased adhesion receptor expression
   - Red cell deformability increases with improved rheology
   - Increases RBC survival
   - Generates increased nitric oxide production
   - Improves intra erythrocytic cell hydration
   - Increases cell potassium content
   - Decreases dense sickle red cell fraction
   - Decreases neutrophil count
   - Decreases platelet count usually below $150 x 10^9/l$

B. BENEFICIAL CLINICAL EFFECTS OF HYDROXYUREA
   1. Adult Subjects
      - Decrease in age specific risk of death
      - Decreases painful events by 50%
      - Decreases frequency of acute chest syndrome
      - Decreases transfusion requirement
   2. Children
      - No effect on risk of stroke or death in short term clinical trials
      - Decreases frequency of acute chest syndrome
      - Decreases hospitalization frequency
      - Increase in body fat
      - Increased splenic perfusion and return of germinal centers
   3. CNS Effects
      - No benefit in already present cerebral ischemia
      - May decrease the rate of penumbral spread adjacent to infarcted areas
      - Increased risk of intracranial hemorrhage in subjects with proliferative vasculopathy (ie Moymoya)
   4. All SS Subjects
      - No benefit in subjects with prior end stage renal failure, retinopathy, osteonecrosis, or those with impotence secondary to priapism
   5. Adverse Effects
      - 25% of SS subjects are non-responders
      - Severe myelosuppression
      - Nausea and vomiting
      - Hair loss
      - Skin rash
      - Pruritus
      - Potential carcinogenesis or teratogenesis

Three potentially beneficial effects of hydroxyurea have been observed in SS subjects. 1) The increase in Hb F above 15% in nearly 50% of SS subjects [36, 164, 165] and 2) the modification of adhesion of the Hb S reticulocyte to the vascular endothelium [10, 26, 76] and 3) myelosuppression [23, 37]. Hydroxyurea therapy improves red cell deformability, decreases cellular dehydration, decreases the irreversible sickle cell fraction, modifies red cell potassium content, improves rheology and RBC survival (Table 6) [23]. Hematocrit elevation increasing whole blood viscosity has not been reported in children. Hydroxyurea decreases the bone marrow production of Hb S reticulocytes, platelets and granulocytes [23, 37]. In clinical trials, poor Hb F responders (25% with no significant change) did demonstrate some improved clinical parameters. The identical hematologic factors (Ie, elevated neutrophil, platelet and reticulocyte count) that can predict an increased risk of cerebral vasculopathy (Table 3) also predict which subjects respond best to hydroxyurea [37]. The dose of hydroxyurea is escalated from 15 to 35 mg/Kg per day monitoring the platelet, neutrophil and reticulocyte counts. Neutropenia of $<2 \times 10^9/1$ should trigger a reduction in dose. Maximum dose for older children and adolescents fluctuates between 1000 mg and 1500 mg orally per day.

The question is: Can hydroxyurea or similar agents prevent the development of cerebral vasculopathy in the very young child [195]? The fact that splenic germinal centers have been shown to return may be a promising model [58, 122, 192]. Long term clinical trials of hydroxyurea beginning during early childhood [85, 102, 152] and a multi-institutional trial in North America are in progress.

Multi-faceted therapeutic effect of hydroxyurea added to other agents in high risk children has great potential benefit and should be evaluated in evidence based randomized clinical trials monitored by neuroimaging and neuropsychologic testing. In order to be clinically effective in the prevention of CNS vasculopathy, these agents must be relatively non toxic in children, cross the blood brain barrier, orally available and not impart on unpleasanet odor (ie butyrate) to the subject. Long term compliance with oral medication is a major problem in young children. This fact was again documented with compliance for oral penicillin at 40% when used to prevent serious or fatal S. Pneumoniae septicemia in young children. This is the same age group (age 1 to 8 years) in whom preventative neuroprotective therapy should be administered.

Nitric Oxide and Precursors

Nitric oxide (NO) was originally known as endothelium -1 or endothelium derived relaxing factor. It has been identified as a vital factor in the maintenance of vascular tone (Table 4) [63]. Arginine is the substrate that endothelial cells use to produce nitric oxide gas. This gas induces smooth muscle to relax and results in dilatation of the blood vessels. In normal subjects, nitric oxide rapidly combines with intra erythrocytic oxyhemoglobin and is destroyed maintaining a narrow physiologic balance in basal vascular tone. However, in subjects with a chronic hemolytic anemia with increased plasma levels of oxyhemoglobin, destruction of NO is further increased as NO binds to oxyhemoglobin to form S-nitroshemoglobin resulting in low plasma levels and vasoconstriction [63].

Decreased availability of nitric oxide has been thought to contribute to the risk of repeat episodes of acute chest syndrome leading to chronic sickle lung disease with pulmonary hypertension, bone marrow embolism and reperfusion injury [17]. Inhaled nitric oxide gas or intravenous arginine has been utilized to treat severe acute chest syndrome which is the sickle equivalent to ARDS with some success. Inhaled NO can be shown to reduce pulmonary artery pressure, improve ventilation and perfusion matching and increase oxygenation [200]. Recent review articles [63] detail the physiologic effects of nitric oxide on adhesion molecules down regulating endothelial VCAM-1 expression and the NO donor effects on hydroxyurea which may add to its therapeutic efficacy. In addition, NO inhibits platelet aggregation.

There appears to be an adverse risk of nitric oxide therapy in subjects with pre-existent cerebral vascular disease. Unrecognized infarctions ('silent') are associated with Moyamoya fragile collateral vessel formations [55]. Observed, but not reported in the literature to date, are subjects treated with inhaled NO coupled with exchange transfusion for acute chest syndrome who developed an intracranial hemorrhage while on therapy. There is a possibility that transfusion induced increased cerebral blood flow along with NO induced cerebral vessel dilatation triggered the rupture of unrecognized fragile vessels. If possible clinically, it seems wise to ascertain the presence of Moyamoya syndrome prior to NO therapy. This problem is confounded by the fact that severe hypoxic ACS is known to trigger an increase in cerebral infarction or leukoencephalopathy in subjects who were not managed using NO, arginine therapy or hydroxyurea [73, 91, 151]. A parallel clinical adverse reaction is reported [58, 152, 183] in which administration of hydroxyurea to children with severe preexisting cerebral vasculopathy was associated with recurrent clinical stroke. This is now thought to be related to the fact that hydroxyurea generates nitric oxide in vivo. This enhances the dilatation of the fragile cerebral microvasculature and can result in intracranial hemorrhage. Thus, how and under what circumstances should inhaled NO or arginine therapy be used urgently requires further investigation.

Antiadhesion Molecular Therapy

The cell adhesion molecules adhere tightly to integrins that are expressed in vascular endothelial cells. The expression of genes associated with the major functions of the endothelial cells include effectors of permissibility and vessel tone, angiogeneses, endothelial cell activation and injury. These are a major target of research in sickle cell anemia (Table 4) [104, 166]. Data supports the deleterious role of VCAM-1 on the blood vessel endothelial cells in SS subjects [62, 156]. VCAM-1 is a cell surface sialoglycoprotein and is elevated in SS subjects at baseline and with acute chest syndrome (ACS). No consistent association of VCAM-1 during 'stroke in progression' has been reported. Perfusion with sickle cells induces VCAM-1 expression in cultured endothelial cells [171]. VCAM-1 influences the neutrophilic inflammatory response and is expressed in the bone marrow stroma and may affect hematopoietic cell mobilization in response to granulocyte colony-stimulating factor (G-CSF) [98]. This effect has potential clinical relevance in that an association between neutrophil infiltration and infarct size has been identified in non-SS adults with clinical stroke. Recently, deaths in SS subjects has been observed in those who responded to G-CSF administration with an intense leukocytosis [9]. It follows that potential anti-VCAM-1 therapy might be protective of the penumbral regions during 'stroke in progression' and prevent recurrent stroke [97]. An allelic variant of the VCAM-1 has been identified (C allele of VCAM-1 G1238C) that may confer protection for completed clinical stroke in SS children [173]. There is a potential for gene therapy if VCAM-1 can be convincingly shown to be a primary mediator of sickle cell induced endothelial damage.

BCAM/Lu is an adhesion molecule that is a major RBC receptor for laminin, an extracellular matrix protein found extensively in the vascular beds. Sickle red cells adhere to laminin and this process is regulated by cyclic AMP mediated activation of BCAM/Lu [78]. Inhibition of this process could have therapeutic benefits.

Other compounds that impair adherence of sickle cells to endothelial cells include polyethylene glycol, arginine-glycine-aspartic (RGD) peptide or anti-integrin molecules (anti VCAM-1) and a number of other erythrocyte "coating" molecules [15]. The few clinical trials of these agents have focused on treating sickle cell crisis. A highly purified form of Rheoth Rx (Flocor) can be administered intravenously and improve microvascular blood flow by lowering frictional forces. An agent such as antibody to P-selectin that can prevent the movement of P-selectin to the outer membrane of the endothelial cell should be theoretically valuable in preventing permanent binding of sickle red cells to the cerebral vascular endothelium [104]. Reperfusion injury with the increased production of oxygen radicals following hypoxia could be possibly treated using NO coupled with an anti-P-selectin antibody [26].

Prevention of Intraerythrocyte Dehydration

Agents that can prevent the loss of red cell potassium and water and prevent red cell dehydration are under investigation [32]. Two major ion transport pathways that mediate sickle red cell dehydration are the Ca^{2+}-activated K^{+} channel (Gardos) and the potassium-chloride cotransport channel. Clotrinozole specifically inhibits Gardos channel mediated red cell dehydration and has been given orally to a few SS subjects at relatively low doses [33]. However dysuria and elevation of liver enzymes precluded long term clinical use and initiated a search for other Gardos channel inhibitors. Some of which, ie Dipyridamole (ICA-17403), are in early phase II clinical trials [32]. Magnesium (Mg^{2+}) can decrease the activity of the K-Cl cotransport system and decrease the red cell mean corpuscular hemoglobin concentration. A small clinical trial in sickle crisis of Mg^{2+} pedolate demonstrated a decrease in painful days but was accompanied with mild diarrhea. Currently 2 randomized Mg^{2+} clinical trails are nearing completion in both adult and pediatric subjects. Magnesium also has independent neuroprotective effects as a NMDA antagonist that can competitively bind to the glutamate site of the NMDA receptor. However, disappointingly in the currently ongoing pilot clinical trials of Mg^{2+} pedolate, no neuroimaging or cognitive assessment is included. Chloride conductance blockers such as a substituted diphenylurea (NS1652) or a bromine substituted tetrazoyl derivative (NS3623) are being considered for clinical trials [32].

NEUROPROTECTIVE THERAPY DURING STROKE IN PROGRESS

During stroke in progression, as part of the 'ischemic cascade', the penumbral regions surrounding new infarction sites are at risk for permanent infarctive damage within a few minutes to 12 hours after the initial vasocclusive event [72, 115]. In 'common' stroke syndrome in adults, the use of acute thrombolysis using Plasminogen Activator Therapy (tPA) is hampered by the restrictive time window of <3 hours after onset of symptoms. Rarely do children present to medical facilities with hemiparetic signs that are quickly recognized. The reasons for this delay has been recently reported [60].

Supportive neuroprotective therapy should be begun immediately before exchange transfusion can be implemented [41]. Exchange red cell transfusion of completely matched erythrocytes is thought to be the most physiologic transfusion regimen removing sickle erythrocytes rapidly. No randomized evidence based evaluation of this procedure in the setting of acute stroke in progression has been performed This could be monitored by metabolic neuroimaging (MRS or MRI (DUI). Each step along the'ischemic cascade' provides a potential target for therapeutic intervention [61]. Glucose infusions maintaining physiologic normal levels are neuroprotective (both hyperglycemia and hypoglycemia are deleterious). Cytoprotection (hypothermia) reduces ischemic neuronal injury in part by decreasing the release of the neurotransmitter glutamate [41], but in SS subjects in may produce rheologic alterations that enhance sickle cell adhesion to the vascular endothelium. Since vasogenic cerebral edema is not a factor during acute stroke, steroids or mannitol are not helpful. Hyperventilation poses the threat of re-perfusion injury and increases intracerebral glutamate. The commonly used free radical scavengers such as • •tocopherol do not penetrate the blood brain barrier effectively.

Pharamcologic neuroprotection has failed in clinical trials in adults including trials of gangliosides, N-methyl-D-aspartate-receptor antagonists, antibodies to adhesion molecules and free-radical scavengers [68]. The explanation for these failed studies may include delay in initiation of treatment, inadequate drug penetration to the ischemic areas or failure to match the drug's mode of action to the mechanisms of brain injury [31]. There has been a disappointing failure of the calcium channel antagonists and the mixed results of the NMDA (N-methyl-D-aspartate) antagonists. One aim is to decrease the presynaptic release of neurotransmitters particularly glutamate which is elevated in ischemia and mediates neuronal death. NMDA antagonists competitively bind to the glutamate site of the NMDA receptor. High incidence of intolerable neuropsychotic side effects associated with several of the NMDA antagonists led to early discontinuation of clinical trials. (Note: phencyclidine (angel dust) and ketamine are classical NMDA antagonists). The use of the NMDA antagonists such as magnesium sulfate (7.5 mg IV immediately with 10 mg continuous IV for 5 days or fructose-1.6 -diphosphate in SS acute stroke could possibly be beneficial [114]. Agents such as the myelin constituent CDP-choline (citocoline) and bFGF, a neuronal growth factor, showed positive results in animals but have failed in phase III clinical adult trials of 'common' stroke. However, neuronal growth factors might be helpful in young SS subjects in terms of decreasing the penumbral damage caused by the 'ischemic cascade'.

SUMMARY

Ischemic brain injury during childhood is the most disabling complication of sickle cell anemia. The cerebral vasculopathy is directly related to the age specific elevated cerebral blood flow and the increased oxygen required for brain maturation. The magnitude of damage is compounded by anemia, abnormal red cell rheology, and sickle reticulocyte induced endothelial hyperplasia. During an acute clinical infarctive stroke, the goals of therapy are to arrest the 'ischemic cascade' and minimize the amount of permanent damage. Further enlargement of the infarction region can be ameliorated by normal hemoglobin (Hb A) red cell transfusion. The combined application of anatomic, functional and physiological neuro-imaging modalities in high risk young SS children can improve the predictive accuracy for impending stroke to greater then 38% during the first decade of life. Neuroimaging abnormalities without a completed infarction defines a 'window of opportunity' that should prompt initiation of preventive therapy. However, cognitive disability is a major consequence of microvascular ischemia without overt clinical stroke.

Transfusion is the only recognized effective modality aimed at the prevention of recurrent infarctive stroke in children. Transfusion of Hb A red cells can prevent the occurrence of overt clinical stroke in 'asymptomatic' subjects with carotid siphon, MCA and ACA stenosis who have borderzone lesions on cMRI or cerebral dysfunction. Long term transfusion therapy is arduous burdened with technical venous access problems coupled with iron overload requiring chelation, induction of irregular transfusion antibodies and hepatitis virus infections.

The ideal treatment for stroke is prevention. Drugs such as hydroxyurea, 5-azocitidine, butyrates, and apiciden that increase the proportion of fetal hemoglobin (Hb F) in the sickle red cell show some promise. Among these, hydroxyurea demonstrates a 2 pronged effect by also decreasing the Hb S reticulocyte adhesion to the endothelium. There is solid theoretical support but no evidence-based clinical trials to supports its use in young high risk children to prevent cerebral ischemia. A number of chemotherapeutic agents that can interfere with sickle red cell adhesiveness to endothelial cells are under investigation. Cellular rehydration with agents that inhibit the Gardas channel or that are chloride conductance blockers might decrease the propensity of deleterious sickle-endothelial cell interaction. Successful erythropoietic cell transplantation including bone marrow, cord blood and stem cell transplantation, can be curative but histocompatibility problems need to be resolved. Safe vectors for gene therapy that can maintain the integrity and function of the inserted • •globin locus control region or hemoglobin gene need to be identified. Identification of appropriate non toxic treatment modalities that can prevent sickle red cell induced neurovascular endothelial damage is the ultimate research (Holy Grail) objective.

REFERENCES

[1] Abound MR, Jackson SM, Barredo J, Holden KR, Cure J, Laver J. Neurologic complications following bone marrow transplantation for sickle cell disease. 1996;*BMT*, 17: 405-407

[2] Adams DM, Shultz WH, Ware RE, Kinney TR. Erythrocytapheresis can reduce iron overload and prevent the need for chelation therapy in chronically transfused pediatric patients. *J Pediatr Hematol/Oncol*, 1996;18: 46-50

[3] Adams RJ. Stroke prevention and treatment in sickle cell disease. *Arch Neurol*, 2001;58:565-568

[4] Adams RJ, Kutlar A, McKie V, Carl E, Nichols FT, Liu JC, McKie K, Clary A. Alpha thalassemia and stroke risk in sickle cell anemia. *Am J Hematol,* 1994;45: 279-282

[5] Adams RJ, McKie VC, Carl EM, Nichols FT, Perry R, Brock K, McKie K, Figueroa R, Litaker M, Weiner MS, Brambilla, D. Long-term stroke risk in children with sickle cell disease screened with transcranial Doppler. *Ann Neurol,* 1997;42: 699-704

[6] Adams RJ, McKie VC, Hsu L, Files B, Vinchinsky E, Pegelow C, Abboud M, Gallagher D, Kutlar A, Nichols FT, Bonds DR, Brambilla D. Prevention of a first stroke by transfusions in children with sickle cell anemia and abnormal results on transcranial doppler ultrasonography. *N Eng J Med,* 1999;98;339: 5-11

[7] Adams R, McKie V, Nichols F, Carl E, Zhang DL, McKie K, Figueroa R, Litaker M, Thompson W, Hess D. The use of transcranial ultrasonography to predict stroke in sickle-cell disease. *N Eng J Med,* 1992;326: 605-610

[8] Adekile A, Yacoub F, Gupta R. Silent cerebral infarcts are rare in Arab sickle cell patients. *Blood*, 1999;94:419a (abstract)

[9] Adler BK, Salzman DE, Carabasi MH, Vaughan WP, Reddy W, Prchal JT. Fatal sickle cell crisis after granulocyte colony-stimulating factor administration. *Blood*, 2001;97:3313-3314

[10] Adragna NC, Fonseca P, Lauf PK. Hydroxyurea affects cell morphology, cation transport, and red blood cell adhesion in cultured vascular endothelial cells. *Blood*, 1994;83: 553-560

[11] Albers GW, Caplan LR, Easton JD, Fayad PB, Mohr JP, Saver JL, Sherman DG. Transient ischemic attack- proposal for a new definition. *N Engl J Med,* 2002;347:1713-1716

[12] Annobil SH, Omojola MF, Adzaku FK, Addae SK, Mohammed S. Cerebrovascular accidents (strokes) in children with sickle cell disease residing at high and low altitudes of Saudi Arabia. *Ann Trop Paediatr*, 1990;10: 191-198

[13] Arena JM. Vascular accident and hemiplegia in a patient with sickle cell anemia. *Am J Dis Child,* 1935;49:722-723

[14] Arena JM. Cerebral vascular lesions accompanying sickle cell anemia. *J Pediatr,* 1939;14:745-751

[15] Armstrong JK, Meiselman HJ, Fisher TC. Covalent binding of poly (ethylene glycol) (PEG) to the surface of red blood cells inhibits aggregation and reduces low shear blood viscosity. *Am J Hematol,* 1997;56:26-28

[16] Armstrong FD, Thompson RJ Jr., Wang W, Zimmerman R, Pegelow CH, Miller S, Moser F, Bello J, Hurtig A, Vass K and the neuropsychology committee of the cooperative study of sickle cell diseases. Cognitive functioning and brain magnetic resonance imaging in children with sickle cell disease. *Pediatr*, 1996;97: 864-870

[17] Aslan M, Ryan TM, Townes TM, Coward L, Kirk MC, Barnes S, Alexander CB, Rosenfeld SS, Freeman BA. Nitric oxide-dependent generation of reactive species in sickle cell disease. *J Biol Chem,* 2003;278:4194-4204

[18] Assessment of brain SPECT: Report of the Therapeutics and Technology Assessment Subcommittee of the American Academy of Neurology. Neurology, 1996;46:278-285

[19] Atweh GF, Loukopoulos D. Pharmacological induction of fetal hemoglobin in sickle cell disease and • •thalassemia. *Sem Hematol*, 2001;38:367-373

[20] Atweh GF, Sutton M, Nassif I, et al. Sustained induction of fetal hemoglobin by pulse butyrate therapy in sickle cell disease. *Blood*, 1999;93:1790-1797

[21] Balkaran B, Char G, Morris JS, Thomas PW, Serjeant BE, Serjeant GR. Stroke in a cohort study of patients with homozygous sickle cell disease. *J Pediatr,* 1992;120: 360-366

[22] Ballas SK. Sickle cell anaemia: progress in pathogenesis and treatment. *Drugs*, 2002;62:1143-1172

[23] Ballas SK, Marcolina MJ, Dover GJ, Barton FB. Erythropoietic activity in patients with sickle cell anaemia before and after treatment with hydroxyurea. *Bri J Haematol*, 1999;105: 491-496

[24] Baron J. Mapping the ischaemic penumbra with PET: implications for acute stroke treatment. *Cerebrovasc Dis,* 1999;9:193-201

[25] Baum C, Dullmann J, Zhixong L, Fehse B, Meyer J, Williams DA, von Kalle C. Side effects of retroviral gene transfer into hematopoietic stem cells. *Blood*, 2003;101:2099-2114

[26] Benkerrou M, Delarche C, Brahimi L, Fay M, Vilmer E, Elion J, Gougerot-Pocidala MA, Elhim C. Hydroxyurea corrects the dysregulated L-selectin expression and increased H_2O_2 production of polymorphonuclear neutrophils from patients with sickle cell anemia. *Blood*, 2002;99:2297-2303

[27] Bernaudin F. Resultats et indications actuelles de l'allogreffe de moelle dans la drepanocytose. Results and current indications for allogeneic bone marrow grafting in sickle cell disease. *Pathologie et Biologie*, 1999;47, 59-64

[28] Bernaudin F, Freard F, Verlhac S, Roudot-thoraval F, Benkerrou M, Thuret I, Mardini R, Vannier JP, Ploix E, Robero M, Casse-Perrot C, Helly M, Gillard E, Lesprit E, Brugieres P. In sickle cell disease, overt and silent strokes, low hematocrit level and high platelet count, significantly and independently badly influence psychometric performances. *Blood*. 1998;92: 496a, (abstr)

[29] Brody AS, Embury SH, Mentzer WC, Wingkler ML, Gooding CA. Preservation of sickle cell blood-flow patterns during MR imaging: an in vivo study. *AM R*, 1988;151: 129-141

[30] Bronspiegel-Weintrob N, Olivieri NF, Tyler B, Andrews DF, Freedman MH, Holland FJ. Effect of age at the start of iron chelation therapy on gonadal function in • • thalassemia major. *N Engl J Med*, 1990;323: 713-719

[31] Brott T, Bogousslavsky J. Treatment of acute ischemic stroke. *N Eng J Med*, 2000;343:710-722

[32] Brugnara C, De Frarceschi L, Beuzard Y. Erythrocyte-active agents and treatment of sickle cell disease. *Sem Hematol,* 2001;38:324-332

[33] Brugnara C, Gee B, Armsby CC, Kurth S, Sakamoto M, Rifai N, Alper SL, Platt OS. Therapy with oral clotrimazole induces inhibition of the Gardos channel and reductioin of erythrocyte dehydration in patients with sickle cell disease. *J Clin Invest*, 1996;97:1227-1234

[34] Buchanan GR, Bowman WP, Smith SJ. Recurrent cerebral ischemia during hypertransfusion therapy in sickle cell anemia. *J Pediatr*, 1983;103: 921-923

[35] Bulas DI, Jones A, Seibert JJ, Driscoll C, O'Donnell R, Adams RJ. Transcranial Doppler (TCD) screening for stroke prevention in sickle cell anemia: pitfalls in technique variation. *Pediatr Radiol*, 2000;30:733-738

[36] Bunn HF. Induction of Fetal Hemoglobin in Sickle Cell Disease. *Blood*, 1999;93: 1787-1789

[37] Charache S, Barton FB, Moore RD, Terrin ML, Steinberg MH, Dover GJ, Ballas SK, McMahon RP, Castro O, Orringer EP, and Investigators of the Multicenter Study of Hydroxyurea in Sickle Cell Anemia. Hydroxyurea and sickle Cell Anemia. *Clinical Utility of a Myelosuppressive "Switching" Agent. Medicine*, 1996;75: 300-326

[38] Charache S, Terrin ML, Moore RD, Dover GJ, Barton FB, Eckert SV, McMahon RP, Bonds DR. Effect of hydroxyurea on the frequency of painful crises in sickle cell anemia. Investigators of the multicenter study of hydroxyurea in sickle cell aneima. *N Engl J Med*, 1995;332:1317-1322

[39] Cheung AT, Harmatz P, Wun T, Chen PC, Larkin EC, Adams RJ, Vichinsky EP. Correlation of abnormal intracranial vessel velocity, measured by transcranial Doppler ultrasonography, with abnormal conjunctival vessel velocity, measured by computer-assisted intravital microscopy, in sickle cell disease. *Blood*, 2001;97:3401-3404

[40] Christakis J, Vavatsi N, Hassapopoulou H, Papadopoulou M, Mandraveli K, Loukopoulos D, Morris JS, Serjeant BE, Serjeant GR. Comparison of homozygous sickle cell disease in northern Greece and Jamaica. *Lancet*, 1990;335:637-640

[41] Chui D, Grotta J. Current clinical status of cytoprotection. In: Welch KMA, Caplan LR, Reis DJ, Siesjo BK, Weir B, (eds). *Primer on cerebrovascular diseases*. San Diego: Academic Press, 1997;731-737

[42] Cohen AR. Sickle cell disease--new treatments, new questions. *N Engl J Med*, 1998;339:42-44

[43] Cohen AR, Martin MB, Silber JH, Kim HC, Frempong KO, Schwartz E. A modified transfusion program for prevention of stroke in sickle cell disease. *Blood*, 1992;79: 1657-1661

[44] Cook WC. Case of sickle cell anemia with associated subarachnoid hemorrhage. *J Med*, 1930;11:541

[45] Craft S, Schatz J, Glauser TA, Lee B, DeBaun MR. Neuropsychologic effects of stroke in children with sickle cell anemia. *J Pediatr*, 1993;123: 712-717

[46] Crisostomo RA, Garcia MM, Tong DC. Detection of diffusion-weighted MRI abnormalities in patients with transient ischemic attack: correlation with clinical characteristics. *Stroke*, 2003;34:932-937

[47] Daubeney P, Pilkington S, Janke E, et al. Cerebral oxygenation measured by near-infrared spectroscopy: Comparison with jugular bulb oximetry. *Ann Thorac Surg*, 1996;61:930-934

[48] DeBaun MR, Glauser TA, Siegel M, Borders J, Lee B. Noninvasive central nervous system imaging in sickle cell anemia. A preliminary study comparing transcranial doppler with magnetic resonance angiography. *J Pediatr Hematol/Oncol*, 1995;17: 29-33

[49] DeBaun MR, Schatz J, Siegel MJ, Koby M, Craft S, Resar L, Chu JY, Launius G, Dadash-Zadeh M, Lee RB, Noetzel M. Cognitive screening examinations for silent cerebral infarcts in sickle cell disease. *Neurology*, 1998;50: 1678-1682

[50] de Ceulaer K, Higgs DR, Weatherall DJ, Hayes RJ, Serejeant BE, Serjeant GR. Alpha thalassemia reduces the hemolytic rate in homozygous sickle-cell disease. (Letter) *New Engl J Med*, 1983;309:189-190

[51] De Reuck J, Leys D, De Keyser J. Is positron emission tomography useful in stroke? *Acta Neurol Belg*, 1997;97:168-171

[52] de Montalembert M, Beauviais P, Bachir D, Galacteros F, Girot R. Cerebrovascular accidents in sickle cell disease. Risk factors and blood transfusion influence. French Study Group on Sickle Cell Disease. *Euro J Pediatr,* 1993;152:201-204

[53] DeSimone J, Heller P, Hall, Zwiers D. 5-azocytidine stimulates fetal hemoglobin (HbF) synthesis in anemic baboons. *Proc Natl Academy Sci, USA*, 1982;79:4428-4431

[54] DeSimone J, Koshy M, Dorn L, Lavelle D, Bressier L, Molokie R, Talischy N. Maintenance of elevated fetal hemoglobin levels by decitabine during dose interval treatment of sickle cell anemia. *Blood*, 2002;99:3905-3908

[55] Dobson SR, Holden KR, Nietert PJ, Cure JK, Laver JH, Disco D, Abboud MR. Moyamoya syndrome in childhood sickle cell disease: a predictive factor for recurrent cerebrovascular events. *Blood*, 2002;99:3144-3150

[56] Driscoll MC, Hurlet A, Styles L, McKie V, Files B, Olivieri N, Pegelow C, Berman B, Drachtman R, Patel K, Brambilla D. Stroke risk in siblings with sickle cell anemia. *Blood*, 2003:101:2401-2404

[57] Ferster A, Corazza F, Vertongen F, Bujan W, Devalck C, Fondu P, Cochaux P, Lambermont M, Khaladji Z, Sariban E. Transplanted sickle cell disease patients with autologous bone marrow recovery after graft failure develop increased levels of fetal haemoglobin which corrects disease severity.*Bri J Haematol,* 1996;90: 804-808

[58] Ferster A, Vermylen C, Cornu G, Buyse M, Corazza F, Devalck C, Fondu P, Toppet M, Sariban E. Hydroxyurea for treatment of severe sickle cell anemia: A pediatric clinical trial. *Blood*, 1996;88: 1960-1964

[59] Figueiredo MS, Kerbauy J, Goncalves MS, Arruda VR, Saad ST, Sonati MF, Stoming T, Costa FF. Effect of alpha-thalassemia and beta-globin gene cluster haplotypes on the hematological and clinical features of sickle-cell anemia in Brazil. *Am J Hematol*, 1996;53: 72-76

[60] Gabis LV, Yangala R, Lenn NJ. Time lage to diagnosis of stroke in children. *Pediatr*, 2002;110:924-928

[61] Garcia JH, Lassen NA, Weiller C, Sperling B, Nakagawara J. Ischemic Stroke and Incomplete Infarction. *Stroke*, 1996;27: 761-765

[62] Gee BE, Platt OS. Sickle reticulocytes adhere to VCAM-1. *Blood*, 1995;85:268-274

[63] Gladwin MT, Schechter AN. Nitric oxide therapy in sickle cell disease. *Sem Hematol,* 2001;38:333-342

[64] Glauser TA, Siegel MJ, Lee BCP, De Baun MR. Accuracy of neurologic examination and history in detecting evidence of MRI-diagnosed cerebral infarctions in children with sickle cell hemoglobinopathy. *J Child Neurol*, 1995;10: 88-92

[65] Goncalves MS, Nechtman JF, Figueiredo MS, Kerbauy J, Arruda VR, Sonati MF, Saad SO, Costa FF, Stoming TA. Sickle cell disease in a Brazilian population from Sao Paulo: a study of the beta s haplotypes. *Human Heredity*, 1994;44: 322-327

[66] Goodman DM, Mendez E, Throop C, Ogata ES. Adult survivors of pediatric illness: The impact on pediatric hospitals. *Pediatrics*, 2002:110-583-589

[67] Goto Y, Yonekawa Y. Worldwide distribution of moyamoya disease. *Neurol Med Chir,* 1992;32:883-886

[68] Grotta J, for the US and Canadian Lubeluzole Ischemic Stroke Study Group. Lubeluzole treatment for acute ischemic stroke. *Stroke*, 1997;28: 2338-2346

[69] Grubb RL, Derdeyn CP, Fritsch SM, Carpenter DA, Yundt KD, Videen TO, Spitznagel EL, Powers WJ. Importance of hemodynamic factors in the Prognosis of Symptomatic Carotid Occlusion. *JAMA*, 1998;280: 1055-1060

[70] Hariman L MF, Griffith ER, Hurtig AL, Keehn MT. Functional outcomes of children with sickle-cell disease affected by stroke. *Arch Phys Med Rehabil*, 1991;72: 498-502

[71] Hebbel RP. Perspectives series: cell adhesion in vascular biology. Adhesive interactions of sickle erythrocytes with endothelium. *J Clin Invest*, 1997;99: 2561-2564

[72] Heiss WD, Thiel A, Grond M, Graf R. Which targets are relevant for therapy of acute ischemic stroke? *Stroke*, 1999;30:1486-1489

[73] Henderson JN, Noetzel MJ, McKinstry RC, White DA, Armstrong M, DeBaun MR. Reversible posterior leukoencephalopathy syndrome and silent cerebral infarcts are associated with severe acute chest syndrome in children with sickle cell disease. *Blood*, 2003;101:415-419

[74] Herold S, Brozovic M, Gibbs J, Lammertsma AA, Leenders KL, Carr D, Fleming JS, Jones T. Measurement of regional cerebral blood flow, blood volume and oxygen metabolism in patients with sickle cell disease using positron emission tomography. *Stroke*, 1986;17: 692-698

[75] Higgs DR, Aldridge BE, Lamb J, Clegg JB, Weatherall DJ, Hayes RJ, Grandison Y, Lowrie Y, Mason KP. Serjeant BE, Serjeant GR. The interaction of alpha-thalassemia and homozygous sickle-cell disease. *N Engl J Med,* 1982;306:1441-1446

[76] Hillery CA, Du MC, Wang WC, Scott JP. Hydroxyurea therapy decreases the in vitro adhesion of sickle erythrocytes to thrombospondin and laminin. *Bri J Haematol*, 2000;322-327

[77] Hillery CA, Du MC, Montgomery RR, Scott JP. Increased adhesion of erythrocytes to components of the extracellular matrix: Isolation and characterization of a red blood cell lipid that binds thrombospondin and laminin. *Blood*, 1996;87:4879-4886

[78] Hines PC, Zen Q, Burney SN, Shea DA, Ataga KI, Orringer EP, Telen MJ, Parise LV. Novel epinephrine and cyclic AMP-mediated activation of BCAM/Lu-dependent sickle (SS) RBC adhesion. *Blood*, 2003;101:3281-3287

[79] Hoppe C, Vinchinsky E, Quirolo K, Van Warmerdam J, Orlen SK. The safety and efficacy of hydroxyurea in 2 to 5 year old children with sickle cell disease. *J Pediatr Hematol,* 2000;22:330-334

[80] Hoppe C, Klitz W, Noble J, Vigil L, Vichinsky E, Styles L. Distinct HLA associations by stroke subtype in children with sickle cell anemia. *Blood*, 2003;101:2865-2869

[81] Horrow MM, Stassi J, Shurman A, Brody JD, Kirby CL, Rosenberg HK. The limitations of carotid sonography: Interpretive and technology-related errors. *AJR Am J Roentgenol*, 2000;174:189-194

[82] Hsu LL, Miller ST, Kutlar A, Wright E, Wang W, Pegelow CH, Driscoll C, Hurlet A, Woods G, Elsas L, Embury S, Adams R, for the Stroke Prevention Trial (STOP) and the Cooperative Study of Sickle Cell Disease (CSSCD). Alpha thalassemia is associated with decreased risk of abnormal TCD in children with sickle cell anemia. *J Pediatr Hematl/Oncol*, In Press, 2003

[83] Hughes JG, Diggs LW, Gillespie CE. The involvement of the nervous system in sickle cell anemia. *J Pediatr*, 1940;17:166-184

[84] Hurlet-Jensen AM, Prohovnik I, Pavlakis SG, Piomelli S. Effects of total hemoglobin and hemoglobin S concentration on cerebral blood flow during transfusion therapy to prevent stroke in sickle cell disease. *Stroke*, 1994;25: 1688-1692

[85] Jayabose S, Tugal O, Sandoval C, Patel P, Puder D, Lin T, Visintainer P. Clinical and hematologic effects of hydroxyurea in children with sickle cell anemia. *J Pediatr*, 1996;129: 559-565

[86] Johnson FL, Mentzer WC, Kalinyak KA, Sullivan KM, Abboud MR. Bone marrow transplantation for sickle cell disease. The United States experience. *Am J Pediatr Hematol-Oncol*, 1994;16: 22-26

[87] Kaul DK, Tsai HM, Liu XD, Nakada MT, Nagel RL, Coller BS. Monoclonal antibodies to alphaVbeta3 (7E3 and LM609) inhibit sickle red cell-endothelium interactions induced by platelet-activating factor. *Blood*, 2000;95:365-367

[88] Kandeel AY, Zimmerman RA, Ohene-Frempong K. Comparison of magnetic resonance angiography anbd conventional angiography in sickle cell disease: clinical significance and reliability. *Neuroradiol*, 1996;38: 409-416

[89] Kinney TR, Sleeper LA, Wang WC, Zimmerman RA, Pegelow CH, Ohene-Frempong K, Wethers DL, Bello JA, Vichinsky EP, Moser FG, Gallagher DM, DeBaun MR, Platt OS, Miller ST and the Cooperative Study of Sickle Cell Disease. Silent Cerebral Infarcts in Sickle Cell Anemia: A Risk Factor Analysis. *Pediatrics*, 1999;103: 640-645

[90] Kirkham FJ, Calamante F, Bynevelt M, Gadian DG, Evans JP, Cox TC, Connelly A. Perfusion magnetic resonance abnormalities in patients with sickle cell disease. *Ann Neurol*, 2001;49:477-485

[91] Kirkham FJ, Hewes DK, Prengler M, Wade A, Lane R, Evans JP. Nocturnal hypoxaemia and central-nervous-system events in sickle-cell disease. *Lancet*, 2001;357:1656-1659

[92] Klijn CMJ, Kappelle LJ, Tulleken CAF, van Gijn J. Symptomatic carotid artery occlusion: a reappraisal of hemodynamic factors. *Stroke*, 1997;28: 2084-2093

[93] Kogutt MS, Goldwag SS, Gupta KL, Kaneko K, Humbert JR. Correlation of transcranial doppler ultrasonography with MRI and MRA in the evaluation of sickle cell disease patients with prior stroke. *Pediatr Radiol,* 1994;24: 204-206

[94] Koroshez WJ, Gonzales RG. Imaging stroke in progress: Magnetic resonance advances but computed tomography is poised for counterattack. *Ann Neurol*, 1999; 46-556-558

[95] Koshy M, Chinnamma T, Goodwin J. Vascular lesions in the central nervous system in sickle cell disease (neuropathology). *JAAMP*, 1990;1: 71-78

[96] Kugler S, Anderson B, Cross D, Sharif Z, Sano M, Haggerty R, Prohovnik I, Hurlet-Jensen A, Hilal S, Mohr JP. Abnormal cranial magnetic resonance imaging scans in sickle-cell disease. Neurological correlates and clinical implications. *Arch Neurol*, 1993;50: 629-635

[97] Kumar A, Eckman JR, Wick TM. Inhibition of plasma-mediated adherence of sickle erythrocytes to microvascular ednothelium by conformationally constrained RGD-peptides. *Am J Hematol*, 1996;53:92-98

[98] Levesque JP, Takamatsu Y, Nilsson SK, Haylock DN, Simmons PJ. Vascular cell adhesion molecule-1 (CD106) is cleaved by neutrophil proteases in the bone marrow following hematopoietic progenitor cell mobilization by granulocyte colony-stimulating factor. *Blood*, 2001;98:1289-1297

[99] Liesner R, Mackie I, Cookson J, McDonald S, Chitolie A, Donohoe S, Evans J, Hann I, Machin S. Prothrombotic changes in children with sickle cell disease: relationships to cerebrovascular disease and transfusion. *Bri J Haematol*, 1998;103: 1037-1044

[100] Locatelli F, Rocha V, Reed W, Bernaudin F, Ertem M, Grafakos S, Brichard B, Li X, Nagler A, Giorgiani G, Haut PR, Brochstein JA, Nugent DJ, Blatt J, Woodard P, Kurtzberg J, Rubin CM, Miniero R, Lutz P, Raja T, Roberts I, Will AM, Yaniv I, Vermylen C, Tannoia N, Garnier F, Ionescu I, Walters MC, Lubin BH, Gluckman E. Related umbilical cord blood transplantation in patients with thalassemia and sickle cell disease. *Blood*, 2003;101:2137-2143

[101] Logan WJ. Functional magnetic resonance imaging in children. *Sem Pediatr Neurol*, 1999;6:78-86

[102] Maier-Redelsperger M, de Montalembert M, Flahault A, Neonato MG, Ducrocq R, Masson MP, Girot R, and Jacques Elion for the French Study Group on Sickle Cell Disease. Fetal hemoglobin and F-cell responses to long-term hydroxyurea treatment in young sickle cell patients. *Blood*, 1998;91: 4472-4479

[103] Malouf AJ Jr., Hamrick-Turner JE, Doherty MC, Dhillon GS, Iyer RV, Smith MG. Implementation of the STOP protocol for stroke prevention in sickle cell anemia by using duplex power Doppler imaging. *Radiology*, 2001;219:359-365

[104] Matsui NM, Borsig L, Rosen SD, Yaghmai M, Varki A, Embury SH. P-selectin mediates the adhesion of sickle erythrocytes to the endothelium. *Blood*, 2001;98:1955-1962

[105] Mendelowitsch A, Sekhar LN, Clemente R, Shuaib A. EC-IC bypass improves chronic ischemia in a patient with moyamoya disease secondary to sickle cell disease: an in vivo microdialysis study. *Neurol Res,* 1997;19:66-70

[106] Mercuri E, Faundez JC, Roberts I, Flora S, Bouza H. Neurological 'soft' signs may identify children with sickle cell disease who are at risk for stroke. European Journal of Pediatrics, 1995;154: 150-156

[107] Miller ST, Sleeper LA, Pegelow CH, Enos LE, Wang WC, Weiner SJ, Wethers DL, Smith J, Kinney TR. Prediction of adverse outcomes in children with sickle cell disease. *N Engl J Med,* 2000;342:83-89

[108] Miller ST, Macklin EA, Pegelow CH, Kinney TR, Sleeper LA, Bello JA, De Witt LD, Gallagher DM, Guarini L, Moser FG, Ohene-Frempong K, Sanchez N, Vichinsky EP, Wang WC, Wethers DL, Younkin DP, Zimmerman RA, DeBaun MR. The Cooperative Study of Sickle Cell Disease. Silent infarction as a risk factor for overt stroke in children with sickle cell anemia: A report from the Cooperative Study of Sickle Cell Disease. *J Pediatr*, 2001;139:385-390

[109] Miller ST, Sleeper LA, Pegelow CH, Enos LE, Wang WC, Weiner SJ, Wethers DL, Smith J, Kinney TR. Prediction of adverse outcomes in children with sickle cell disease. A report from the Cooperative Study (CSSCD). *NEJM*, 2000;342:83-89

[110] Mohandas N, Evans F. Rheological and adherence properties of sickle cells. Potential contribution to hematologic manifestations of the disease. *Ann NY Acad Sci,* 1989;565:327-337

[111] Moran CJ, Siegel MJ, DeBaun MR. Sickle cell disease: imaging of cerebrovascular complications. *Radiology*, 1998;206:311-321

[112] Moritani T, Shrier DA, Numaguchi Y, Takase Y, Takahashi C, Wang HZ, Shibata DK, Abe T, Ukisu R, Ohgiya Y, Tsuchiya A, Kushihashi T, Gokan T, Munechika H. Diffusion-weighted echo-planar MR imaging: clinical applications and pitfalls--a pictorial essay. *Clinical Imag*, 2000;24:181-192

[113] Moser FG, Miller ST, Bello JA, Pegelow CH, Zimmerman RA, Wang WC, Ohene-Frempong K, Schwartz A, Vichinsky EP, Gallagher D, Kinney TR. The spectrum of brain MR abnormalties in sickle-cell disease: a report from the Cooperative Study of Sickle Cell Disease. *AJNR*, 1996;17:965-972

[114] Muir KW, Lees KR. A randomized, double-blind, placebo-controlled pilot trial of intravenous magnesium sulfate in acute stroke. *Stroke*, 1995;26: 1183-1188

[115] Nagesh V, Welch KM, Windham JP, Patel S, Levine SR, Hearshen D, Peck D, Robbins K, D'Olhaberriague L, Soltanian-Zadeh H, Boska MD. Time course of ADCw changes in ischemic stroke: beyond the human eye! *Stroke*, 1998:29:1778-1782

[116] Neish AS, Blews DE, Simms CA, Merritt RK, Spinks AJ. Screening for stroke in sickle cell anemia: comparison of transcranial Doppler imaging and nonimaging US techniques. *Radiol*, 2002;222:709-714

[117] Nietert PJ, Abboud MR, Silverstein MD, Jackson SM. Bone marrow transplantation versus periodic prophylactic blood transfusion in sickle cell patients at high risk of ischemic stroke: a decision analysis. *Blood*, 2000;95:3057-3064

[118] Nifong TP, Domen RE. Oxygen saturation and hemoglobin A content in patients with sickle cell disease undergoing erythrocytapheresis. *Therapeutic Apheresis* 2002;6:390-393

[119] Novotny E, Ashwal S, Shevell M. Proton magnetic resonance spectroscopy: An emerging technology in pediatric neurology research. *Pediatric Res*, 1998;44:1-10

[120] Numaguchi Y, Haller JS, Humbert JR, Robinson AE, Lindstrom WW, Gruenauer LM, Carey JE. Cerebral blood flow mapping using stable xenon-enhanced CT in sickle cell cerebrovascular disease. *Neuroradiology*, 1990;32: 289-295

[121] Ohene-Frempong K, Weiner SJ, Sleeper LA, Miller ST, Embury S, Moohr JW, Wethers DL, Pegelow CH, Gill FM and the Cooperative Study of Sickle Cell Disease.

Cerebrovascular accidents in sickle cell disease: Rates and risk factors. *Blood*, 1998;91: 288-294

[122] Olivieri NF, Vichinsky EP. (1998) Hydroxyurea in children with sickle cell disease: Impact on splenic function and compliance with therapy. *J Pediatr Hematol/Oncol,* 1998;20:26-31

[123] Oyesiku NM, Barrow DL, Eckman JR, Tindall SC, Colohan ART. Intracranial aneurysms in sickle-cell anaemia: clinical features and pathogenesis. *J Neurosurg*, 1991;75:356-363

[124] Ozsoylu S, Altinoz N. Sickle-cell anaemia in Turkey. Evaluation of 97 cases (with parents findings). *Scand J Haematol*, 1977;19: 85-92

[125] Pawliuk R, Westerman KA, Fabry ME, Payen E, Tighe R, Bouhassira EE, Acharya SA, Ellis J, London IM, Eaves CJ, Humphries RK, Beuzard Y, Nagel RL, Leboulch P. Correction of sickle cell disease in transgenic mouse models by gene therapy. *Science*, 2001;294:2368-2371

[126] Pegelow CH. Stroke in children with sickle cell anaemia: aetiology and treatment (Review) *Pediatr Drugs*, 2001;3:421-432

[127] Pegelow CH, Adams RJ, McKie V, Abbound M, Berman B, Miller ST, Oliveieri N, Vichensky E, Wang W, Brambilla D. Risk of recurrent stroke in patients with sickle cell disease treated with erythrocyte transfusions. *J Pediatr*, 1995;1995:896-899

[128] Pegelow CH, Macklin EA, Moser FG, Wang WC, Bello JA, Miller ST, Vichinsky EP, DeBaun MR, Guarini L, Zimmerman RA, Younkin DP, Gallagher DM, Kinney TR. Longitudinal changes in brain magnetic resonance imaging findings in children with sickle cell disease. *Blood*, 2002;99:3014- 3018

[129] Pegelow CH, Wang W, Granger S, Hsu LL, vichinsky E, Moser FG, Bello J, Zimmerman RA, Adams RJ, Brambilla D. STOP Trial. Silent infarcts in children with sickle cell anemia and abnormal cerebral artery velocity. *Arch Neurol,* 2001;58:2017-2021

[130] Perrine SP, Miller BA, Faller DV, et al. Sodium butyrate enhances fetal globin gene expression in erythroid progenitors of patients with Hb SS and beta thalassemia. *Blood,* 1989;74:454-459

[131] Perrine RP, Pembrey ME, John P, Perrine S, Shoup F. Natural history of sickle cell anemia in Saudi Arabs. *Ann Intern Med,* 1978;88:1-6

[132] Platt OS, Brambilla DJ, Rosse WF, Milner PF, Castro O, Steinberg MH, Klugg PP. Mortality in sickle cell disease. Life expectancy and risk factors for early death. *N Engl J Med*, 1994;330: 1639-1644

[133] Powars D, Adams RJ, Nichols FT, Milner P, Charache S, Sarnaik S. Delayed intracranial hemorrhage following cerebral infarction in sickle cell anemia. *J Assoc Acad Minority Phys*, 1990;1:79-82

[134] Powars D, Chan LS, Schroeder WA. The variable expression of sickle cell disease is genetically determined. *Sem Hematol*, 1990;27: 360-376

[135] Powars DR, Conti PS, Wong WY, Groncy P, Hyman C, Smith E, Ewing N, Keenan RN, Zee CS, Harold Y, Hiti AL, Teng EL, Chan LS. Cerebral vasculopathy in sickle cell anemia: Diagnostic contribution of positron emission tomography *Blood*, 1999;93:71-79

[136] Powars DR, Weiss JN, Chan LS, Schroeder WA. Is there a threshold level of fetal hemoglobin which ameliorates morbidity in sickle cell anemia? *Blood*, 1984;63: 921-926

[137] Powars DR, Wilson B, Imbus C, Pegelow C, Allen J. The natural history of stroke in sickle cell disease. *Am J Med*, 1978;65:461-471

[138] Prohovnik I, Pavlakis SG, Piomelli S, Bello J, Bohr JP, Hilal S, De Vivo DC. Cerebral hyperemia, stroke and transfusion in sickle cell disease. *Neurology*, 1989;39: 344-348

[139] Provenzale JM, Engelter ST, Petrella JR, Smith JS, MacFall JR. Use of MR exponential diffusion-weighted images to eradicate T2 "shine'through" effect. *AJR*, 1999;172:537-539

[140] Racoff WR, Ohene-Frempong K, Month S, Scott JP, Neahring B, Cohen AR. Neurologic events after partial exchange transfusion for priapism in sickle cell disease. *J Pediatr* 1992;120: 882-885

[141] Rana S, Houston PE, Surana N, Shalaby-Rana EI, Castro OL. Discontinuation of long-term transfusion therapy in patients with sickle cell disease and stroke. *J Pediatr* 1997;131:757-760

[142] Reed W, Jagust W, Al-Mateen M, Vichinsky E. Role of positron emission tomography in determining the extent of CNS ischemia in patients with sickle cell disease. *Am J Hematol*, 1999;60: 268-272

[143] Resar LMS, Segal JB, Fitzpatric LK, Friedmann A, Brusilow SW, Dover GJ. Induction of fetal hemoglobin synthesis in children with sickle cell anemia on low-dose oral sodium phenylbutyrate therapy. *J Pediatr Hematol Oncol,* 2002;24:737-741

[144] Rosse WR, Gallagher D, Kinney TR, Castro O, Dosik H, Moohr J, Wang W, Levy PS, and the Cooperative Study of Sickle Cell Disease. Transfusion and alloimmunization in sickle cell disease. *Blood*, 1990;76:1431-1437

[145] Rothman SM, Fulling KH, Nelson JS. Sickle cell anemia and central nervous system infarction: a neuropathological study. *Ann Neurol*, 1986;20:684-690

[146] Russell MO, Goldberg HI, Hodson A, Kim HC, Halus J, Reivich M, Schwartz E. Effect of transfusion therapy on arteriographic abnormalities and on recurrence of stroke in sickle cell disease. *Blood*, 1984;63:162-169

[147] Sarnaik SA. Prevention of stroke by transfusions in children with sickle cell anemia. *N Engl J Med*, 1998;339:1477-1478

[148] Sarnaik S, Soorya D, Kim J, Ravindranath Y, Lusher J. Periodic transfusions for sickle cell anemia and CNS infarction. *Am J Dis Child,* 1979;133: 1254-1257

[149] Schatz J, Brown RT, Pascual JM, Hsu L, DeBaun MR. Poor school and cognitive functioning with silent cerebral infarcts and sickle cell disease. *Neurol*, 2001;56:1109-1111

[150] Schoning M, Hartig B. Age dependence of total cerebral blood flow volume from childhood to adulthood. *J Cerebral Blood Flow and Metabolism*, 1996;16:827-833

[151] Scothorn DJ, Price C, Schwartz D, Terrill C, Buchanan GR, Shurney W, Sarniak I, Fallon R, Chu JY, Pegelow CH, Wang W, Casella JF, Resar LS, Berman B, Adamkiewicz T, Hsu LL, Ohene-Frempong K, Smith-Whitley K, Mahoney D, Scott JP, Woods GM, Watanabe M, DeBaun MR. Risk of recurrent stroke in children with sickle

cell disease receiving blood transfusion therapy for at least five years after initial stroke. *J Pediatr*, 2002;140:348-354

[152] Scott JP, Hillery CA, Brown ER, Misiewicz V, Labotka RJ. Hydroxyurea therapy in children severly affected with sickle cell disease. *J Pediatr*, 1996;128: 820-828

[153] Seibert JJ, Glasier CM, Kirby RS, Allison JW, James CA, Becton DL, Kinder DL, Cox KS, Flick EL, Lairry F, Jackson JF, Graves RA. Transcranial Doppler, MRA, and MRI as screening examination for cerebrovascular disease in patients with sickle cell anemia: an 8-year study. *Pediatr Radiol* 1998;28:138-142

[154] Seibert JJ, Miller SF, Kirby RS, Becton DL, James CA, Glasier CM, Wilson AR, Kinder DL, Berry DH. Cerebrovascular disease in symptomatic and asymptomatic patients with sickle cell anemia: screening with duplex transcranial Doppler US-correlation with MR imaging and MR angiography. *Radiol*, 1993;189: 457-466

[155] Serjeant G. Chronic transfusion programmes in sickle cell disease: problem or panacea? *Br J Haematol*, 1997;97:253-255

[156] Setty BN, Stuart MJ. Vascular cell adhesion molecule-1 is involved in mediating hypoxia-induced sickle red blood cell adherence to endothelium: Potential role in sickle cell disease. *Blood*, 1996;88:2311-2320

[157] Shiu YT, Udden MM, McIntire LV. Perfusion with sickle erythrocytes up-regulates ICAM-1 and VCAM-1 gene expression in cultured human endothelial cells. *Blood*, 2000;95:3232-3241

[158] Siegel MJ, Luker GD, Glauser TA, DeBaun MR. Cerebral infarction in sickle cell disease: transcranial Doppler US versus neurologic examination. *Radiol*, 1995;197:191-194

[159] Silliman CC, Peterson VM, Mellman DL, Dixon DJ, Hambidge KM, Lane PA. Iron chelation by deferoxamine in sickle cell patients with severe transfusion-induced hemosiderosis: a randomized, double-blind study of the dose-response relationship. *J Lab Clin Med*, 1993;122: 48-54

[160] Slates RB, Farahani K, Shao Y, Marsden PK, Taylor J, Summers PE, Williams S, Beech J, Cherry SR. A study of artefacts in simultaneous PET and MR imaging using a prototype MR compatible PET scanner. *Phys Med Biol*, 1999;44:2015-2027

[161] Solovey A, Lin Y, Browne P, Choong S, Wayner E, Hebbel RP. Circulating activated endothelial cells in sickle cell anemia. *N Engl J Med*, 1997;337:1584-1590

[162] Steen RG, Emudianughe T, Hankins GM, Wynn LW, Wang WC, Xiong X, Helton KJ. Brain imaging findings in pediatric patients with sickle cell disease. *Radiology*, 2003; 228: 216-225

[163] Steen RG, Reddick WE, Mulhern RK, Langston JW, Ogg RJ, Bieberich AA, Kingsley PB, Wang WC. Quantitative MRI of the brain in children with sickle cell disease reveals abnormalities unseen by conventional MRI. *J Mag Res Imag*, 1998;8:535-543

[164] Steinberg MH, Barton F, Castro O, Pegelow CH, Ballas SK, Kutlar A, Orringer E, Bellevue R, Olivieri N, Eckman J, Varma M, Ramirez G, Adler B, Smith W, Carlos T, Ataga K, DeCastro L, Bigelow C, Saunthararajah Y, Telfer M, Vichinsky E, Claster S, Shurin S, Bridges K, Waclawiw M, Bonds D, Terrin M. Effect of hydroxyurea on mortality and morbidity in adult sickle cell anemia. Risks and benefits up to 9 years of treatment. *JAMA*, 2003:289:1645-1651

[165] Steinberg MH, Lu ZH, Barton FB, Terrin ML, Charache S, Dover GJ and the multicenter study of hydroxyurea. Fetal hemoglobin in sickle cell anemia: determinants of response to hydroxyurea. Multicenter Study of Hydroxyurea. *Blood*, 1997;89: 1078-1088

[166] Stins MF, Gilles F, Kim KS. Selective expression of adhesion molecules on human brain microvascular endothelial cells. *J Neuroimmunol*, 1997;76:81-90

[167] Stocker JW, DeFranceschi L, McNaughton-Smith G, Corrocher R, Beuzard Y, Brugnara C. ICA-17043, a novel Gardos channel blocker, prevents sickled red blood cell dehydration in vitro and in vivo in (SAD) mice. *Blood*, 2003; 101:2412-2418

[168] Stuart MJ, Setty BN. Sickle cell acute chest syndrome: pathogenesis and rationale for treatment. *Blood*, 1999;94:1555-1560

[169] Styles LA, Hoppe C, Klitz W, Vichinsky E, Lubin B, Trachtenberg E. Evidence for HLA-related susceptibility for stroke in children with sickle cell disease. *Blood*, 2000;95:3562-3567

[170] Sugihara K, Sgihara T, Mohandas N, et al. Thrombospondin mediates adherence of CD36+ sickle reticulocytes to endothelial cells. *Blood*, 1992;80:2634-2642

[171] Sultana C, Shen Y, Rattan V, Johnson C, Kalra VK. Interaction of sickle erythrocytes with endothelial cells in the presence of endothelial cell conditioned medium induces oxidant stress leading to transendothelial migration of monocytes. *Blood*, 1998;92:3924-3935

[172] Swift AV, Cohen MJ, Hynd GW, Wisenbaker JM, McKie KM, Makari G, McKie VC. Neuropsychologic impairment in children with sickle cell anemia. *Pediatr*, 1989;84: 1077-1085

[173] Taylor TG IV, Tang DC, Savage SA, Leitman SF, Heller SI, Serjeant GR, Rodgers GP, Chanock SJ. Variants in the VCAM1 gene and risk for symptomatic stroke in sickle cell disease. *Blood*, 2002;100:4303-4309

[174] Tournier-Lasserve, E. New players in the genetics of stroke. *N Engl J Med*, 2002;347:1711-1712

[175] Ueki K, Meyer FB, Mellinger JF. Moyamoya Disease: The disorder and surgical treatment. *Mayo Clin Proc*, 1994;67:749-757

[176] Valles J, Santos MI, Aznar J, Osa A, Lago A, Cosin J, Sanchez E, Broekman MJ, Marcus AJ. Erythrocyte promotion of platelet reactivity decreases the effectiveness of aspirin as an antithrombotic therapeutic modality: The effect of low-dose aspirin is less than optimal in patients with vascular disease due to prothrombotic effects of erythrocytes on platelet reactivity. *Circulation*, 1998;97:350-355

[177] Venketasubramanian N, Prohovnik I, Hurlet A, Mohr JP, Piomelli S. Middle cerebral artery velocity changes during transfusion in sickle cell anemia. *Stroke*, 1994;25:2153-2158

[178] Verlhac S. Imaging of cerebrovascular disease in sickle cell anemia. *Pathologie et Biologie* 1999;47:31-38

[179] Verlhac S, Bernaudin F, Tortrat D, Brugieres P, Mage K, Gaston A, Reinert P. Detection of cerebrovascular disease in patients with sickle cell disease using transcranial Doppler sonography: correlation with MRI, MRA and conventional angiography. *Pediatr Radiol*, 25:Suppl 1, 1995;1: 14-19

[180] Vermeer SE, Prins ND, den Heijer T, Hofman A, Koudstaal PJ, Breteler MB. Silent brain infarcts and the risk of dementia and cognitive decline. *N Engl J Med,* 2003;348:1215-1222

[181] Vermylen C, Cornu G. Bone marrow transplantation for sickle cell disease. The European experience. *Am J Pediatr Hematol/Oncol*, 1994;16:18-21

[182] Vernet O, Montes JL, O'Gorman AM, Baruchel S, Farmer JP. Encephaloduroarterio-synangiosis in a child with sickle cell anemia and moyamoya disease. *Pediatr Neurol,* 1996;14:226-230

[183] Vichinsky EP, Lubin BH. A cautionary note regarding hydroxyurea in sickle cell disease. *Blood*, 1994;83:1124-1128

[184] Walters MC, Patience M, Leisenring W, Rogers ZR, Dinndorf P, Davies SC, Roberts IAG, Yeager A, Kurtzberg J, Bunin N, Scott JP, Wall DA, Wayne AS, Wiley J, Darbyshire PJ,Mentzer WC, Smith FO, Sullivan KM. Collaborative multicenter investigation of marrow transplantation for sickle cell disease: current results and future directions. *Biol Bone Marrow Transplant*, 1997;3:310-315

[185] Walters MC, Storb R, Patience M, Leisenring W, Taylor T, Sanders JE, Buchanan GE. Rogers ZR, Dinndorf P, Davies SC, Roberts IA, Dickerhoff R, Yeager AM, Hsu L, Kurtzberg J, Ohene-Frempong K, Bunin N, Bernaudin F, Wong WY, Scott JP, Margolis D, Vichinsky E, Wall DA, Wayne AS, Pegelow C, Redding-Lallinger R, Wiley J, Klemperer M, Mentzer WC, Smith FO, Sullivan KM. Impact of bone marrow transplantation for symptomatic sickle cell disease: an interim report. Multicenter investigation of bone marrow transplantation for sickle cell disease. *Blood,* 2000;95:1918-1924

[186] Walters MC, Sullivan KM, Bernaudin F, Souillet G, Vannier JP, Johnson FL, Lenarsky C, Powars D, Bunin N, Ohene-Frempong K, Wall D, Michel G, Plouvier ME, Bodigoni P, Lutz P, Sanders JE, Matthews DC, Patience M, Appelbaum FR, Stork R. Neurologic complications after allogeneic marrow transplantation for sickle cell anemia. *Blood,* 1995;85:879-884

[187] Wang WC, Gallagher DM, Pegelow CH, et al. Multicenter comparison of magnetic resonance imaging and transcranial Doppler ultrasonography in the evaluation of the central nervous system in children with sickle cell disease. *J Pediatr Hematol Oncol,* 2000;22:335-339

[188] Wang WC, Grover R, Gallagher D, Espeland M, Fandal A. Developmental screening in young children with sickle cell disease. Results of a cooperative study. *Am J Pediatr Hematol/Oncol*, 1993;15:87-91

[189] Wang WC, Kovnar EH, Tonkin IL, Mulhern RK, Langston JW, Day SW, Schell MJ, Wilimas JA. High risk of recurrent stroke after discontinuance of five to twelve years of transfusion therapy in patients with sickle cell disease. *J Pediatr,* 1991;118:377-382

[190] Wang WC, Langston JW, Steen RG, Wynn LW, Mulbern RK, Wilimas JA, Kim FM, Figueroa RE. Abnormalities of the central nervous system in very young children with sickle cell anemia. *J Pediatr,* 1998;132:994-998

[191] Wang W, Riester K, Gallagher D, Thompson R, Guarini L, Vichinsky E, Wright E, Armstrong D. Neuropsychometric performance declines with age in children with

sickle cell disease: A report from the cooperative study of sickle cell disease (CSSCD). *Blood*, 1998;92:496a (abstr)

[192] Wang WC, Wynn LW, Rogers ZR, Scott JP, Lane PA, Ware RE. A two-year pilot trial of hydroxyurea in very young children with sickle-cell anemia. *J Pediatr,* 2001;139:790-796

[193] Wang Z, Bogdan AR., Zimmerman RA, Gusnard DA, Ohene-Frempong K. Investigation of stroke in sickle cell disease by ^{1}H nuclear magnetic resonance spectroscopy. *Neuroradiology*, 1992;35: 57-65

[194] Wang Z, Zimmerman RA, Sauter R. Proton MR Spectroscopy of the Brain: Clinically useful information obtained in assessing CNS diseases in children. *AJR*, 1996;167: 191-199

[195] Ware RE, Zimmerman SA, Schultz WH. Hydroxyurea as an Alternative to Blood Transfusions for the Prevention of Recurrent Stroke in Children with Sickle Cell Disease. *Blood*, 1999;94: 3022-3026

[196] Wasserman AL, Wilimas JA, Fairclough DL, Mulhern RK, Wang W. Subtle neuropsychologic deficits in children with sickle cell disease. *Am J Pediatr Hematol/Oncol*, 1991;13: 14-20

[197] Watkins KE, Hewes KD, Connelly A, Kendall BE, Kingsley DP, Evans JE, Gadian DG, Vargha-Khadem F, Kirkham FJ. *Cognitive deficits associated with frontal-lobe infarction in children with sickle cell disease.* 1998;40:536-543

[198] Wayne AS, Schoenike SE, Pegelow CH. Financial analysis of chronic transfusion for stroke prevention in sickle cell disease. *Blood*, 2000;96:2369-2372

[199] Weiner DL, Brugnara C. Hydroxyurea and sickle cell disease. A chance for every patient. *JAMA*, 2003:289:1692-1694

[200] Weiner DL, Hibberd PL, Betit P, Cooper AB, Botelho CA, Brugnara C. Preliminary assessment of inhaled nitric oxide for acute vaso-occlusive crisis in pediatric patients with sickle cell disease. *JAMA*, 2003;289:1136-1142

[201] Wertham F, Mitchell N, Angrist A. Brain in sickle cell anemia. *Arch Neurol Psychiat*, 1942;47:752

[202] White DA, DeBaun M. Cognitive and behavioral function in children with sickle cell disease: a review and discussion of methodological issues. *J Pediatr Hematol/Oncol*, 1998;20:458-462

[203] White DA, Salorio CF, Schatz J, DeBaun M. Preliminary study of working memory in children with stroke related to sickle cell disease. *J Clin Exp Neuropsy*, 2000;22:257-264

[204] Wilimas J, Goff JR, Anderson HR Jr., Langston JW, Thompson E. Efficacy of transfusion therapy for one to two years in patients with sickle cell disease and cerebrovascular accidents. *J Pediatr*, 1980;96:205-209

[205] Witt O, Monkemeyer S, Ronndahl G, Erdlenbruch B, Reinhardt D, Kanbach K, Pekrun A. Induction of fetal hemoglobin expression by the histone deacetylase inhibitor apicidin. *Blood*, 2003;101:2001-2007

[206] Yahata T, Ando K, Sato T, Miyatake H, Nakamura Y, Muguruma Y, Kata S, Hotta T. A highly sensitive strategy for SCID-repopulating cell assay by direct injection of

primitive human hematopoietic cells into NOD/SCID mice bone marrow. *Blood*, 2003;101:2905-2913

[207] Yamauchi H, Fukuyama Y, Nagahama Y, Nabatame H, Nakamura K, Yamamoto Y, Yonekura Y, Konishi J, Kimura J. Evidence of misery perfusion and risk for recurrent stroke in major cerebral arterial occlusive diseases from PET. *J Neurol Neurosurg Psychiatry,* 1996;61:18-25

[208] Zimmerman RA, Gill F, Goldberg HI, Bilaniuk LT, Hackney DB, Johnson M, Grossman RI, Hecht-Leavitt C. MRI of sickle cell cerebral infarction. *Neuroradiol*, 1987;29:232-237

In: Focus on Sickle Cell Research
Editor: Ralph L. Plasmar, pp. 59-67
ISBN 1-59033-920-7

Chapter III

STROKE IN SICKLE CELL ANEMIA IN THE MID-SOUTHERN REGION OF TURKEY

Yurdanur Kilinç[1,*], Ilgen Şaşmaz[1], Bülent Antmen[1], H. Hayriye Kozanoğlu[2], Süreyya Soyupak[3] and Şakir Altunbaşak[4]

Çukurova University, Faculty of Medicine
[1] Division of Pediatric Hematology-Oncology
[2] Department of Paediatric Haematology
[3] Department of Radiodiagnostics.
[4] Division of Pediatric Neurology
Adana, Turkey

ABSTRACT

Stroke is one of the most serious complications at crisis period in SCA patients. If it is not prevented in time, various motor and mental problems may appear in these patients. The SCA patients may show clinical patterns as severe or mild courses. If the patient has severe clinical pattern, he or she may have suffered from frequent vaso-occlusive crises, hemolytic, sequestration crisis and cerebrovascular accidents from the early ages of life and may need RBCs transfusions. 320 registered SCA patients with HbSS pattern is in follow-up clinics in Pediatric Hematology Department of Çukurova University. In last ten years, 16 of the patients had suffered from stroke. This conforms 5% of SCA population. This means we have to take care of the SCA patients carefully. The patients ages were between 11 months-17 years, 8 of them were females. In 16 patients, admitted with stroke, hematological and blood chemistry findings was determined. Also, neurological manifestations and findings were evaluated. The radiodiagnostics studies have been done. They were brought to the hospital with paresis, paralysis, confusion, loss of consciousness. They have hospitalized, have had partial exchange transfusions. They

* Correspondence address: Prof. Dr Yurdanur Kılınç, Head of the Department of Pediatric Hematology-Oncology, Medical Faculty of Çukurova University, Balcalı, 01330 Adana / TURKEY, Telefax:++90-322-3386906, email: kyurdnur@mail.cu.edu.tr.

are in follow-up if alive and in last five years, we began hydroxyurea in therapy and planned BMT in some cases. The mortality rate from stroke in study group is 2/16 (12.5 %)

Key Words: Stroke- Sickle cell anemia -Ischemia- Cerebrovascular accident.

In sickle cell anemia (SCA) patients, extracellular matrix underlying the endothelium may be exposed to pathological changes. The sickled RBCs interact with additional adhesive elements including proteoglycans, laminin, thrombospondin and collagen [1, 2]. The most but not all patients with Hb SS and nonhemorrhagic stroke have large-vessel disease when studied angiographically, and many have stenotic lesions involving vascular territories not symptomatic at the time of study [3]. All these vents assumed as cerebro-vascular accidents(CVA) in SCA. Spontanous intracranial hemorrhagy in patients with SCA is secondary to cerebral vasculopathy arising from intimal damage from sickled RBCs [4, 5]

Sickle cell anemic patients may suffer from various SCA crises especially because of the loss of deformability of RBCs. Initiation with vaso-occlusion, cerebrovascular events lead to stroke and if it is not prevented, may result with severe sequela or death [6].

Subjects and Methods

The study population is composed of 16 SCA patients with stroke. The patients were in the ages of 11 months to 17 years with the mean age of 9 years 2 months ± 4 years 4 months. The gender distribution was equal (8 / 8 patients). The eligibility criteria for the study was the findings of stroke and /or neurological findings and complications. All the patients was proved to have SCA with clinical and laboratory findings and family studies. The patients were evaluated in hematological, neurological and radiological profiles. They admitted to clinics with the outcome of stroke without other predisposing factors.

Results

The hematological profile and the results of blood chemistry is given in Table 1. All the patients were anemic, mean ISCs 9.3%, mean HbF 8.7%. In blood chemistry, renal functions were normal; SGPT levels were differing from normal to high as 53 IU/ml.

The clinical and neurological evaluation, CT findings of SCA patients suffered from stroke are given in Table 2, and Table3.

Table 1. The hematological parameters and blood chemistry of SCA patients

	mean±sd	Low-High
Hb (g/dl)	8.31±1.30	6.30-10.60
MCV (fl)	90.67 ±5.75	78.00-100.00
Retics(%)	6.00±5.43	0.60-20.000
ISC (%)	9.30±3.93	3.00-15.00
Plt (/mm^3)	367533.33±210481.00	1260000-925000
Hb F (%)	8.7±5.84	3.5-18.5
BUN (mg/dl)	12.20±5.97	5.00-26.00
Creatinin (mg/dl)	0.65±0.11	0.50-0.80
Indirect reacting Bilirubin (mg/dl)	2.22±1.22	0.80-5.20
SGOT (IU/ml)	83.70±39.08	35.00-149.00
SGPT(IU/ml)	33.72±13.20	10.00-53.00

Table 2. The clinical manifestations and prognosis of SCA patients with stroke

Name	Complaints and neurological findigs	HM	SM	Prognosis
YE *	Convulsion	+	+	Total recovery
NÇ +	Convulsion, vomiting, loss of consciousness	+	_	Total recovery
ACÖ**	Hemiparesis in left side	+	_	+, hemiparesis, facial paralysis
NA *	Headache, convulsion	+	_	Total recovery
CY +	Convulsion	_	_	+, monoparesis
MS *	Convulsion, back pain	_	_	Total recovery
GY **	Convulsion, abdominal and limb pain	_	_	Total recovery
NÇ +	Hemiplegy, loss of consciousness	+	_	+, epilepsy, hemiparesis
SA +	Loss of consciousness, hemiparesis	+	_	+, cerebral palsy
SP +	Loss of consciousness, hemiparesis, convulsion	+	_	+, hemiparesis
AK **	Loss of consciousness, arthralgia	+	_	Total recovery
GÇ **	Loss of consciousness	+	_	Total recovery
SG +	Limb pain, loss of consciousness	_	_	exitus (CVA)
SS +	Loss of consciousness, convulsion	+	+	Total recovery
FP **	Loss of consciousness	+	+	Total recovery
ÖK +	Loss of consciousness, convulsions	+	_	Exitus (interventricular bleeding)

CT: *: Not obtained **: With normal findings + :With pathological findings

Table 3. The CT Findings in SCA with stroke

Name	CT FINDINGS
NÇ	Subarachnoidal cyst at left temporal fossae
CY	Local old infarct at right parietal area
SA	Acute and chronic infarct in frontal area
SP	Minimal cerebral oedema, subarachnoidal hemorrhagi,calcification in the basal ganglia
SG	Cerebral oedema, acute infarct, chronic ischemic changes
SS	Acute infarct in right and left temporopariatal area
ÖK	Bleeding above and between the lateral ventricles interrupted corpus callosum, blood density all over the ventricular system

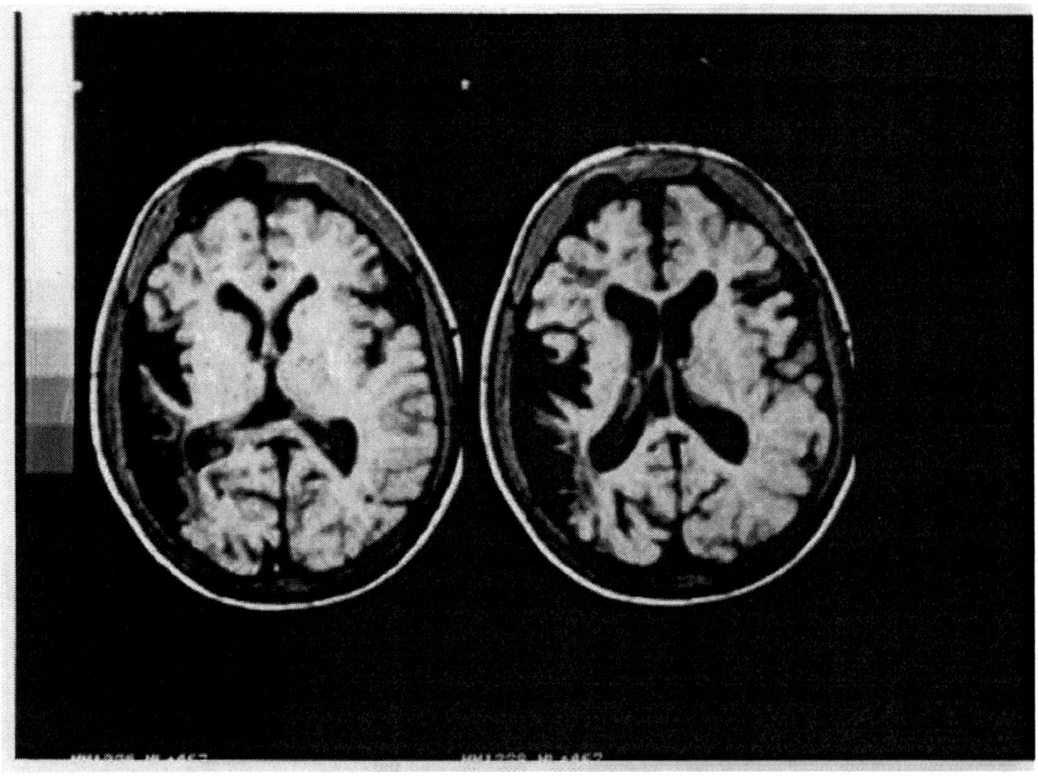

Picture 1. N.Ç. Huge tissue loss due to chronic infarct at right temporo-parietal and frontal area (Axial T^1 sections of MR)

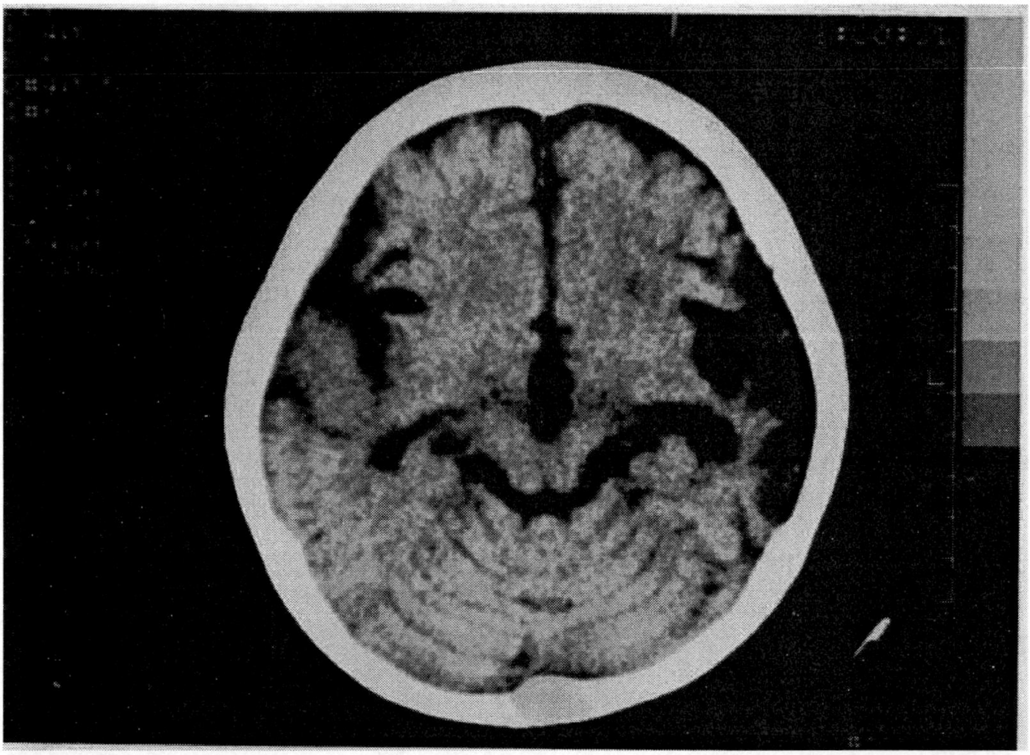

Picture 2. S.A. The hypodense areas, subcortical and cerebral atrophy in the inflow area of the left arteria cerebri media (Axial CT)

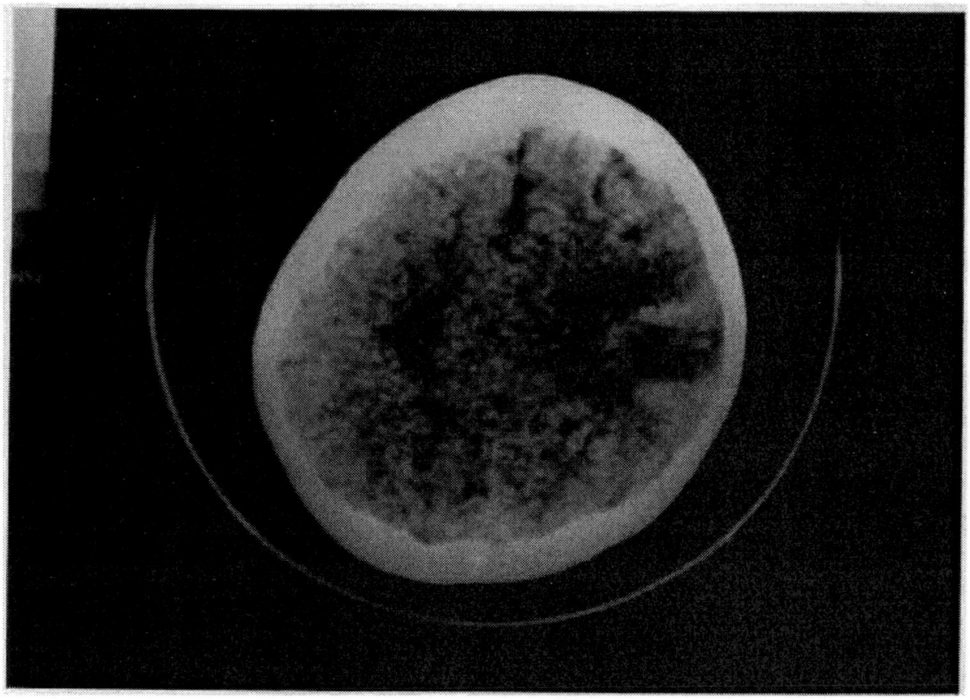

Picture 3. The hypointens area due to tissue loss by way of chronic infarct at left parietal area (Axial CT).

All the patients were admitted with neurological findings and/or convulsion. The CT findings are given in Table 4 and Picture 1, 2 and 3. The earlier the admittance and therapy, the better the prognosis. Two patients were deceased of serious complications of stroke (one CVA-, one interventricular bleeding). Therapeutic modalities were given in Table 4.

Table 4. The treatment modalities of SCA patients with stroke

Name	Hydration	Partial Exchange (RBC)s transfusion	Hydroxyurea Treatment	Antiepileptic Therapy
YE	+	+	_	+
NÇ	+	+	+	+
ACÖ	+	+	_	_
NA	+	+	_	+
CY	+	_	_	+
MS	+	+	_	+
GY	+	+	_	+
NÇ	+	+	_	+
SA	+	+	+	+
SP	+	+	_	+
AK	+	+	_	_
GÇ	+	+	+	_
SG	+	+	_	_
SS	+	+	_	+
FP	+	_	_	+
ÖK	+	+	_	_

Nine patients were totally recovered from stroke. In five patients, neurological sequela were found because of the long duration of stroke and the lag of initiation therapy. In last three patients, we began hydroxyurea therapy in addition to hydration and erythroctapheresis, zinc and folate supplementation have been given.

DISCUSSION

Stroke is a major cause of death in SCA [7]. Both clinical and subclinical stroke in SCA are resulted or associated with significant cognitive deficits [8]. The cerebrovascular damage typically occurs in either the microcirculation or in the medium to large size arteries [9, 10]. Decreased RBC deformability and increased adhesive properties contribute to the pathogenesis of cerebro-vascular events in SCA [2, 11]. The increased adhesion of sickle RBCs to endothelial cells as well as to components of the subendothelial matrix has been shown [1, 12]. The mechanism of RBC- endothelial cell interaction such as paranchymal lesions attributable microvascular occlusion or embolism [3] also depends on the source of the endothelial cell, such as microvascular versus large vein endothelium [13]. In addition to the vascular endothelium, abnormal vasomotor tone regulation contributes to vaso-occlusion, including stroke in SCA [14]. Increased adhesion of SS-RBCs to brain vasculature and the combination of nitric oxid inhibition and sickled RBC accumulation predispose to cessation of cerebral blood flow (stroke) and death in animal models [15]. The enhanced adhesion of SS-RBCs to the cerebral microvascular endothelium and subsequent perturbation of endothelial cell function may contribute to the initiation perpetuation of clinically significant vaso-occlusion in sickle cell disease.

In most studies of mortality, the age of death is determined from autopsy data or from clinical records. In the study of Thomas et al., the acute chest syndrome is the principal cause of death after 10 years of age, with chronic organ damage such as renal or cardiac failure, cerebro-vascular accidents as concomittant causes of death [16]. Also Platt et al., reported 15 stroke cases in 20 years or elder SCA patients [17]. In this study, 16/320 of the outpatients with SCA had suffered from stroke in last ten years. This conforms 5% of SCA population, two of them had deceised of complicatios. The prevalence of ischemic brain injury with paresis as SCA complications nears 10% in North America, 8% in jamaica and Nigeria, 8% in Turkey, 10-18 % in Brasil and 1% in Saudi Arabia [18-24]. The incidence of stroke is elevated in patients with SCA, but its recurrence is preventable by chronic transfusion programme [3, 6, 25, 26]. The aim of transfusion therapy is keeping hemoglobin S fraction below 20% and lifetime treatment may be indicated in some patients [25, 26]. The frequency of recurrent clinical stroke was reduced by 90% by some reports. They often die of massive intracranial hemorrhage and adult respiratory distress syndrome or complications of transfusion induced hemochromatosis [27-30].

In our cases, stroke incidence is 16/320 (5.0%). The lower incidence in this study-comparing with Özsoylu and Altınöz's study may be explained by cumulation of the cases for follow-up in our center, education of the patients and families in time, medical and issurance facilities and feasibilities for therapeutic intervention. For preventing severe sequela or death in SCA patients, the standard schedule may be developed. First of all, patients must be educated for their problems and medical team including - physician, hematolog, psycholog, physical therapist, surgean, etc must be ready for medical intervention. In therapy, first goal must be prevention of crises. The parenteral fluid therapy, erythrocytapheresis or partial exchange transfusions for decreasing Hb S concentrations below 20%, hydroxyurea therapy to increase Hb F levels, folate and zinc supplementation for erytropoiesis must be given. Bone marrow transplantation must be considered after 6 months follow-up of clinical recovery, if the neurological findings resist. The lag period may cause another stroke and loss of patients with infarcts and bleeding. Otherwise, the patient may be in crippled condition and may need personal and medical help for life-long duration.

REFERENCES

[1] Joneckis CC, Ackley RL, Orringer EP, Wayner EA, Parise LV: Integrin α_4 β_1 and glycoprotein IV (CD36) are expressed on circulating retyculocytes in sickle cell anemia. *Blood* 1993:**82**:3548-3555

[2] Francis RB, Johnson CS: Vascular occlusion in sickle cell disease: Current concepts and unanswered questions. *Blood* 1991;**70**:1405-1414

[3] Adams RJ, Nichols FT, McKie V, Milner P, Gammal TE. Cerebral infarction in sickle cell anemia. *Neurology.*1988;**38:**1012-1017

[4] Van Hoff J, Kitchey K, Shayerits BA: Spontaneous intracranial hemorrhage in patients with SCA is secondary to cerebral vasculopathy arising from intimal damage from sickle cell. *Am J Dis Child* 1986**;** **140**:505-506

[5] Earley J, Kýttner SJ, Feeser BR, Gardner J, Epstein A, Wozniak MA, Wityk R, Stern BJ, Price TR, Macko RF, Jhonson C, Sloan MA, and Buchola D: Stroke in chidren and sickle cell disease: Baltimore-Washington Cooperative Young Stroke Study. *Am Acad Neurol* 1998**:S1**:169-176

[6] Powars D, Wilson B, Dmbus C, Pegelow C, Allen J: The natural history of stroke in sickle cell disease. *Am J Med* 1985;**65**:461-471

[7] Balkaran B, Char G, Morris JS, Thomas PW, Serjeant GR: Stroke in a cohort of patients with homozygous sickle cell disease. *J. Pediatr* 1992, **120**:360-366

[8] Armstronog FD, Thompson RJ, Wang W, Zimmermen R, Pagelow CH, Willer S, Moser F, Bello J, Hurtig A, Vass K: Neuropsychologyst Committee of the Cooperative Study of Sickle Cell Disease. Cognitive functioning and brain magnetic resonance imaging in children with sickle cell disease. *Pediatrics* 1996;**97**:864-869

[9] Pavlakis SG, Belli J, Prohevnik I, Sutton M, Ince C, Mohr JP, Piomelli S, HÝllal S, De Vivo DC: Brain infarction in sickle cell anemia: Magnetic resonance imaging correlates. *Ann Neurol* 1988;**23**:125-130

[10] Stockman JA, Nigro MA, Mishkin MM, Oski FA: Occlusion of large cerebral vessels in sickle cell anemia. *N Engl J Med* 1972;**287**:846-849

[11] Hebbel RP: Beyond hemoglobin polymerization: The red blood cell membrane and sickle cell disease pathophsiology. *Blood* 1991;**70**:1405-1411

[12] Kaul DK, Fabry ME, Constantini F, Rubin EM, Nagel RL: In vivo demonstration of res cell -endothelial interaction, sickling and altered microvascular response to oxygen in the sickle transgenic mouse. *J Clin Invest* 1985;**65**:2845-2851.

[13] Brittain HA, Eckman JR, Wick TM; Sickle erythrocyte adherence to large vessel and microvascular endothelium under physiologic flow is calitatively different. *J Lab Clin Med* 1992;**120**:538-545

[14] Faller DV: Vascular modulation, in Embury SH, Hebbel RP, Mohandar N, Steinberg MH (eds): *Sickle Cell Disease: Basic Principles Clinical Practice.* New York, NY, Raven, 1994, p-236-242

[15] French JA, Kenny O, Scott JP, Hoffman RG, Wood JD, Hudetz AG, Hillery CA: Mechanisms of stroke in sickle cell disease: sickle erythrocytes decrease cerebral blood flow in rats after nitric oxide synthase inhibition. Blood 1997;89:4591-4599

[16] Thomas AN, Pattison C, Serjeant GR: Causes of death in sickle cell disease in Jamaica. *BMJ* 1982;**285**:633-635

[17] Platt OS, Brambilla DJ, Rosse WF, Milner PF, Castro O, Steinberg M, Klug PP: Mortality in sickle cell disease: life expectancy and risk factors for early death. *New Eng J Med.* 1994; 330:**23**,1639- 1644.

[18] Powars DR, Wilson B, Imbus C, Pegelow C, ana AllenJ: The natural history of stroke in sickle cell disease. *Amer J Med* 1978;**65**:461-471.

[19] Balkaran B, Char G, Morris JS, Thomas PW, Serjeant BE, and Sergeant G: Stroke in a cohort study of patients with homozygous sickle cell disease. *J Pediatr* 1992;**120**:160-66.

[20] Ohene-Frempong K, Weiner SJ, Sleeper LA, Miller ST, Embury S, Moohr JW, Wethers DJ, Pegelow CH, Gill MF, and "the Cooperative Study of Sickle Cell Disease: Cerebro-vascular accidents in sickle cell disease: rates and risk factors. *Blood* 1998;**91**:288-294.

[21] Özsoylu Ş, and Altınöz N: Sickle cell anemia in Turkey. Evaluation of 97 cases (with parents findings). *Scand J Haematol* 1977:**19**:85-92.

[22] Perrine RF, Pembrey ME, John P, Perrine S, ana Shoup F:Natural history of sickle cell anemia in Saudi Arabs. *Ann Int Med* 1978;**88:**1-6.

[23] Goncalves MS, Nechtman JF, Figueiredo MS, Kerbauy J, Arruda VR, Sonati MF, Saad SO, Costa FE, and Stoming TA: Sickle cell disease in a Brazilian population from Sao Paulo:a study of beta s haplotypes. *Human Heredity* 1994;**44:**122-127.

[24] Annobil SH, Omojola ME, Adzaku FK, Addae SK, and Mohammed S:Cerebrovascular accidents(strokes) in children with sickle cell disease residing at the high and low altitudes of Saudi Arabia. *Ann Trop Pediatr* 1990;**10**:191-198.

[25] Hurlet-Jensen AM, Prohovnic I, Pavlokis SG, Piomelli S. Effects of total hemoglobin S concentration on cerebral blood flow during transfusion therapy to prevent stroke in sickle cell disease. *Stroke* 1994 Aug; **25**:8,1688-1692

[26] Sarnaik S: Prevention of stroke by transfusion in children with sickle cell anemia. *New Eng J Med* 1998; **339**:1477-1478.

[27] Buchanon GR, Bowman WP, and Smith SJ: Recurrent cerebral ischemia during hypertransfusion therapy in sickle cell anemia. *J Pediatr* 1983;**103**:921-923.

[28] Cohen AR: Sickle cell disease-new treatments, new questions. *New Engl J Med* 1998;**339,** 42-44.

[29] Powars DR: Management of cerebral vasculopathy in children with sickle cell anemia. *Brit J Haematol* 2000;**108**:666-678.

[30] Russel MO, Goldberg HI, Hudson α, Kim HC, Halus J, Retwich M, and Schwartz E: Effect of transfusion therapy in arteriographic abnormalities and on recurrence of stroke in sickle cell disease. *Blood* 1984:**63**, 162-169.

In: Focus on Sickle Cell Research
Editor: Ralph L. Plasmar, pp. 69-80

ISBN 1-59033-920-7

Chapter IV

STROKE IN SICKLE CELL DISEASE

Jawad A. Arshad*, Howard A. Klausner and Christopher Lewandowski

Dept. of Emergency Medicine
Henry Ford Hospital
2799 W. Grand Boulevard, Detroit, MI 48202

ABSTRACT

Stroke in sickle cell disease (SCD) is the leading cause of cerebrovascular accident in children, and is the leading cause of death in sickle cell patients. SCD is caused by the substitution of a valine for a glutamate in the hemoglobin. This leads to rigidity of the hemoglobin and it precipitates readily during hypoxemia. SCD affects both small and large blood vessels. The sludging of the red blood cells causes reactive changes to blood vessels leading to intimal hyperplasia. The Cooperative Study of Sickle Cell Disease has reported four risk factors for stroke in sickle cell patients: i) previous transient ischemic attack, ii) low steady state hemoglobin, iii) frequent/recent acute chest syndrome, and iv) elevated systolic blood pressure. Other risk factors are genetic, environmental, and infectious. Stroke in sickle cell disease is usually "silent," and so most cerebrovascular accidents are not clinically apparent. Young children with SCD are especially at risk for stroke, and require close neuropsychological testing to monitor their performance. Transcranial Doppler is a useful modality that compares well with MRI to assess for stroke. The mainstay of therapy is preventive. In acute presentations of stroke, the standard antiplatelet therapy including thrombolytics can be used. Hydroxyurea and a routine transfusion regimen is used for prevention of stroke in SCD.

* For correspondence please contact Dr. Jawad A. Arshad, Henry Ford Hospital, Dept of Emergency Medicine, 2799 West Grand Blvd., ECFP-1, Detroit, MI 48202; E-mail: jawad.arshad@mail.com

INTRODUCTION

Stroke in sickle cell disease (SCD) has been recognized as a major cause of morbidity and mortality since Dr. Sydenstricker's report of hemiplegia in a young boy at the Medical College of Georgia in 1923. Sickle cell disease has been known for centuries but the sickled red blood cells were first described in 1910. It was not until 1949 that Pauling and colleagues determined an abnormal hemoglobin, hemoglobin S (HbS), to be the cause of this disease. Ingram, in the 1950s, showed that HbS resulted from an amino acid substitution. There are variants of SCD depending upon the genotype. For example, HbS is formed from the substitution of a valine for the glutamate amino acid at the sixth position on the beta-globin chain which results in a hemoglobin tetramer (alpha2/beta S2); this hemoglobin solubilizes poorly in a deoxygenated environment. Other genotype variants of SCD are Hb SC, Hb S-beta (+) thalassemia, Hb S beta (0) thalassemia; these variants arise from inheritance of one sickle cell gene mutation plus another mutation at the beta-globin gene. Other variants also exist which involve alpha chain mutations. These sickle cell variants have some important prognostic value in determining the risk factor for stroke in SCD. Pathogenesis of stroke in SCD is multi-factorial including changes in red cell membrane structure and function, disordered cell volume control, and increased adherence to vascular endothelium. These factors induce chronic endothelial changes which lead to accelerated atherosclerosis, and increased risk for cerebrovascular accidents.

EPIDEMIOLOGY

Sickle cell disease is the most common cause of stroke in childhood. Prevalence of stroke in SCD varies from 5 to 17% with cerebral infarction accounting for 75% of these events[3]. It is the leading cause of death in both children and adults with SCD. The incidence of stroke is 0.61 to 0.76 percent per year during the first 20 years of life[26]. The Cooperative Study of Sickle Cell Disease (CSSCD) [1], a prospective study of the natural history of SCD in 4082 patients, reveals that the incidence of stroke in early childhood from age 2 to 5 years is 1.02%, 0.79% at 6 to 9 years of age, and 0.41% in patients aged 10-19 years. The highest incidence of first infarction is between ages 2 to 5 years, the lowest is in the ages 20 to 29, and then there is another increase in risk over age 30. (See Table 1) The lifetime risk of ischemic stroke in SCD patients is 25-30% with risk rising to 67% for a second event in patients who have had a prior stroke [28]. SCD patients are living longer with better diagnostic and therapeutic interventions. In a study by Platt *et al.* [25] they found that almost 50% of SCD patients survived beyond the fifth decade. Those who died had no overt chronic organ failure, and usually died during an acute phase of either pain syndrome or stroke. Hemorrhagic stroke is most common in the age group of 20 to 30 years but is not uncommon in children. The prognosis for hemorrhagic events is dismal as compared to ischemic strokes. In a study by Ohene-Frempong *et al.* [23] the ischemic vs. hemorrhagic stroke related mortality was evaluated in SCD patients. All deaths occurring less than 14 days after a stroke were considered to be stroke related. A total of 104 patients (87 with first episode and 17 recurrent with stroke) had 133 episodes of CVAs in the study. Eleven (10.6%) of the 104 patients died, 9 after hemorrhagic stroke and 2 after strokes of unidentified type. Seven of the 11 deaths resulted from the first CVA; of these, 6 had a hemorrhagic stroke and 1 had stroke of unidentified type. All 11 patients were in the Hgb SS group without any other co-existing hemoglobinopathy (11.7% of Hgb SS CVA patients), and ranged in age from 12 to 58 years. Six died on the day of the CVA, whereas the others died within 1 week after the CVA. The mortality rate for hemorrhagic stroke was 24% overall, and 26% for Hgb SS patients. No deaths occurred within 14 days after 62 ischemic strokes. Despite these dismal statistics, SCD patients and their caregivers have limited awareness of the risk or symptoms of stroke. In a study by Katz *et al.* [15] which assessed the ability of children and their caregivers to determine presence of stroke, only 36% of caregivers were aware that their children were at higher risk for stroke, and 46% were unable to identify signs of a stroke. Information about stroke was provided by 82% of health care providers in this study.

Table 1. Incidence of First CVA

Age (yr)	SS	SC	S-$^{+}$	S-^{0}	Total
N	2,436	839	188	184	3,647
< 2	0.13 (1)	0.00	0.00	0.00	0.08 (1)
2-5	1.02 (20)	0.27 (2)	0.00	0.00	0.75 (22)
6-9	0.79 (15)	0.00	0.00	0.00	0.55 (15)
10-19	0.41 (15)	0.09 (1)	0.00	0.00	0.30 (16)
20-29	0.52 (14)	0.16 (1)	0.46 (1)	0.43 (1)	0.45 (17)
30-39	0.59 (8)	0.00	0.00	0.00	0.39 (8)
40-49	0.74 (3)	1.01 (2)	0.00	0.00	0.76 (5)
> 50	1.28 (2)	0.76 (1)	0.00	0.00	0.91 (3)
Overall	0.61 (78)	0.17 (7)	0.11 (1)	0.10 (1)	0.46 (87)
Age-adjusted	0.61	0.15	0.09	0.08	

The number of CVA per 100 patient-years, by age group at occurrence and hemoglobin genotype, is shown. The number in parentheses represents the number of events.

SS--Sickle Cell Anemia, homozygous

SC-- Heterozygous for Hb S and Hb C

Sβ^{+}--Sickle Cell with beta-thalassemia major

Sβ^{0}--Sickle Cell with beta-thalassemia minor

Adapted from Ohene-Frempong *et al.* Blood. 1998;91:288-294 [23]

PATHOPHYSIOLOGY

The pathogenesis of stroke in SCD involves the molecular abnormality in hemoglobin, with resultant change in RBC membrane, and damage to vasculature. Molecular sickling in HbS results from the substitution of the valine for the glutamate which is inconsequential in ligand state but readily polymerizes in a deoxygenated state resulting in a gel. This causes the red blood cells to become elongated, less pliable and to develop a higher density. Factors such as hypoxemia, infections, or acidosis precipitate sickling. Higher concentrations of HbA or even HbF (fetal hemoglobin) decreases gel formation. HbF affords protection and increases life expectancy for SCD patients [25]. SCD patients tend to have occlusions of their larger cerebral vessels such as the distal internal carotid artery and the middle cerebral artery. The small vessels are occluded by the sludging of the red blood cells due to the rigidity of their membrane and hyper-viscosity when sickled. Infarcts in arterial border zones suggest loss of distal small vessels, as they usually can not be imaged reliably. The larger vessels usually demonstrate occlusion and stenosis on imaging. In a study of 30 stroke patients, only 3 had normal angiograms [3]. The large vessels on histological studies reveal non-inflammatory endothelial hyperplasia that is caused by the abnormal adherence of sickle shaped red blood cells to the endothelium and non-laminar flow. There is also an abnormal pattern of collateral vessels which gives a hazy appearance to the dilated blood vessels on radiographic imaging. This type of disease pattern is seen in Moyamoya disease, a connective tissue disorder. The vasculopathy of SCD patients is therefore termed *moyamoya.* Hyperviscosity with platelet aggregation predisposes to stroke in an already stenosed cerebral vasculature. Endothelial hyperplasia is also a nidus for thrombus formation which leads to ischemic events. Other causes should always be entertained such as hyperventilation which reduces blood flow to the brain, fat emboli from bone infarction, and cardiac emboli. Nocturnal hypoxia has also been implicated with increased number of both platelet-erythrocyte complexes and monocytes which enhance sickling [28].

Hemorrhagic strokes are usually the result of aneurysmal rupture. Endothelial hyperplasia leads to aneurysm due to hyperemia, turbulent flow, and hemodynamic stress which can then rupture leading to intracranial hemorrhage. The collateral vasculature that mimics Moyamoya disease is also at high risk for rupture and cause small hemorrhages. The prognosis is worse with hemorrhagic strokes than with ischemic events.

RISK FACTORS

The Cooperative Study of Sickle Cell Disease (CSSCD) has reported the following risk factors for stroke in sickle cell disease: (1) previous transient ischemic attack, (2) low steady state hemoglobin, (3) more frequent or recent acute chest syndrome, and (4) elevated systolic blood pressure [18]. The genotype in SCD has been shown to help in risk stratification as well. In one series of 3647 patients from CSSCD, the age-adjusted incidence of stroke was 0.61% for HbSS, 0.15% for HbSC, 0.09% for HbS-beta (+) thalassemia, and 0.08% for Hb S-beta (0) thalassemia [23]. (See Figure 1) A previous stroke/TIA is a significant risk factor for a recurrent event as reported by Miller *et al.* [19] from a subgroup of patients from CSSCD. Other factors have been explored as well. A study by Driscoll *et al.* [10] compared 2353 patients with HbS for risk of stroke; of these there were 207 sibships with SCD. 42 of the 207 sibships had at least one sibling with a stroke. The stroke prevalence was statistically higher ($p = 0.0012$) in families with at least two children with a stroke as compared to the expected number of strokes in general population. According to this study, familial predisposition was the only significant predictor of stroke when compared with sex or mean age. This study raises the interesting possibility that there is a multi-factorial genetic component involved in predicting stroke in SCD. Adams *et al.* [2] compared a group of SCD patients with and without alpha-thalassemia for stroke risk. In their subgroup of 44 patients with a stroke, there is a prevalence of alpha-thalassemia of 20.5%. However, there is a statistically significant (p

= 0.02) higher prevalence at 38% of alpha-thalassemia in the subgroup of patients without a stroke. Alpha-thalassemia seems to be protective against stroke in SCD.

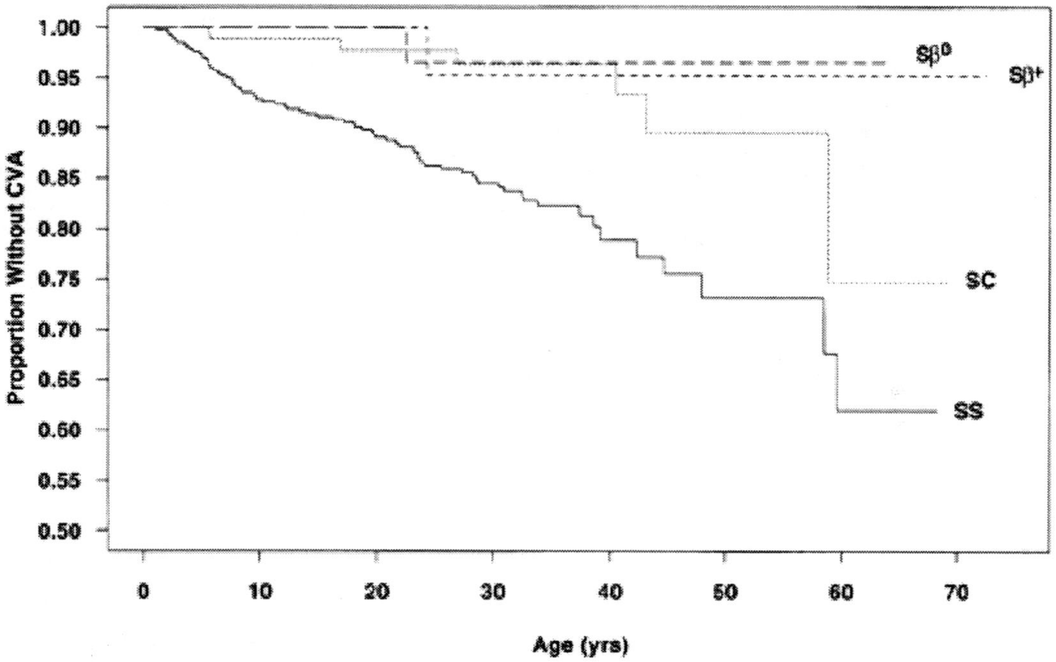

SS--Sickle Cell Anemia, homozygous
SC--Heterozygous for Hb S and Hb C
$S\beta^{+}$--Sickle Cell with beta-thalassemia major
$S\beta^{0}$--Sickle Cell with beta-thalassemia minor
Adapted from Ohene-Frempong *et al.* Blood. 1998;91:288-294 [23]

Figure 1

Genetics has been implicated by many authors as the culprit for having influence in determining the probability and risk of stroke in SCD. Styles *et al.* [32] presented a study of 53 patients with sickle cell anemia who underwent HLA typing at both HLA class I (HLA-A, B) and HLA class II (HLA-DR, DQ, DP) loci. 22 of the 53 patients had MRI evidence of stroke. There was a statistically significant higher prevalence of a mutation at the class I HLA-B, class II HLA-DRB1, and class II HLA-DQB1 loci for patients with a stroke. However, mutation at the class II DRB1*1501 locus was found to be protective against stroke. Taylor *et al.* [35] sequenced the *VCAM1* gene and its alleles. In a small pilot study of 10 patients they reported that a variant allele of *VCAM1* G1238C is associated with a statistically significant lower prevalence of stroke in SCD ($p = 0.04$, 95% CI of 0.15-0.83). Furthermore, Tang and associates [34] have studied the polymorphism in the angiotensinogen gene and the risk of stroke in SCD. There are different alleles of the angiotensinogen gene with varying repetitions of the bases G and T. The study group consisted of 21 stroke and 42 non-stroke patients with SCD who were age and sex matched for analysis. Upon genetic analysis, allele A3 and/or A4 of the angiotensinogen gene had a four fold higher ($p < 0.05$) predilection for the non-stroke group. This study suggests a lower incidence of stroke in SCD patients with alleles A3 and/or A4 of the angiotensinogen gene. These studies highlight the importance of molecular genetic mapping to identify patients at higher risk for stroke.

Other hematologic factors are poorly understood in sickle cell disease and cerebrovascular accidents. For example, in 1997 Houston *et al.* [13] studied 100 patients with SCD. 16 of the 100 patients were diagnosed with stroke. Serum homocysteine levels were measured for all patients. The authors found there to be a statistically significant higher incidence of hyperhomocysteinemia ($p < 0.02$) in the stroke subgroup. Multiple regression analysis showed that homocysteine levels are independently correlated with stroke. In the patients with hyperhomocysteinemia, folate levels were inversely correlated to homocysteine. With logistic regression, this study found a serum homocysteine level of $>10.1 \mu mol/L$ to be associated with a 3.5 fold increase in risk for stroke. However, two years later Balasa *et al.* [5] failed to reproduce this result and found a non-significant increase in homocysteine levels and association with stroke in SCD. This study assessed the role of mutation C677T in the gene encoding for the enzyme methylenetetrahydrofolate reductase (MTHFR), which is involved in the metabolism of homocysteine. It failed to demonstrate elevated levels of homocysteine in SCD, and its association with risk for stroke. Although this study was much smaller with only 11 SCD patients with stroke, it highlights the confusion that surrounds the clinicians in attempting to risk stratify SCD patients for stroke. Khanduri *et al.* [16] studied protein C deficiency and stroke risk in SCD patients. Three subgroups of SCD patients with stroke, patients in steady state--i.e. without any active pain or neurologic symptoms, and patients with vaso-occlusive crisis were evaluated. Protein C, protein S, anti-thrombin III, and factor V Leiden levels were measured. The only statistically significant finding was a decreased level of protein C activity and antigen levels in the stroke subgroup when compared to the vaso-occlusive and the steady state subgroups. Comparison of the vaso-occlusive and the steady state groups revealed no significant findings in the studied variables. Since these patients are predisposed to coagulopathy, further research is needed to discern whether SCD with stroke may benefit from anticoagulation over a long term.

There have been some exposure related studies in assessing the risk for stroke. Wierenga *et al.* [39] presented a retrospective study by reviewing charts between 1978 and 1999 in Jamaica to assess for a causal relationship with parvovirus B19 infection induced aplastic crisis in SCD and stroke. In the 346 patients who were identified with aplastic crisis and SCD, 10 patients were found to have neurologic symptoms from 2 days to 5 weeks which were suggestive of stroke. This is a 58 times greater than the expected risk of stroke in SCD which suggests a causal relationship between parvovirus B19 infection and stroke in SCD. These environmental factors are not completely understood, and present new venues for research. In a paper from Kuwait by Adekile and colleagues [4], they presented a study group of 30 patients with no obvious neurologic damage in whom MRI was performed to assess for stroke. Only one patient had an abnormal scan giving a prevalence of 3.3% which is considerably less than the sickle cell patients in the United States where as high as 20% prevalence has been shown. It is unclear if there is an environmental factor which is protective in these children from the Middle East, or whether there are deleterious factors affecting the SCD patients in North America.

NEURO-PSYCHOLOGICAL EFFECTS

Stroke in sickle cell disease has a significant neuro-cognitive effect quite different from the traditional stroke in adults due to atherosclerosis. Stroke in SCD affects children most often at ages before or during peak of schooling and learning years. This leads to a significant disadvantage for these children, especially since most of these children have "silent" strokes which are not readily apparent. Thus these children are sometimes mislabeled as attention deficit without necessarily addressing the underlying issues. Several studies have been done that show differences in intellect in children with "silent" strokes and without strokes in SCD patients. Noll *et al.* [22] conducted a study in which 31 case control and 31 SCD children were given a standardized battery of test assessing their verbal, attention/memory, and total scores. SCD patients scored lower then their healthy counterparts. In another study presented by Boni *et al.* [6] compared the ability of children with SCD and stroke to correctly interpret facial and vocal emotional cues with children who only had SCD but no evidence of stroke on MRI. Children with stroke performed poorly in being able to decode facial and vocal emotions as compared to the control group. SCD children with stroke are severely challenged in social adjustment as they are unable to interpret non-verbal language effectively. Nabors and Freymouth [20] conducted a study of 12 children with SCD and stroke, 14 children with SCD but no evidence of stroke, and 13 children without SCD to assess for attention deficit using the Coding subtest of the Wechsler Intelligence Scale for Children-Revised, and subtests of reading, arithmetic, and spelling from the Wide Range Achievement Test-Revised. They found that children without evidence of stroke, with or without SCD, performed better than children with SCD and stroke. DeBaun and colleagues [9] designed a study to see if a specific test is more useful in identifying children with stroke in SCD. They constructed groups of 7 children with SCD and "silent" stroke, 21 children with SCD and overt stroke, and 17 normal children without SCD. Cerebral infarct was determined via MRI and children were matched. The Test of Variables of Attention especially assessing attention and executive domains was most sensitive (86%) and specific (81%) for identifying SCD children with stroke. Thus a more focused battery of test can be administered to SCD patients to quickly gage for neurocognitive function on a routine basis. Wang *et al.* [37] showed similar results from a cohort of students taken from the Cooperative Study of Sickle Cell Disease database. Patients with stroke performed worse when compared to their control counterparts. The neurocognitive deficits seem to arise early in SCD patients. Steen *et al.* [31] tested kindergarten children with SCD and determined that in children with SCD and stroke, there was significant deficit in auditory discrimination ($p < 0.01$) with a trend toward language impairment ($p < 0.10$). White and colleagues [38] have shown similar results of memory impairment in their research. Neurocognitive testing in SCD should be started early to identify patients who have learning disabilities and difficulty with social adjustments so that focused programs can be instituted for these patients. Patients with "silent" strokes can also be identified early so that aggressive preventive therapies can be initiated as these patients are at higher risk for another stroke [7].

Diagnosis

Stroke in sickle cell disease is a major problem with serious social, psychological and financial implications. MRI has been used by many studies as the gold standard for diagnosing cerebral infarcts. However, it is far too expensive and exclusive a tool to be used as a screening modality. Thus alternative imaging techniques have been explored. The large Stroke Prevention in Sickle-Cell Anemia Trial (STOP) evaluated sickle cell disease patients using transcranial Doppler ultrasound, and then assigning high risk patients to either receiving blood transfusion or not. This study was terminated early by the National Heart Lung and Blood Division of NIH due to overwhelming success of transcranial Doppler (TCD) in identifying high risk patients. TCD evaluates cerebral artery velocity. Flow greater than 200cm/sec in the STOP trial had a 10-20 fold higher risk of stroke. Thus TCD became standard of care for screening of high risk patients, as any good screening tool, it is less expensive than MRI and more readily available. Jones *et al.* [14] compared the conventional TCD, which is a non-imaging Doppler, to the more widely available and familiar imaging transcranial Doppler ultrasound (TCDI). Although this study found the mean velocities for TCDI were about 15% less than those for TCD per STOP protocol, the correlation was adequate such that a velocity of about 180cm/sec on TCDI would correlate to TCD of 200cm/sec. This readjustment in scale would allow for the use of TCDI in evaluating patients. In the study by Neish *et al.* [21], the use of TCD and TCDI was compared. They found that TCD required less examination time and the mean velocities did not vary substantially. Their center has instituted TCD as the primary screening tool due to decreased time in obtaining the doppler study.

Other more investigational techniques have been reported as well. Kirkham and colleagues [17] have reported a series of 48 patients who underwent perfusion MRI. 24 of the 25 patients with positive perfusion MRI scans had no neurologic symptoms. The perfusion abnormality was larger than the area of infarction for 9 of the patients. Although more expensive and less available, perfusion MRI scanning adds another option in the arsenal to diagnose stroke in SCD. Positron Emission Tomography (PET) scanning is an additional tool that can be used to further assess neurologic damage in SCD. Positron Emission Tomography (PET) was compared with MRI in an evaluation of 49 SCD patients. Of the 19 subjects with overt stroke, 17 had abnormal MRI, 17 had abnormal PET scans, but all 19 of the patients had either an abnormal MRI or PET scan or both. Since PET scanning can evaluate metabolic improvement, it can be used to re-assess patients after therapeutic intervention to document their effectiveness [27].

Treatment

The treatment of acute stroke in SCD is similar to that for conventional atherosclerotic stroke. In the emergency department, an emergent CT Scan should be obtained to rule out the possibility of a hemorrhagic stroke. A thorough history with the exact time of onset of symptoms must be elicited. A thorough neurologic exam should be performed and the NIH stroke scale should be completed. If the patient is within the 3 hour window for thrombolysis, risks and benefits of t-PA should be explained and with consent, t-PA should be given to the patient. t-PA has not been studied in children and is not labeled for patients under age 18 years. If thrombolysis is not an option, then treatment should consist of antiplatelet therapy with agents such as aspirin or clopidogrel, and a neurology consult should be obtained.

The mainstay of therapy for stroke in SCD has been prevention with either the use of transfusion therapy or the use of hydroxyurea. Transfusion therapy decreases the concentration of HbS and thus reduces sickling. The incidence of stroke can be reduced to below 10% with chronic blood transfusions and HbS concentration <30% [29]. It seems that cessation of transfusion therapy returns the patients to high risk again. In one study, 5 of 10 patients who had received chronic transfusion therapy had transient ischemic attack or stroke within one year of cessation of transfusions [37]. Blood transfusions are not without complications such as alloimmunization, infection, and iron overload. Therefore, Cohen *et al.* [8] studied 15 patients who had been stroke free for at least four years on the transfusion program, and decided to let the HbS level increase to <50% instead of the conventional <30%. At a median follow-up of 84 months, no new neurologic events had been described in their series. Pegelow and colleagues [24] found concurrent results with the STOP trial and saw more favorable outcomes with transfusion therapy as well. Despite increasing the threshold for transfusion, some patients are unable to tolerate the procedure due to alloantibodies, autoantibodies, recurrent strokes even with transfusion therapy, iron overload, allergy to deferoxamine therapy, or noncompliance. Therefore, an alternative approach has been sought with hydroxyurea which causes hematologic stress on the body and causes an increase in HbF. Hydroxyurea was studied by Sumoza *et al.* [33] who found increased hemoglobin concentration, and increased HbF above 14.7% throughout the study with no adverse events in a 42-112 month follow-up. No adverse outcomes such as leukopenia or thrombocytopenia were reported. In a larger study by Ferster *et al.* [11] of 93 patients with varying mean follow-up times, there was a decrease in hospitalization, severe pain syndromes and stroke, which were statistically significant. Steinberg *et al.* [30] showed similar results with decreased mortality with the use of hydroxyurea. In one case report, however hydroxyurea was shown to decrease the number of vascular events but did not alter the progression of parenchymal damage in an advanced case of SCD [12].

Conclusion

Sickle cell disease is an inherited disorder with a significant vasculopathic profile. Stroke in SCD has the highest mortality of all the complications. Though there is a higher incidence of ischemic stroke in younger children and older SCD patients, the middle age group in their 20s and 30s have a higher risk of hemorrhagic stroke. Hemorrhagic stroke though less common, has a worse prognosis. The cerebral vasculature of SCD patients has endothelial damage from the sickled red blood cells, and turbulent blood flow which leads to intimal hyperplasia. These factors predispose SCD patients to have strokes. Stroke in SCD is a heterogeneous disorder which has varying protective and some deleterious risk factors. Familial predisposition seems to be strongly correlated with high incidence of stroke in SCD. It is important to identify patients with stroke in SCD. These patients are at higher risk for repeat stroke. They also have higher incidence of learning disabilities, and require special attention. The mainstay of treatment is with transcranial doppler as screening tools. MRI is however the gold standard. The acute treatment of stroke in SCD is the same as with the conventional atherosclerotic stroke. The mainstay of therapy in SCD patients is prevention with chronic blood transfusions, and therapy with hydroxyurea to improve outcome.

REFERENCES

[1] Adams RJ. *Stroke prevention in sickle cell disease. Current opinion in Hematology* 2000; 7(2):101-105.

[2] Adams RJ, Kutlar A, McKie V, Carl E, *et al. Alpha thalassemia and stroke risk in sickle cell anemia. American Journal of Hematology* 1994; 45:279-82.

[3] Adams RJ, Nichols FT, Hartlage P, *et al. Stroke in sickle cell disease. Journal of the Medical Association of Georgia* 1986; 75(5):271-74.

[4] Adelike AD, Yacoub F, Gupta R, *et al. Silent brain infarcts are rare in Kuwaiti children with sickle cell disease and high Hb F. American Journal of Hematology* 2002; 70(3):228-31.

[5] Balasa VV, Gruppo RA, Gartside PS, Kalinyak KA. *Correlation of C677T MTHFR genotype with homocysteine levels in children with sickle cell disease. Journal of Pediatric Hematology/Oncology* 1999; 21(5):397-400.

[6] Boni LC, Brown RT, Davis PC, Hsu L, Hopkins K. *Social information processing and magnetic resonance imaging in children with sickle cell disease. Journal of Pediatric Psychology* 2001; 26(5):309-19.

[7] Brown RT, Davis PC, Lambert R, Hsu L, Hopkins K, Eckman J. *Neurocognitive functioning and magnetic resonance imaging in children with sickle cell disease. Journal of Pediatric Psychology* 2000; 25(7):503-13.

[8] Cohen AR, Martin MB, Silber JH, *et al. A modified transfusion program for prevention of stroke in sickle cell disease. Blood* 1992; 79:1657.

[9] DeBaun MR, Schatz J, Siegel MJ, *et al. Cognitive screening examinations for silent cerebral infarcts in sickle cell disease. Neurology* 1998; 50(6):1678-82.

[10] Driscoll MC, Hurlet A, Styles L, *et al. Stroke in siblings with sickle cell anemia. Blood* 2003; 101(6):2401-04.

[11] Ferster A, Tahriri P, Vermylen C, *et al. Five years of experience with hydroxyurea in children and young adults with sickle cell disease. Blood* 2001; 97(11):3628-32.

[12] Helton KJ, Wang WC, Wynn LW, Khan RB, Steen RG. *The effect of hydroxyurea on vasculopathy in a child with sickle cell disease. American Journal of Neuroradiology* 2002; 23(10):1692-96.

[13] Houston PE, Rana S, Sekhsaria S, *et al. Homocysteine in sickle cell disease: relationship to stroke. American Journal of Medicine* 1997; 103(3):192-96.

[14] Jones AM, Seibert JJ, Nichols FT, *et al. Comparison of transcranial color doppler imaging (TCDI) and transcranial doppler (TCD) in children with sickle cell anemia. Pediatric Radiology* 2001; 31:461-69.

[15] Katz ML, Smith-Whitley K, Ruzek SB, Ohene-Frempong K. *Knowledge of stroke risk, signs of stroke, and the need for stroke education among children with sickle cell disease and their caregivers. Ethnicity and Health* 2002; 7(2):115-23.

[16] Khanduri U, Gravell D. *Reduced Protein C levels—a contributory factor for stroke in sickle cell disease. Thrombosis and Haemostasis* 1998; 79(4):879-80.

[17] Kirkham FJ, Calamante F, Bynevelt M, *et al. Perfusion Magnetic Resonance abnormalities in patients with sickle cell disease. Annals of Neurology* 2001; 49(4):477-85.

[18] Klausner HA, Lewandowski C. *Infrequent causes of Stroke. Emergency Medicine Clinic of North America* 2002; 20:657-70.

[19] Miller ST, Macklin EA, Pegelow CH, *et al. Silent infarction as a risk factor for overt stroke in children with sickle cell anemia: a report from the Cooperative Study of Sickle Cell Disease. Journal of Pediatrics* 2001; 139(3):385-90.

[20] Nabors NA, Freymouth AK. *Attention deficits in children with sickle cell disease. Perceptual and Motor Skills* 2002; 95:57-67.

[21] Neish AS, Blews DE, Simms CA, Merritt CA, Spinks AJ. *Screening for stroke in sickle cell anemia: comparison of transcranial doppler imaging and nonimaging US techniques. Radiology* 2002; 222(3):709-14.

[22] Noll RB, Stith L, Gartstein MA, Ris MD, *et al. Neuropsychological functioning of youths with sickle cell disease: comparison with non-chronically ill peers. Journal of Pediatric Psychology* 2001; 26(2):69-78.

[23] Ohene-Frempong K, Weiner SJ, Sleeper LA, *et al. Cerebrovascular accidents in sickle cell disease: rates and risk factors. Blood* 1998; 91:288-94.

[24] Pegelow CH, Wang W, Granger S, Hsu LL, *et al. Silent infarcts in children with sickle cell anemia and abnormal cerebral artery velocity. Archives of Neurology* 2001; 58(12):2017-21.

[25] Platt OS, Brambilla DJ, Rosse WF, *et al. Mortality in sickle cell disease. New England Journal of Medicine* 1994; 330(23):1639-44.

[26] Powars D, Wilson B, Imbus C, *et al. The natural history of stroke in sickle cell disease. American Journal of Medicine* 1978; 65:461.

[27] Powars DR, Conti PS, Wong WY, *et al. Cerebral vasculopathy in sickle cell anemia: diagnostic contribution of Positron Emission Tomography. Blood* 1999; 93(1):71-9.

[28] Prengler M, Pavlakis SG, Prohovnik I, Adams RJ. *Sickle cell disease: the neurologic complications. Annals of Neurology* 2002; 51(5):543-52.

[29] Russell MO, Goldberg HI, Hodson A, *et al. Effect of transfusion therapy on arteriographic abnormalities and on recurrence of stroke in sickle cell disease. Blood* 1984; 63:162.

[30] Steinberg MH, Barton F, Castro O, *et al. Effect of Hydroxyurea on mortality and morbidity in adult sickle cell anemia. The Journal of the American Medical Association* 2003, 289(13):1645-51.

[31] Steen RG, Hu XJ, Elliott VE, Miles MA, Jones S, Wang WC. *Kindergarten readiness skills in children with sickle cell disease: evidence of early neurocognitive damage? Journal of Child Neurology* 2002; 17(2):111-16.

[32] Styles LA, Hoppe C, Klitz W. *et al. Evidence for HLA-related susceptibility for stroke in children with sickle cell disease. Blood* 2000; 95(11):3562-67.

[33] Sumoza A, De Bisotti R, Sumoza D, Fairbanks V. *Hydroxyurea for prevention of recurrent stroke in sickle cell anemia. American Journal of Hematology* 2002; 71(3):161-5.

[34] Tang DC, Prauner R, Liu W, Kim K, *et al. Polymorphisms within the angiotensinogen gene (GT-Repeat) and the risk if stroke in pediatric patients with sickle cell disease: a case control study. American Journal of Hematology*

[35] Taylor JG, Tang DC, Savage SA, *et al. Variants in the VCAM1 gene and risk for symptomatic stroke in sickle cell disease. Blood* 2002; 100(13):4303-09.

[36] Wang W, Enos L, Gallagher D, *et al. Neuropsychologic performance in school-aged children with sickle cell disease: a report from the Cooperative Study of Sickle Cell Disease. The Journal of Pediatrics* 2001; 139(3):391-97.

[37] Wang WC, Kovnar EH, Tonkin IL, *et al. High risk of recurrent stroke after discontinuance of five to twelve years of transfusion therapy in patients with sickle cell disease. Journal of Pediatrics* 1991; 118:377.

[38] White DA, Salorio CF, Schatz J, DeBaun M. *Preliminary study of working memory in children with stroke related to sickle cell disease. Journal of Clinical and Experimental Neuropsychology* 2000; 22(2):257-64.

[39] Wierenga KJ, Serjeant BE, Serjeant GR. *Cerebrovascular complications and parvovirus infection in homozygous sickle cell disease. Journal of Pediatrics* 2001; 139(3):438-42.

In: Focus on Sickle Cell Research
Editor: Ralph L. Plasmar, pp. 81-97
ISBN 1-59033-920-7

Chapter V

SICKLE CELL DISEASE AND STROKE: USING TRANSCRANIAL DOPPLERS AND OTHER NEURODIAGNOSTIC TESTS TO PROTECT THE BRAIN

Jeffrey A. Switzer and Robert J. Adams
Medical College of Georgia
Department of Neurology

Sickle Cell Disease (SCD) affects numerous organ systems; its affect on the cerebrovascular system may be its most devastating. The association between SCD and stroke has been recognized since the early twentieth century. In 1923, Syndenstricker reported the case of a five year old sickle cell patient with hemiparesis and recurrent seizures. [1] Twelve years later, Arena described another sickle cell child with headache, stupor and hemiplegia. [2] Several other case reports of SCD and stroke surfaced in the first half of the century. [3, 4] It was not until 1972, when Stockman and colleagues published angiographic results on seven children with neurologic deficits, six of which had large cerebral vessel occlusions, that the significance of in intracranial large vessel disease in the pathogenesis of sickle cell stroke was first suggested. [5] Despite almost a century of work, our understanding of the pathogenesis, sequelae, treatment and prevention of stroke in the sickle cell patient is still in its infancy, with many of the recent advances mirroring advances in neuroimaging technology.

In general, the treatment of stroke, whether from SCD or more common etiologies (atherothrombosis, embolism, small vessel vasculopathy, etc.) has been disappointing. There has been only one randomized, controlled trial in either adults or children that has shown sufficient statistical benefit in the acute treatment of ischemic stroke to warrant FDA approval. [6] Therefore, the emphasis in stroke therapeutics has been placed on prevention. Although the prevalence of stroke in SCD is significant, the annual incidence is less than 1% per year [7], that is, not all children with SCD have comparable stroke risks. The current effort in sickle cell stroke targeted towards identifying the subset of patients who are at the greatest risk through the use of neurodiagnostic testing for the purpose of implementing protective strategies. Adams et al. published the seminal work in this regard, identifying high-risk subjects using transcranial Dopplers. [8] Subjects with elevated cerebral blood velocities who received transfusion therapy had a greater than 90% reduction in stroke risk. The purpose of this chapter will be to review the current understanding of the relationship of SCD and stroke. Epidemiology, risk factors and pathophysiology will be discussed. The emphasis of the chapter will be on efforts to prevent stroke in high-risk children using neurodiagnostic testing.

Incidence and Prevalence of Stroke

To appreciate the need for intervention, one must recognized the scope of the problem. Although, stroke in the general population of children is rare, it is not an uncommon sequelae of SCD. The Baltimore-Washington Cooperative Young Stroke Study was a retrospective study that identified all cases of ischemic and hemorrhagic stroke among children and young adults within a catchement area that totaled 46 hospitals over a three-year period between 1988 and 1991. [9] The total population of the region was based on 1990 census data. The population of children with SCD was estimated from the *National Newborn Screening Report.* A total of thirty-five strokes, eighteen ischemic infarcts and seventeen intracerebral hemorrhages (ICH), were identified. The overall incidence of childhood stroke was calculated at 1.29 per 100,000 per year in the Baltimore-Washington area, but for those with SCD the incidence rate was 285 per 100,000 per year (0.28% per year). The risk of both ischemic infarction and hemorrhage was elevated in the sickle cell patient. The incidence of childhood ischemic stroke was 0.58 per 100,000 and ICH was 0.71 per 100,000. Conversely, for children with SCD, the incidence rates per 100,000 were 238 and 47.5 respectively.

Similar incidence rates in SCD were obtained in the Cooperative Study of Sickle Cell Disease. [7] The CSSCD collected data on 4,082 patients with SCD at twenty three clinical centers within the United States over a ten-year period from 1978 to 1988. In this study, transient ischemic attack (TIA) was included with infarction and ICH. The annual incidence of first stroke was 0.46% per year. This result included SCD variants including those who inherited a hemoglobin C gene (SCD-SC), or a β-thalassemia gene (SCD-Sβ^+ and SCD-Sβ^o), in addition to one sickle cell gene mutation. Children homozygous for the sickle cell gene mutation (SCD-SS) had an even higher rate of 0.61% per year. The highest rate of first stroke was in children between two to five years, followed by those from six to nine years with incidences of 1.02% per year and 0.68% per year respectively. A second peak is seen in adults greater than thirty years old. The incidence of ICH peaks in adults between twenty and twenty nine years of age. The calculated incidence of first stroke in SCD-SS by age twenty was 11%, and by age forty-five was 24%.

Recurrence of stroke is high in SCD. Repeat clinical strokes occur in 67%, and 70% of these are within the first three years. [10]

Advances in neuroimaging have identified sickle cell children with structural defects in the brain corresponding to infarction without any history of focal neurologic deficits, the clinical syndrome by which stroke is defined. Perhaps poorly named due to their effect on cognitive abilities, these lesions have been titled "silent infarcts". Their significance will be discussed in the following section. The prevalence of silent infarction in SCD has been detailed as well [11, 12], and magnetic resonance imaging (MRI) lesions that correspond with subclinical stroke are identified in 17% of patients between ages six and twelve. A more recent study has placed the prevalence at 21.8% possibly due to the increased sensitivity of current neuroimaging techniques. [13] Therefore, depending on one's definition of stroke, studies on stroke rate may have underestimated its true frequency. The cumulative risk of stroke in childhood, including both subclinical and clinical events, may be as high as 30%. [14] This represents a several hundred-fold increase in the risk of childhood stroke when compared with the general population.

SILENT INFARCTS

As suggested above, it has been recognize for some time that neuroimaging of patients with SCD may show evidence of prior infarction despite an absence of neurologic signs. [15] For the purpose of study, these silent infarcts have been defined by the researchers as areas of abnormally increased signal on intermediate and T2-weighted MRI images of the brain. [12] In the past decade, significant effort has been undertaken to characterize these lesions and assess their significance. The distribution and size of cerebral vascular lesions in patients without a clinical history of a neurologic event are distinct from those with a documented clinical stroke. [12, 13] Basal ganglia and thalamic lesions were identified with greater frequency in those with a history of stroke. Stroke subjects with frontal lobe infarcts had involvement of both cortex and deep white matter as opposed to silent infarcts, which involved the deep white matter alone. Also, silent infarcts also tended to be smaller than lesions in patients with history of a stroke.

So, as overt strokes predict future strokes, silent infarctions predict future silent infarctions. Whereas almost one quarter of children with lesions on brain MRI consistent with silent infarction subsequently developed additional silent infarcts on repeat imaging, only 2.5% of children with a normal baseline MRI developed silent infarcts. [13] Overt strokes also occur with a greater frequency in patients with prior silent infarcts, but not to the degree that they recur in those with prior symptomatic cerebrovascular events. [13]

The sequelae of overt infarction are readily evident including hemiparesis, seizures, and eventually spastic quadriparesis and pseudobulbar palsy with repeated events. [10] However, the consequences of silent infarction are more subtle. Cognitive impairments in children with SCD have been reported since the late 1980's. [16, 17] Separate research groups have demonstrated deficits in children with stroke involving language skills [18], visuospatial [19], and executive function [20] respectively. Data collected by the CSSCD allowed for the comparison of MRI findings with neuropsychologic testing. [21] Patients underwent MRI of the brain and a series of neuropsychologic tests, which included the Wechsler Intelligence Scale for Children and the Woodcock-Johnson Math and Reading Achievement Tests. Patients with T2 hyperintensities and no history of clinical stroke had statistically significant lower scores on all neuropsychometric tests. This corresponded to lower Full-Scale IQ,

Verbal IQ, Performance IQ and math and reading achievement when compared with children with normal MRIs. Children with a history of infarction had comparable scores to the children with prior silent infarction. There remains little doubt of the significance of silent infarcts regarding cognitive dysfunction in children with SCD.

RISK FACTORS

Numerous clinical and laboratory features have been proposed as independent risk factors for stroke in SCD. The best data for stroke risk are derived from the CSSCD, as it is a population-based study [7]. As mentioned previously, stroke rate is influenced by age with the peak rate of infarctive stroke during infancy, from ages two to five, followed by a decrement in incidence over the subsequent two decades, and a second peak after thirty years of age. ICH, conversely, peaks during the third decade of life. [7] Previous stroke portends future events as well. This is the case for both overt and silent infarcts. [10, 13]

Phenotypic heterogeneity of SCD in relation to stroke is probably due to at least in part to modifier genes. Driscoll and colleagues examined 3425 patients with SCD (2533 with SCD-SS) of which 168 had a clinical history of stroke. [22] Of the 2533, 443 were in sibships and fifty-two of the 443 had a reported clinical stroke. The study established an increased risk of stroke among siblings greater than would be expected by chance. Potential candidate genes include those involved in cell adhesion [23], inflammatory pathways, and coagulation. Certain HLA subtypes confer an increased stroke risk whereas other offer protection. [24, 25] Conversely, polymorphisms of the methylenetetrahydrofolate reductase gene C677T [26] and the Factor V Leiden gene [27] do not increase stroke rate. It is likely that stroke risk is polygenic.

SCD subtype plays a role as well. Alpha-thalassemia appears to provide some protection from stroke in children SCD. The incidence of α-globin gene deletions was significantly lower in a cohort of SCD patients with prior stroke than those without a history of infarction. [28] More recently, the CSSCD has shown that the incidence of stroke, including both hemorrhages and infarcts, in patients who inherit both α-thalassemia and sickle cell anemia is significantly lower than those with pure SCD. [7] When these data were analyzed by stroke subtype, statistical significance was lost. This is possibly due to a decrease in the number of total events. The etiology of the suggested protective effect is not established, but may be from decreased hemolysis and increased oxygen carrying capacity.

In assessing for risk factors for first stroke, the CSSCD evaluated infarctive and hemorrhagic strokes independently due to their disparate pathogenesis. Variables analyzed included TIA, gender, systolic blood pressure, Hb F level, mean Hb level, mean leukocyte count mean platelet count, α-thalassemia; history of meningitis; presentation for seizure, surgery, priapism, acute anemia, acute chest syndrome (ACS), and transfusion within two weeks before stroke; and rates of painful crises and ACS. [7] Five predictors were significant at a $P<.05$ for infarctive stroke and these were prior TIA, low steady-state Hb, ACS within two weeks prior to event, ACS rate and elevated systolic blood pressure. TIA had the greatest significance, however, the vast majority with first infarction had no history of a TIA.

Multivariate analysis identified decrease in baseline Hb and increase in baseline white blood cell count as the only significant predictors of ICH.

Risk for silent infarction has been studied as well. The CSSCD has published data on 230 children with SCD-SS of which forty-two had silent infarcts identified on MRI. [29] Multivariate analysis identified a history of seizures and a low rate of painful crises as the strongest clinical predictors of ischemic lesions. Patients with increased white blood cell counts and SEN β globin haplotype were also at higher risk. Other variables analyzed including Hb F level, platelet count, reticulocytosis, and total bilirubin were not significant. Risk factors for silent infarction are clearly different than those for overt stroke.

PATHOGENESIS

Cerebral Angiography

Early theories into the mechanism of stroke in SCD concentrated on occlusion of small or penetrating arteries. The pathogenesis was felt most likely to be the result of intravascular sickling and consequent sludging of red blood cells in the setting of hypoxemia and acidosis. In 1972, Stockman and colleagues published angiographic results on seven children with SCD and stroke forcing a revision of this hypothesis. [5] Six of the seven patients had severe large vessel occlusive disease involving the supraclinoid internal carotid arteries, as well as the anterior and middle cerebral arteries. The vertebrobasilar circulation was relatively spared. Collateral circulation with dilatation of penetrating vessels was identified in several of the patients. The authors remarked on the similarity to the pattern of basal vessel occlusive disease and collateralization seen in Moyamoya disease. Subsequent studies have supported these findings [30-32] and 86% of children with SCD and stroke have large vessel occlusive disease of the anterior circulation. [33] There have been concerns in the past of angiographic dye inducing sickling, and report of two patients who had strokes after angiography. [34] Adverse outcomes can be avoided with hydration and transfusion or exchange transfusion with reduction of Hb S to less than 30%.

Contrast angiography is not typically necessary to evaluate SCD patients with stroke. Magnetic resonance angiography (MRA) is 85% accurate in comparison with conventional angiography. [35] In a study of twenty-two SCD patients, short focal areas of abnormality on MRA were not associated with infarction, whereas disease in a long segment (six mm) with reduced distal flow correlated with subclinical infarction [36]. MRA was performed on twenty-nine patients between the ages of seven and forty-eight months. [36] Three children had large vessel stenoses further substantiating that large vessel disease may begin at a very early age.

Radiographic Findings

Computed tomography (CT) and magnetic resonance imaging (MRI) have been used to better define the mechanism of stroke. Adams et al. evaluated twenty-five patients with SCD and stroke. [37] The patterns of infarction were consistent with large vessel occlusion.

Twelve patients had strokes in the vascular territories supplied by the anterior or middle cerebral arteries or internal carotid arteries. Nine patients had infarction in a border zone pattern between the anterior and middle cerebral arteries, middle and posterior cerebral arteries or in the centrum semiovale between the superficial and deep middle cerebral artery territories. Strokes in other distributions, either small cortical branch vessel occlusions, or isolated subcortical infarcts, together totaled only 28%. Other researchers have duplicated these results. Among eighteen patients who had suffered cerebral infarction, sixteen had patterns of border zone stroke. [38] Five of the sixteen also had infarction in the middle cerebral artery territory. Considering angiography, CT and MRI data the predominant role of large vessel disease in cerebral infarction is clear.

Anatomic Pathology

Neurologic complications in SCD were long thought to be the result of occlusion of small vessels from sickled erythrocytes; however, we now know that large vessel disease plays a prominent role as well. Baird et al. described cerebral arterioles, capillaries and venules distended and obliterated by sickled red cells in the post-mortem analysis of five patients. [39] There was microinfarction within the subcortical white matter. Greer and Schotland corroborated these findings and detailed "endothelial hyperplasia" in the capillaries. [40] Wertham et al. described "hypertrophy and proliferation of endothelial and adventitial elements of the walls of small blood vessels". [41] Infarcts were distributed in region between the cortex and subcortical white matter.

Bridgers was the first to detail large vessel occlusive disease. [4] He described a girl with SCD who developed a right hemiparesis at four years of age, and subsequently died form a subarachnoid hemorrhage three years later. Microscopic examination of the cerebral vessels revealed "obliteration of the lumen with endothelial proliferation, fibroblastic reaction and hyalinization, occasional loss of internal elastic lamina, and fragmentation of the persistent internal elastic lamina". There was occlusion of the right middle cerebral artery and partial obliteration of the left middle cerebral artery and both anterior cerebral arteries.

In a review of six cases of SCD with cerebrovascular complications, Hughes et al. was the first to describe organizing thrombus in a stenotic cerebral vessel. [42] In 1942, Connel detailed recent thrombosis of the left middle cerebral artery in a twenty year old female. [43] Merkel and colleagues detailed the case of a seven year old child with SCD who succumbed to bihemispheric strokes. [44] Angiography revealed bilateral distal internal carotid artery occlusion. Multiple collaterals supplying blood flow to the basal ganglia were present in a pattern consistent with Moyamoya disease. Pathologically, there was occlusion of the proximal portions of both the right and left middle, anterior and posterior communicating arteries. The authors describe intimal hyperplasia due to "proliferation of fibroblasts and smooth muscle cells as well as focal splitting or clumping the internal elastic lamina". Thrombus was present in the left middle cerebral artery. They concluded that intimal expansion and superimposed thrombosis were primary and secondary events respectively.

Rothman et al. provided further evidence concerning the importance of large vessel disease in cerebral infarction. [45] They identified cerebral infarcts in twelve of twenty-four patients at autopsy. Infarction in the border zone between the anterior and middle cerebral arteries was the most prominent location of involvement and was present in all patients with infarcts. Infarcts in the striatum, thalamus, posterior border zone (between middle and posterior cerebral artery territories) and the boundary area between the superior and inferior cerebellar arteries were present to a lesser degree. Organized mural thrombus was present in all patients with infarcts, often in association with reduplication of the internal elastic membrane and scarring of the media. The authors proposed two mechanisms of infarction: distal perfusion failure from stenosis of the intracranial internal carotid artery and proximal middle and anterior cerebral arteries and artery to artery embolization.

Koshy et al. reviewed twenty post-mortem cases of patients with SCD, eleven of which had died from cerebral infarction or hemorrhage. [46] Large vessel disease was described in thirteen and characterized by intimal proliferation as well as fragmentation and reduplication of the internal elastic lamina involving the terminal portion of the internal carotid and proximal middle and anterior cerebral arteries. The authors identified sickled red blood cells adhering to the endothelium and incorporated into large vessel intima as the earliest changes and proposed that repeated injury to the endothelium results in thrombosis and plaque formation. Fifteen patients had evidence of small vessel abnormalities, including two without large vessel obliterative lesions. Koshy et al. concluded that infarctions were due to both small and large vessel disease. [46]

Cerebral Blood Flow

In the 1980s, technology became available to evaluate the relationship between cerebral perfusion and infarction. Huttenlocher and colleagues utilizing a xenon-133 inhalation technique on patients with SCD and suspected cerebrovascular disease were the first group to demonstrate global and regional hypoperfusion abnormalities. [47] Studies obtained after exchange transfusion demonstrated normalization of blood flow. In a small study utilizing positron emission tomography (PET), Herold et al. compared regional cerebral blood flow and cerebral blood volume in six children with SCD with fourteen age- and sex-matched controls. [48] Patients with SCD had elevated regional cerebral blood flow and blood volume when compared with non-SCD subjects. Fractional oxygen extraction was not significantly different from controls.

The discovery of increased cerebral blood flow was an apparent contradiction to the fact that patients with SCD suffer cerebral infarctions related to perfusion failure. Prohovnik and colleagues undertook a larger study, performing xenon-133 inhalation technique on sixty-seven patients. [49] Cerebral blood flow was 68% higher when compared with age-matched controls and proportional to the degree of anemia. Cerebral blood volume was correlated to blood flow. Transfusion therapy normalized cerebral hyperemia. The reduction in blood flow was greater than would be expected from correction of hematocrit alone. This has been corroborated in other studies. [50] Also, decrease in percent Hb S may contribute to the decrease in cerebral blood flow. In summary, SCD is characterized by chronic hyperemia and hypervolemia due to anemia, and probably, abnormal red cell morphology as well.

Pathophysiology

Neuroimaging data have displayed that strokes in SCD occur in a variety of vascular territories. The largest proportion of overt infarctions occurs in border zone territories, principally in the distal field between the anterior and middle cerebral artery, but also between the middle and posterior cerebral artery and between the superficial and deep middle cerebral artery territories. Isolated subcortical strokes occur but are less frequent. Silent infarcts tend to be in smaller in size and involve the deep white matter, but spare the cortex. Based on angiographic and pathologic studies, it is clear that large vessel disease plays a preeminent role in the pathogenesis of clinically evident strokes. Nevertheless, a minority of patients with stroke has a normal cerebral angiogram performed shortly after their event. [5, 51, 52] Therefore, a variety of mechanisms, involving both large and small vessels, must be at play to explain stroke in SCD.

The cause of stenosis of large vessels in SCD has been debated. Stockman et al. initially proposed that obliterative disease of large intracerebral vessels was the result of damage to the vaso vasorum by sickled cells. [5] This is unlikely, as the large intracranial vessels have been subsequently shown to lack vaso vasorum. [53] The etiology of large vessel occlusion is not known, but most surmise a response-to-injury hypothesis. The mechanisms by which sickled red cells may damage the endothelium include hemodynamic factors causing turbulence at large vessel bifurcations, as well as abnormal interactions between sickled erythrocytes and the endothelium. [54] Damage to the endothelium promotes "intimal hyperplasia" and mural thrombus formation.

Large vessel disease causes stroke primarily by a relative hypoperfusion of susceptible arterial territories. Anemia and abnormal rheology create a condition of steady state hyperemia and hypervolemia. At baseline the fraction of oxygen extraction is unchanged, suggesting that this high flow state tenuously compensates for proximal large vessel occlusions most likely by dilatation of the intracerebral vasculature. When stressed, there is inability to increase perfusion passed large vessel occlusions, leading to distal field insufficiency and border zone infarction. Artery to artery embolism may be responsible for a smaller subset of large vessel strokes. The abnormal physical properties of sickled erythrocytes and abnormal flow through distal lenticulostriate arteries results in small vessel infarcts. Large and small vessel disease may play more or less significant roles in individual patients with SCD and stroke.

Intracerebral Hemorrhage

ICH represents a smaller but sizable proportion of intracerebral vascular events in SCD. A multitude of mechanisms are responsible for intracranial hemorrhages. First, hemorrhagic conversion of infarcted tissue may occur. In addition, the same pathogenesis that has been proposed for large vessel occlusion may cause weakening of large intracerebral vessels. [55] Consequently, hemorrhages may result from rupture of abnormally dilated large intracerebral vessels. Many authors have noted similarities between SCD and Moyamoya disease. [5, 54] Children with SCD may have angiographic features compatible to Moyamoya with distal internal carotid artery occlusions and a network of basal collaterals. There is clinical overlap as well with a similar natural history of infarctive stroke in infancy and hemorrhages in adulthood. In this context a third manner of ICH may result from bursting of fragile collaterals.

Alternatively, subarachnoid hemorrhage (SAH) may result from rupture of berry aneurysms. Aneurysms are often multiple, and occur frequently in the vertebrobasilar circulation. [55, 56] SAH in SCD has been managed successfully with craniotomy and clipping, and more recently via endovascular coiling. [57] To avoid missing potential correctable anomalies such as saccular aneurysms, arteriography should be performed on all patients with ICH. [54]

TRANSCRANIAL DOPPLER ULTRASOUND AND IDENTIFYING PATIENTS AT RISK

Carotid duplex and transcranial Doppler ultrasound (TCD) have been used for decades to identify extracranial and intracranial arterial stenoses. Increased velocities reflect elevated cerebral blood flow when identified diffusely, while focal abnormalities are a sign of a reduction in arterial diameter. [58] Mean velocities in children with SCD are therefore elevated at baseline due to the effects of low hematocrit. [59, 60] Whereas normal children have middle cerebral artery velocities in the range of 90 cm/sec, children with SCD have velocities of 130-140 cm/sec without increased stroke risk.

More than a decade ago, it was hypothesized that primary stroke prevention in SCD would be possible, if a noninvasive test could be performed that would identify the subset of patients with large vessel intracranial disease and thus at highest risk for cerebral infarction. With this goal in mind, TCD was compared with cerebral angiography, the gold standard for identifying cerebrovascular disease. Using a mean velocity of 190 cm/sec or greater, the sensitivity and specificity of greater than fifty percent middle cerebral artery stenosis is 90% and 100% respectively. [8] Correlation between TCD abnormalities and arteriography has been confirmed by other groups. [61] More significantly, increased velocity in the middle cerebral artery and carotid siphon have been shown to predict first stroke. [62, 63] Velocities over 200 cm/sec indicate a stroke risk of 10-13%/year on top of a baseline rate of .5-1%/year. An intermediate risk is implied with velocities between 170 and 200. These results provided the basis for the Stroke Prevention Trial in Sickle Cell Anemia (STOP study), the only randomized clinical trial for prevention of stroke in SCD. [64]

There are several important technical issues regarding the use of TCD and the identification of intracranial stenosis that are worth discussion. First, the velocities obtained in STOP were time averaged mean of the maximum velocities as opposed to more conventional peak systolic values. Velocities of greater than 200 cm/sec measured by time averaged mean of the maximum may correlate with a peak systolic figure of 280-300 cm/sec. [14] Use of improper protocol could misidentify children without significant intracranial disease as having large vessel stenosis, and target them for a potential unnecessary and risky therapy. Alternatively, improper technique might fail to identify children at risk who would benefit from transfusion therapy. A second technique to insonate the intracranial vessels has been recently developed. Transcranial color doppler imaging (TCDI) superimposes color

Doppler flow information of vessels onto a B-mode doppler image. TCDI has been compared to TCD for the evaluation of intracranial disease. [65, 66] TCDI values are 10-15% lower when compared with TCD in the middle cerebral and distal internal carotid arteries. Although no firm guidelines have been established, treatments based on cerebral blood flow velocities may need to be adjusted accordingly.

For the purpose of comparing the results of TCD and MRI, data was analyzed on seventy-eight children who had taken part in both the CSSCD and STOP study groups. [67] Children with a history of overt stroke were excluded. Only 29% of subjects with a silent infarct had elevated velocities by TCD. Among the sixty-one patients without MRI abnormality, 18% had velocities greater than 170 cm/sec. From these results, it is apparent that TCD and MRI reveal disparate aspects of central nervous system disease in SCD, and that TCD is a poor predictor of silent infarction. Considering the detrimental effects of subclinical stroke on cognitive function, better tests to identify children at risk for silent infarction need to be assessed. MRA, PET, computer-assisted intravital microscopy, and neuropsychometric testing require further examination in this regard.

TREATMENT

Among the therapies used to prevent stroke in SCD, transfusion therapy has the longest history of study. Both partial exchange transfusion and simple transfusion have been performed. The goal of transfusion is a hemoglobin and hematocrit of 12 g/dL and 36% respectively and an HbS concentration that is less than thirty percent of the total. Erythocytapheresis increases oxygen saturation by increasing hemoglobin oxygen affinity and arterial oxygen pressure. [68] In 1984, Russell et al. showed that transfusion therapy could decrease progression of large vessel stenosis by arteriography. [69] Other researchers have shown that transfusion causes a rapid and significant decrease in MCA mean velocities in patients with prior stroke as measured by TCD. [70]

To date, there has been only one randomized clinical trial that has evaluated stroke prevention, primary or secondary, in SCD. Among over 2000 children between the ages of two and sixteen, 130 were identified as high risk for stroke based upon middle cerebral or internal carotid artery velocities greater than 200 cm/sec. [64] Patients were randomly assigned to standard care or transfusion therapy. Eleven subjects receiving standard therapy had strokes (including one ICH) versus only one cerebral infarction in the transfusion group reflecting a 92% difference in stroke risk. Stated another way, annual stroke risk was decreased from 10% to 1%. The overwhelming results were associated with early termination of the study. The National Heart Lung and Blood Institute published a Clinical Alert calling for the TCD screening of asymptomatic children and the consideration of transfusion for prevention of first stroke. The duration of transfusion for primary prevention has not been determined.

Although there are no clinical data to direct therapy in the setting of acute stroke, erythocytapheresis is typically advocated to decrease percent HbS without increasing blood viscosity. [71]

No clinical trials have investigated the role of transfusion therapy in preventing stroke recurrence. Prospective data was collected on sixty subjects with a history of overt stroke who were placed on chronic transfusion therapy. [72] The patients were followed for a total of 191.7 patient-years, during which eight had recurrent stroke for a prevalence of 13.3%. Considering the natural history data reported by Powars et al. [10] and others showing risk of recurrence at greater than fifty percent, the benefit of transfusion therapy in secondary stroke prevention appears considerable. In children with a history of silent infarction and abnormal intracranial velocities as measured by TCD, transfusion therapy lowers the risk of new subclinical ischemic events as well. [73] After several years of rigorous therapy, a reduction in transfusion intensity appears to be tolerated without an increase in rate of stroke recurrence. [74, 75] Whether transfusion therapy can be safely discontinued altogether is not clear. [76, 77]

Serious complications are associated with chronic transfusion. Alloimmunization occurs in as many as 30% [78], although this may be reduced using leukocyte-reduced red blood cells matched for E, C, and Kell. [79] There is a small risk of transmitting infection during transfusion. Iron overload is an inevitable consequence of chronic transfusion. Desferoximine, the only available iron chelator, is associated with its own complications including acute respiratory distress syndrome as well as the potential for growth, visual and hearing disabilities. Compliance with transfusions and chelation therapy are often poor.

While transfusion after cerebral infarction is performed as a matter of routine, acceptance of transfusion therapy to prevent a first stroke has been incomplete. Whether a 10% annual risk of stroke warrants the risks of alloimmunization, hemosiderosis, and infection associated with transfusion therapy is debated. In addition, the duration of transfusions and risks of termination have not been determined.

Alternative interventions have been investigated, but as of yet no clinical trials have been performed. Bone marrow transplantation (BMT) is potentially curative. Among 26 patients followed for median of 57.0 months after transplantation, ten had history of prior overt stroke and four of silent infarction. [80] None had a clinical stroke after BMT.

Currently, there are numerous impediments to transplantation. BMT is available only for patients who have an HLA-identical sibling, although improvements in techniques for HLA matching and supportive care may make transplantation from unrelated donors more feasible in the future. [81, 82] In addition, graft rejection occurs in 15% and mortality is as high as 10%. [83] Peritransplant neurologic complications including seizures and ICH are more common in patients with a history of cerebral infarction. [80] Preliminary studies using umbilical cord blood for transplantation are encouraging and appear to be associated with a lower risk of graft-versus-host disease. [84, 85]

Hydroxyurea (HU) is a potential chemotherapeutic alternative to transfusion therapy. It increases Hb F concentration [86, 87], decreases adherence of sickled erythrocytes to basal lamina proteins [88], and reduces levels of neutrophils, monocytes and reticulocytes. [89] HU has been shown to decrease the frequency of painful crises, ACS, hospitalization and need for blood transfusion in a double blind, placebo-controlled study. [86] Controlled trials on stroke prevention are lacking. In a pilot study by Wang and colleagues, there was one stroke and one transient ischemic attack (TIA) among 28 children followed for two years on therapy. [90] There was no stroke recurrence on HU among five patients with a history of stroke or

TIA followed for 42 to 112 months. [91] Switching to HU in patients unable to tolerate transfusion therapy may be reasonable. [92] Ware and colleagues followed 16 children with SCD and prior stroke who discontinued erythrocytapheresis (as a result of noncompliance, hemosiderosis, alloimmunization, etc.) on HU for a period of 3 to 52 months. Three strokes occurred; all during the first four months after transfusion therapy was discontinued. Patients receiving HU need to have blood counts monitored periodically. The risk of leukemic transformation on HU is likely low, however the longterm risks of HU therapy in children are not known. [83]

Surgical Revascularization may be an alternative for a minority of patients. Children with SCD, stroke and Moyamoya pattern of collateralization may be candidates for encephaloduroarteriosynangiosis. [93]

CONCLUSION

Strokes, both overt and subclinical, have a tremendous impact on a large subset of patients with SCD. In those who are predisposed for ischemic events, changes in cerebral vasculature and brain parenchyma have been detected as early as infancy. Disease of both large and small intracranial vessels are important in the pathogenesis of stroke, and may be more or less significant in different patients.

TCD has been shown to identify high risk subjects, and intervening with transfusion therapy can prevent a first stroke. [64] The duration and consequences of discontinuing transfusion therapy, though, are not yet established. Considering the complications of transfusion, alternatives should be investigated. BMT offers the promise of cure, but currently is available only to a limited number, and associated with a not insignificant mortality risk. Data on HU for stroke prevention are sparse and surgery is not a consideration for most patients. Future research in SCD and stroke will most likely involve the use of neurodiagnostic testing to better identify high risk patients, including those with silent infarcts. Defining the parameters of transfusion therapy and improving transplantation technique represent opportunities for future investigators to make an impact on stroke in sickle cell patients. Clinical trials are needed to evaluate the capacity of HU and other alternative therapies to protect the brain.

REFERENCES

[1] Syndenstricker VP, Mulherin WA, Houseal RW. Sickle cell anemia. *Am J Dis Child.* 1923;26:132-154.

[2] Arena JM. Vascular accident and acute hemiplegia in sickle cell anemia. *Am J Dis Child.* 1935;49:722-723.

[3] Kampmeier RH. Sickle cell anemia as a cause of cerebral vascular disease. *Arch Neurol Psychiat.* 1936;36:1323-1329.

[4] Bridgers WA. Cerebral vascular disease accompanying sickle cell anemia. *Am J Pathol.* 1939;15:353.

[5] Stockman JA, Nigro MA, Mishkin MM. Occlusion of large cerebral vessels in sickle-cell anemia. *N Engl J Med.* 1972;287:846-848.

[6] The National Institute of Neurological Disorders and Stroke rt-PA Stroke Study Group. Tissue plasminogen activator for acute ischemic stroke. *N Engl J Med.* 1995;333:1581-1587.

[7] Ohene-Frempong K, Weiner SJ, Sleeper LA, et al. Cerebrovascular accidents in sickle cell disease: rates and risk factors. *Blood.* 1998;91:288-294.

[8] Adams RJ, Nichols FT, Figueroa R, et al. Transcranial doppler correlation with cerebral angiography in sickle cell disease. *Stroke.* 1992;23(8):1073-1077.

[9] Earley MD, Kittner SJ, Feeser BR, et al. Stroke in children and sickle-cell disease. Baltimore-Washington Cooperative Young Stroke Study. *Neurology.* 1998;51:169-176.

[10] Powars D, Wilson B, Imbus C, et al. The natural history of stroke in sickle cell disease. *Am J Med.* 1978;65:461-471.

[11] Armstrong FD, Thompson RJ, Wang W, et al. Cognitive functioning and brain magnetic resonance imaging in children with sickle cell disease. *Pediatrics.* 1996;97:864-870.

[12] Moser FG, Miller ST, Bello JA, et al. The spectrum of central nervous system abnormalities in sickle cell disease as defined by magnetic resonance imaging: A report from the Cooperative Study of Sickle Cell Disease. *Am J Neuroradiol.* 1996;17:965-972.

[13] Pegelow CH, Macklin EA, Moser FG, et al. Longitudinal changes in brain magnetic resonance imaging findings in children with sickle cell disease. *Blood.* 2002;99:3014-3018.

[14] Adams RJ, Ohene-Frempong K, and Wang W. Sickle cell and the brain. *Hematology.* 2001:31-46.

[15] Hindmarsh PC, Brozovic M, Brook CG, et al. Incidence of overt and covert neurological damage in children with sickle cell disease. *Postgrad Med J.* 1987;63:751-753.

[16] Fowler MG, Whitt JK, Lallinger RR, et al. Neuropsychologic and academic functioning of children with sickle cell anemia. Dev Behav Pediatr. 1988;9:213-220.

[17] Swift AV, Cohen MJ, Hynd GW, et al. Neuropsychologic impairment in children with sickle cell anemia. *Pediatrics.* 1989;84:1077-85.

[18] Davis P, Landers A, Gentry B, et al. Speech and language characteristics of children with strokes due to sickle cell disease. *Percept Mot Skills.* 1997;85:809-810.

[19] Craft S Schatz J, Glauser TA, et al. Neuropsychologic effects of stroke in children with sickle cell anemia. *J Pediatr.* 1993;123:712-717.

[20] Brown RT, Davis PC, Lambert R, et al. Neurocognitive functioning and magnetic resonance imaging in children with sickle cell disease. *J Pediatr Psychol.* 2000;25:503-513.

[21] Wang W, Enos L, Gallagher D, et al., for the Cooperative Study of Sickle Cell Disease. Neuropsychological performance in school-aged children with sickle cell disease: A report from the Cooperative Study of Sickle Cell Disease. *J Pediatr.* 2001;139:391-397.

[22] Driscoll MC, Hurlet A, Styles L, et al. Stroke risk in siblings with sickle cell anemia. *Blood*. 2003;101(6):2401-2404.

[23] Taylor JG, Tang DC, Savage SA, et al. Variants in the VCAM 1 gene and risk for symptomatic stroke in sickle cell disease. *Blood*. 2002;100:4303-4307.

[24] Styles LA, Hoppe C, Klitz W, et al. Evidence for HLA-related susceptibility for stroke in children with sickle cell disease. *Blood*. 2000;95(11):3562-3567.

[25] Hoppe C, Klitz W, Noble J, et al. Distinct HLA associations by stroke subtype in children with sickle cell anemia. *Blood*. 2003;101(7):2865-9.

[26] Cumming AM, Olujohungbe A, Keeney S, et al. The methylenetetrahydrofolate reductase gene C677T polymorphism in patients with homozygous sickle cell disease and stroke. *Br J Haematol*. 1999;107:569-571.

[27] Kahn MJ, Scher C, Rozans M. Factor V Leiden is not responsible for stroke in patients with sickling disorders and is uncommon in African Americans with sickle cell disease. *Am J Hematol*. 1997;54:12-15.

[28] Adams RJ, Kutlar A, McKie V, et al. Alpha thalassemia and stroke risk in sickle cell anemia. *Am J Hematol*. 1994;45:279-82.

[29] Kinney TR, Sleeper LA, Wang WC, et al. Silent cerebral infarcts in sickle cell anemia: a risk factor analysis. *Pediatrics*. 1999;103(3):640-645.

[30] Adeloye A, Odeku E. Nervous system in sickle cell disease. *Afr J Med Sci*. 1970;1:33-39.

[31] Borosh RC, Weiner WJ. Large vessel disease in sickle cell anemia. *J Neurol Neurosurg Psychiatr*. 1986;39:1236-1243.

[32] Russell MO, Goldberg HI, Hodson, et al. Effect of transfusion therapy on arteriographic abnormalities and on recurrence of stroke in sickle cell disease. *Blood*. 1984;63:162-169.

[33] Pavlakis SG, Prohovnik I, Piomelli S, DeVivo DC. Neurological complications of sickle cell disease. *Adv Pediatr*. 1989;36:247-276.

[34] Richards D, Nulsen FE. Angiographic media and the sickling phenomenon. *Surg Forum*. 1971;22:403-404.

[35] Kandeel AY, Zimmerman RA, Ohene-Frempong K. Comparison of magnetic resonance angiography and conventional angiography in sickle cell disease: clinical significance and reliability. *Neuroradiol*. 1996;38:409-416.

[36] Gilliams AR, McMahon L, Weinberg G, Carter AP. MRA of the intracranial circulation in asymptomatic patients with sickle cell disease. *Pediatr Radiol*. 1998;28:283-287.

[37] Adams RJ, Nichols FT, McKie V, et al. Cerebral infarction in sickle cell anemia: mechanism based on CT and MRI. *Neurology*. 1988;38:1012-1017.

[38] Pavlakis SG, Bello J, Prohovnik I, et al. Brain infarction in sickle cell anemia: magnetic resonance imaging correlates. *Ann Neurol*. 1988;23:125-130.

[39] Baird RL, Weiss DL, Ferguson AD, et al. Studies in sickle cell anemia. XXI Clinico-pathological aspects of neurological manifestations. *Pediatrics*. 1964;34:92-100.

[40] Greer M, Schotland D. Abnormal hemoglobin as a cause of neurological disease. *Neurology*. 1962;12:114-120.

[41] Wertham F, Mitchell N, Angrist A. The brain in sickle cell anemia. *Arch Neurol Psych*. 1942;47:752-767.

[42] Hughes JG, Diggs LW, Gillespie CE. The involvement of the nervous system in sickle cell anemia. *J Pediatr.* 1948;17:166-184.

[43] Connel JH. Cerebral necrosis in sickle cell disease. *JAMA*. 1942;188:893-895.

[44] Merkel KH, Ginsberg PL, Parker JC, et al. Cerebrovascular disease in sickle cell anemia: a clinical, pathological and radiological correlation. *Stroke*. 1978;9:45-52.

[45] Rothman SM, Fulling KH, Nelson JS. Sickle cell anemia and central nervous system infarction: a neuropathological study. *Ann Neurol.* 1986;20:684-690.

[46] Koshy M, Thomas C, Goodwin J. Vascular lesions in the central nervous system in sickle cell disease (neuropathology). *JAAMP*. 1990;1:71-78.

[47] Huttenlocher PR, Mohr JW, Johns L, et al. Cerebral blood flow in sickle cell cerebrovascular disease. *Pediatrics*. 1984;73:155-181.

[48] Herold S, Brozovic M, Gibbs J, et al. Measurement of regional cerebral blood flow, blood volume and oxygen metabolism in patients with sickle cell disease using positron emission tomography. *Stroke*. 1986;17(4):692-698.

[49] Prohovnik I, Pavlakis SG, Piomelli S, et al. Cerebral hyperemia, stroke, and transfusion in sickle cell disease. *Neurology*. 1989;39(3):344-348.

[50] Hurlet-Jensen AM, Prohovnik I, Pavlakis SG, Piomelli, S. Effects of total hemoglobin and hemoglobin S concentration on cerebral blood flow during transfusion therapy to prevent stroke in sickle cell disease. *Stroke*. 1994;25(8):1688-1692.

[51] Gerald B, Sebes JI, Langston JW. Cerebral infarction secondary to sickle cell disease: arteriographic findings. *Am J Radiol.* 1980;134:1209-1212.

[52] Jeffries BF, Lipper MH, Kishure RP. Major intracerebral arterial involvement in sickle cell disease. *Surg Neurol.* 1980;14:291-295.

[53] Clower BR, Sullivan DM, Smith RR. Intracerebral vessels lack vasa vasorum. *J Neurosurg*. 1984;61:44-48.

[54] Hess DC, Adams RJ, Nichols FT. Sickle cell anemia and other hemoglobinopathies. *Seminar in Neurology*. 1991;11(4):314-328.

[55] Oyesiku NM, Barrow DL, Eckman JR, et al. Intracranial aneurysms in sickle-cell anemia: clinical features and pathogenesis. *J Neurosurg*. 1991;75:356-363.

[56] Preul MC, Cendes F, Just N, Mohr G. Intracranial aneurysms and sickle cell anemia: multiplicity and propensity for the vertebrobasilar territory. *Neurosurg*. 1998;42(5):971-978.

[57] Firth PG, Peterfreund RA. Management of multiple intracranial aneurysms: neuroanesthetic considerations of sickle cell disease. *J Neurosurg Anesth.* 2000;12(4):366-371.

[58] Aaslid R, Markwalder TM, Nornes H. Noninvasive transcranial doppler ultrasound recording of flow velocity in basal cerebral arteries. J Neurosurg. 1982;57(6):769-774.

[59] Brass LM, Pavlakis SG, DeVivo D, et al. Transcranial doppler measurements of the middle cerebral artery. Effect of hematocrit. *Stroke*. 1988;19(12):1466-1469.

[60] Adams RJ, Nichols FT, Aaslid R, et al. Cerebral vessel stenosis in sickle cell disease: criteria for detection by transcranial doppler. *Am J Pediatr Hematol Oncol.* 1990;12(3):277-282.

[61] Adams RJ, McKie VC, Hsu L, et al. Prevention of a first stroke by transfusion in children with sickle cell anemia and abnormal results on transcranial doppler ultrasonography. *NEJM.* 1998;338:5-11.

[62] Verlhac S, Bernaudin F, Tortrat D, et al. Detection of cerebrovascular disease in patients with sickle cell disease using transcranial doppler sonography: correlation with MRI, MRA and conventional angiography. *Pediatr Radiol.* 1995;25 suppl 1:S14-19.

[63] Adams R, McKie V, Nichols F, et al. The use of transcranial ultrasonography to predict stroke in sickle cell disease. *NEJM.* 1992;326:605-610.

[64] Adams RJ, McKie VC, Carl EM, et al. Long-term stroke risk in children with sickle cell disease screened with transcranial doppler. *Ann Neurol.* 1997;42:699-704.

[65] Bulas DI, Jones A, Seibert JJ, et al. Transcranial doppler (TCD) screening for stroke prevention in sickle cell anemia: pitfalls in technique variation. *Pediatr Radiol.* 2000;30(11):733-738.

[66] Jones AM, Seibert JJ, Nichols FT, et al. Comparison of transcranial color doppler imaging (TCDI) and transcranial doppler (TCD) in children with sickle-cell anemia. *Pediatr Radiol.* 2001;31:461-469.

[67] Wang WC, Gallagher DM, Pegelow CH, et al. Multicenter comparison of magnetic resonance imaging and transcranial doppler ultrasonography in the evaluation of central nervous system in children with sickle cell disease. *J Pediatr Hematol Oncol.* 2000;22(4):335-339.

[68] Uchida K, Rackoff WR, Ohene-Frempong K, et al. Effect of erythrocytapheresis on arterial oxygen saturation and hemoglobin oxygen affinity in patients with sickle cell disease. *Am J Hematol.* 1998;59(1):5-8.

[69] Russell MO, Goldberg HI, Hodson A, et al. Effect of transfusion therapy on arteriographic abnormalities and on recurrence of stroke in sickle cell disease. *Blood.* 1984;63(1):162-9.

[70] Venketasubramanian N, Prohovnik I, Hurlet A, et al. Middle cerebral artery velocity changes during transfusion in sickle cell anemia. *Stroke.* 1994;25(11)2153-2158.

[71] Powars DR. Management of cerebral vasculopathy in children with sickle cell anaemia. *Br J Haematol.* 2000;108:666-678.

[72] Pegelow CH, Adams RJ, McKie V, et al. Risk of recurrent stroke in patients with sickle cell disease treated with erythrocyte transfusions. *J Pediatr.* 1995;126:896-899.

[73] Pegelow CH, Wang W, Granger S, et al. Silent infarcts in children with sickle cell anemia and abnormal cerebral artery velocity. *Arch Neurol.* 2001;58:2017-2021.

[74] Miller ST, Jensen D, and Rao SP. Less intensive long-term transfusion therapy for sickle cell anemia and cerebrovascular accident. *J Pediatr.* 1992;120:54-57.

[75] Cohen AR, Martin MB, Silber JH, et al. A modified transfusion program for prevention of stroke in sickle cell disease. *Blood.* 1992;7:1657-1661.

[76] Wang WC, Kovnar EH, Tonkin IL, et al. High risk of recurrent stroke after discontinuance of five to twelve years of transfusion therapy in patients with sickle cell disease. *J Pediatr.* 1991;118(3):377-382.

[77] Rana S, Houston PE, Surana N, et al. Discontinuation of long-term transfusion therapy in patients with sickle cell disease and stroke. *J Pediatr.* 1997;131:757-760.

[78] Vichinsky EP, Earles A, Johnson RA, et al. Alloimmunization in sickle cell anemia and transfusion of racially unmatched blood. *NEJM.* 1990;322:1617-21.

[79] Vichinsky EP, Luban NL, Wright E, et al. Prospective RBC phenotype matching in a stroke-prevention trial in sickle cell anemia: a multicenter transfusion trial. *Transfusion.* 2001;41:1086-1092.

[80] Walters MC, Storb R, Patience M, et al. Impact of bone marrow transplantation for symptomatic sickle cell disease: an interim report. *Blood.* 2000;95(6):1918-1924.

[81] Walters MC. Bone marrow transplantation for sickle cell disease: where do we go from here. *J Pediatr Hematol Oncol.* 1999;21(6):467-474.

[82] Krishnamurti L, Abel S, Maiers M, and Flesch S. Availability of unrelated donors for hematopoietic stem cell transplantation for hemoglobinopathies. *Bone Marrow Transplant.* 2003;31(7):547-550.

[83] Wood AJ. Management of sickle cell disease. *NEJM.* 1999;340(13):1021-1030.

[84] Gore L, Lane PA, Quinones RR and Giller RH. Successful cord blood transplantation for sickle cell anemia from a sibling who is human leukocyte antigen-identical: implications for comprehensive care. *J Pediatr Hematol Oncol.* 2000;22(5):437-440.

[85] Locatelli F, Rocha V, Reed W, et al. Related umbilical cord blood transplantation in patients with thalassemia and sickle cell disease. *Blood.* 2003;101(6):2137-2143.

[86] Charache S, Terrin ML, Moore RD, et al. Effect of hydroxyurea on the frequency of painful crises in sickle cell anemia. *NEJM.* 1995;332:1317-1322.

[87] Steinberg MH, Lu Z-H, Barton FB, et al. Fetal hemoglobin in sickle cell anemia: determinants of response to hydroxyurea: multicenter study of hydroxyurea. *Blood.* 1997;89:1078-1088.

[88] Hillery CA, Du MC, Wang WC and Scott JP. Hydroxyurea therapy decreases the *in vitro* adhesion of sickle erythrocytes to thrombospondin and laminin. *British J Haematol.* 2000;109:322-327.

[89] Charache S, Barton FB, Moore RD, et al. Hydroxyurea and sickle cell anemia-clinical utility of a myelosuppressive "switching" agent: the multicenter study of hydroxyurea in sickle cell anemia. *Medicine (Baltimore).* 1996;75:300-326.

[90] Wang W, Wynn LW, Rogers ZR, et al. A two year pilot trial of hydroxyurea in very young children with sickle cell anemia. *J Pediatr.* 2001;139:790-796.

[91] Sumoza A, de Bisotti R, Sumoza D and Fairbanks V. Hydroxyurea for prevention of recurrent stroke in sickle cell anemia. *Am J Hematol.* 2002;71(3):161-165.

[92] Ware RE, Zimmerman SA and Schultz WH. Hydroxyurea as an alternative to blood transfusions for the prevention of recurrent stroke in children with sickle cell disease. *Blood.* 1999;94(9):3022-3026.

[93] Vernet O, Montes JL, O'Gorman AM, et al. Encephaloduroarteriosynangiosis in a child with sickle cell anemia and Moyamoya disease. *Pediatr Neurol.* 1996;14(3):226-230.

In: Focus on Sickle Cell Research
Editor: Ralph L. Plasmar, pp. 99-112
ISBN 1-59033-920-7

Chapter VI

SICKLE CELL CRISIS AND MALARIA – THE BAND 3 CONNECTION

J. Randall Kennedy
Manatee Memorial Hospital
Department of Pediatrics

ABSTRACT

The severity of the vaso-occlusive process that characterizes a sickle cell crisis would seem to be an irreversible one but it usually resolves with only symptomatic treatment. This reversibility suggests a precarious balance between an erythrocyte adhesive process and an equally energetic anti-occlusive mechanism. This paper presents a hypothesis addressing this duality that evolved from consideration of the ability of the sickle trait to prevent the similar and equally deleterious vaso-occlusion pathology that occurs in falciparum malaria. The malaria benefit is thought to be the result of natural antibodies whose normal function is to eliminate senescent red cells that display band 3 clusters on their surface. These band 3 clusters also appear on malaria infected and sickle cells. It is proposed that prematurely denatured sickle hemoglobin in sickle trait erythrocytes is responsible for generating the band 3 clusters that evoke the antibody response that benefits a malaria patient. The presence of an even greater abundance of these clusters and their antibodies in sickle cell disease is proposed as a major factor in both the cause and of the resolution of a sickle crisis.

Sickle erythrocytes and malaria infected erythrocytes that display band 3 clusters adhere to endothelial CD36 and thrombospondin molecules and this adhesion can be prevented by certain band 3 peptides and by antibodies that recognize these peptides. If natural band 3 specific antibodies block adhesion to both CD36 and thrombospondin they will not only prevent adhesion of erythrocytes bearing these clusters, they will also disrupt the CD36 thrombospondin bridge that helps reticulocytes to adhere to the endothelium. These antibodies exist and their proposed up-regulation in sickle cell disease and malaria suggests a therapeutic potential that deserves further investigation.

A single substitution of valine for glutamic acid in the hemoglobin molecule makes all the difference in the world to the millions of people with sickle cell disease who have had their lives shortened and irrevocably changed. The enormity of this problem has lead to research that has greatly expanded our understanding of the myriad complexities of the hematologic, genetic, metabolic, immunologic and physiologic changes that occur in this disease. Recent technological advances have allowed investigation of new and re-examination of old areas of interest. In spite of this we still have very little to offer these people. As a result, the vaso-occlusive pathology that this disease produces still results in a painful and an abbreviated life span.

From infancy on, these patients have to deal with recurring painful attacks that leave almost no organ system or physiologic function untouched. The disease subjects them to overwhelming infections, damages their cardiovascular, pulmonary, nervous, and renal systems and eventually leads to an early death. Medical management for this disorder is, for the most part, merely supportive with the treatment of crisis limited to the management of pain, the administration of intravenous fluids for hydration, the selective use of antibiotics if infection is suspected, blood transfusions if anemia is severe, and oxygen for hypoxia. Even though the disease is called sickle cell anemia the patients seem to be well accommodated to this component of their disease. Transfusions are more often given to try and elevate the level of non-sickle hemoglobin and thereby preventing these attacks in those who are critically ill.

The diagnosis of this disorder is relatively simple and in developed countries the diagnosis of sickle cell disease is even automatic in that neonatal screening is done at birth. With the introduction of this program a spot of blood taken in the neonatal nursery is all that is needed to detect this disease and its trait. Though we have no cure to offer these newborns, this rapid diagnosis provides vital information that allows physicians to begin prophylactic antibiotics to prevent the infections that these children are subject to and to introduce the child into the medical system in preparation for the difficult times that may lie ahead. The neonatal detection of the sickle trait is equally important in that it makes the parents aware of the possibility that future children may have the full blown disease. It allows the parents to be tested to see if they both have the trait.

The bizarre shaped sickled cell that is produced when a sickle erythrocyte is exposed to a hypoxic environment was once used to diagnose this disease but that use has now been reduced to a historical artifact. The graphic image of these malformed cells entwined in a vascular logjam was responsible for the original thought that these cells were the primary cause of the vaso-occlusion responsible for sickle crisis but it is now apparent that this is not true. The logjam principle is still valid but the vascular occlusion is now known to occur because of the adhesive nature of non-sickled and fully oxygenated cells that adhere to a sticky endothelium and to each other [1]. While the obstruction produced by the rigid deformed sickle cells is still important in the vaso-occlusive process it cannot be the major factor in sickle crisis because the irreversibly deformed cell is incompatible with the fact that crisis attacks are reversible.

The investigation of these adhesive molecules, both those on the erythrocytes, the vascular endothelium, and adhesion inducing modalities in the plasma has been vigorous and rigorous and much solid information has been obtained. The evidence of an adhesive rather than a mechanical induction for the vascular occlusion that occurs in sickle cell disease is such that, unlike the jagged cell model, it is unlikely to go away. However, no unifying concept has yet evolved to tie the large amount of data together and to enable effective treatment. This discussion concerns a molecule that has not heretofore been considered a player in sickle cell crisis, the band 3 molecule. It presents evidence of band 3's adhesive nature and a rational for its consideration as a major player in both the etiology and, equally important, the resolution of a sickle cell crisis. This hypothesis was suggested by the observed ability of the sickle trait to prevent an equally lethal vaso-occlusive process that occurs in falciparum malaria.

BAND 3

The band 3 molecule is the anion channel that functions as a chloride/bicarbonate exchanger that is involved in carbon dioxide transport and is present on the surface of every cell in the body [2]. There are 3 different types of band 3 molecules but only the AE1 molecule that is present on erythrocytes will be considered. This protein molecule comprises two domains that are structurally and functionally distinct. The N-terminal domain is located in the cytoplasm, with no exposure on the erythrocytes surface, where it acts as an attachment site for the red cell skeleton by binding ankyrin (a structural protein in the red cell membrane), thus helping to maintain the mechanical integrity of the red cell. The glycosylated C-terminal of this molecule carries out the anion transport and it loops through the red cell membrane between 12 and 14 times, having both a cytoplasmic and extracellular presence. There are approximately one million of these molecules that are widely dispersed on each erythrocyte. This molecule exists on the erythrocyte surface primarily as a dimer but under certain conditions these molecules become clustered and this clustering results in two very significant changes. First, these red cells become adhesive to the endothelium and second, they become immunogenic and are recognized by naturally occurring antibodies of the immune system [3, 4].

The etiology of the band 3 clustering that changes this ion channel into an immunogenic-adherent structure is the breakdown of hemoglobin which, in turn leads to the formation of Heinz bodies which are the actual clustering agents. This band 3 clustering may also come about as a result of a genetic mutation that results in a condition called Southeast Asian ovalocytosis. This mutation occurs at the hinge area between the two domains and results in more rigid red cells with natural band 3 clusters on their surface. This condition, like sickle cell trait, also reduces the severity of a malaria infection.

There are many reasons for hemoglobin to become denatured. Among them are certain chemicals, the normal aging of red cells, the premature breakdown of abnormal hemoglobins that occurs in the different hemoglobinopathies, abnormal cytoplasmic environments such as occur in G6PD deficiency, and in parasitic infections like malaria. The hemoglobinopathies that modify the course of malaria are the mild forms of sickle cell disease and thalassemia. When Heinz bodies form, their physical-chemical configuration causes them to immediately become attached to the cytoplasmic surface of the erythrocyte membrane and to attract several of the cell membrane's protein molecules that are in their vicinity [5], one of these molecules is band 3. The extra cellular portions of the band 3 molecule will then be clustered on the red cell membrane just above the Heinz body.

The band 3 molecules located on normal erythrocytes are not adhesive but the adhesive properties of the sickle cell's band 3 clusters have been well documented experimentally and are not in doubt. Several adhesive peptide loci on the exofacial band 3 molecule have been delineated. They and the antibodies specific to them have been used to demonstrate the specificity of band 3's adhesive nature on both sickle cells and on malaria parasite infected erythrocytes [3, 6, 7, 8, 9, 10, 11, 12]. They accomplished this experimentally by blocking the adhesion of sickle erythrocytes to certain endothelial surfaces. There are three separate adhesive band 3 peptides (476-485, 547-553 and 542-555) that have been discovered and evaluated. They are short peptides (6-13 peptides in length) that were able to block the adhesion between the endothelial surface and the sickle cells and the cells infected with the parasite of Plasmodium falciparum. The difficulty involved in experimental evaluation of the post capillary venule has resulted in the use of several in-vitro models, primarily, human umbilical vein endothelial cells and amelanotic melanoma cells. These two models have not only demonstrated band 3's adhesive properties, they have also identified two different receptors for band 3, CD36 and thrombospondin, and shown that either receptor is sufficient for adhesion. The only evaluation of the sickle cell's band 3 clusters adhesion to the endothelium was done by Thevenin [3] and he used human umbilical endothelial cells, which do not contain CD36. It was noted that the endothelial cells retracted when the sickle cells were added and they adhered to thrombospondin in the cell interspaces. This test was done in the absence of plasma.

Both CD36 and thrombospondin have been found on the endothelium of the post capillary venule. Thrombospondin is also found in the matrix of the vessel wall and it is also actively secreted into the circulation both by the endothelium and by activated platelets [13]. This circulatory thrombospondin presents bridging possibilities as it has a receptor for band 3 clusters and it also has a receptor for the CD36 molecule that is located on the vascular endothelium. In addition, it can bridge between reticulocytes that have the CD36 molecule on their surface and the endothelium's CD36 molecules. This bivalent ability of thrombospondin to adhere to both the CD36 molecule and the band 3 clusters and the possibility that the adhesion can be blocked by band 3 specific antibodies may play an important role in the induction and resolution of sickle crisis. Certainly a confluence of sickle erythrocytes with band 3 clusters on their surface, CD36 bearing reticulocytes, plasma and endothelial thrombospondin and endothelial CD36 in the post capillary venule has the potential to cause vaso-occlusion.

The original investigation of these clusters revealed them to have a physiologic function, the removal of senescent erythrocytes [14, 15]. The passage of time had resulted in the break down of the dysfunctional hemoglobin molecules in these old cells and their elimination was required. These cells are supposed to be removed from the circulation by the spleen but the adhesive clusters on their surface would have prevented or at least delayed this by causing them to adhere to the vascular endothelium. The adhesion to the vascular endothelium is avoided, however, because the band 3 clusters are rapidly recognized by naturally occurring IgG antibodies that block this adhesion. Once these antibodies attach to band 3 they rapidly appropriate a C3b complement component [16] that labels these cells for removal by macrophages of the spleen. Apparently, these antibodies are able to prevent adhesion of the clusters in the same manner as monoclonal antibodies used experimentally to identify, define or interfere with receptor ligand complexes. Both the endothelial adhesion and the immune recognition of these band 3 clusters are brought about by the exposure of cryptic band 3 antigens or by the close approximation of naturally exposed peptide antigens. One or both of these mechanisms make it possible for the endothelial receptors and IgG antibodies to adhere to these clusters.

It is obvious that clustered band 3 molecules on sickle cells have the potential to adhere to the post capillary venule and produce the vaso-occlusive process that causes a sickle crisis. However, aside from the fact that the immune response to band 3 clusters presents a possible mechanism for reversing the vaso-occlusive process, this adhesive molecule has no more credence as the etiology of a sickle crisis than any of the others that have been investigated. Indeed, almost certainly, all of the adhesive molecules play a part in the vaso-occlusive process but there is circumstantial evidence of a convincing nature that implies a more prominent role for band 3.

MALARIA

A Fable

It was the first of many rains that would end the long dry season in a small, never to be named African village when a momentous, but totally unheralded, event took place that would change the lives of millions. Unknown to the tribal chief or one of his many wives, the fusion of one of his sperm with his mate's recently released ovum irrevocably altered the future. One of the sub-microscopic participants of this union was different, not visibly, but a single note in the score of life's symphony was flat.

Nine months later, when the drought was still on the land, a son was born. He was a fine boy who thrived on his mother's milk and did what normal babies do. When he was 5 months old and the annual rains had begun he became ill and was irritable and very hot and the mother was deeply concerned because she knew that this was the season when many of the village babies and infants would become ill and many would die. And many did, but he did not.

The boy grew up, became a chief and had many wives and was completely unaware that fate had smiled on him with his special trait. Many of his children would survive the monsoon sickness that would otherwise have been lost, a special blessing in this land where so many babies did not survive long enough to even become children.

The chief's children grew up and had children and their children did the same, all still unaware of their good fortune. Generations later however, things were not the same. The unrecognized benefit was still present in many of the children but a few became very ill. Unless these babies caught the monsoon sickness in the first few months of their life they almost always succumbed to it and if they survived they suffered with recurring severe painful attacks. Apparently the chief's trait was not a blessing when both parents endowed their child with it. Twice as much of a good thing was bad, still, most of the children were still blessed and the trait increased among the people.

Millennia pass and now the people live all over the world. Numbers are now used and their obtuse interpretation has revealed the previously concealed benefit of the trait and called it sickle. Many of the people no longer live in the area of the monsoon illness, that is now called malaria, and the trait that was once a blessing has become a curse with no redeeming grace.

Malaria is a parasitic disease of tropical climates that infects two to three hundred million people each year. One to two million of these people, mostly children, die from it. Malaria results when erythrocytes are invaded by any of four species of protozoan parasites but for clinical and diagnostic purposes, malaria may be regarded as two disease entities. The more dangerous one is caused by the parasite Plasmodium falciparum that produces a variety of acute clinical manifestations and if untreated may be fatal in a few days. The less serious forms are caused by P. vivax, P. Ovale, and P. malariae and they are more typically paroxysmal and almost never fatal.

A sporozoite is injected into the blood stream after the bite of an infected mosquito and in a very short time it enters the cytoplasm of a hepatic cell. Growth and nuclear division are rapid in microscopic cysts (a schizont) containing merozoite forms. In 6-15 days the cyst ruptures and the erythrocytic phase begins. The merozoites that enter the red cell appear in blood smears as bluish rings and eight to eighteen hours after the cell is invaded it becomes increasingly sticky and the cells adhere to the vascular endothelium where they complete their development. The growing parasites, called trophozoites, consume the cell's hemoglobin to meet its protein requirements, an action that produces hemichromes, the precursor of Heinz bodies. The mature schizont, containing a variable number of merozoites ruptures and releases them and they enter new erythrocytes and another asexual cycle begins. Certain of the growing parasites become differentiated into male or female forms that are capable of infecting mosquitoes.

Enhanced malaria survival in people who have one of the mild forms of sickle cell disease, or thalassemia or G6PD deficiency [17, 18] has resulted in the increased genetic frequency in all of these diseases in spite of the fact that their severe forms have zero survival advantage in malaria. All of these hemoglobinopathies and all types of malaria have at least one thing in common, the presence of band 3 clusters on their erythrocytes.

Heinz bodies and band 3 clusters occur in malaria because hemoglobin is metabolized by the parasites, not because it becomes denatured. The band 3 clusters that result from this action then perform a valuable service for these infected cells. They help them to adhere to the vascular endothelium and thereby reduce the likelihood of their reaching the spleen where parasitic antigens displayed on the erythrocytes surface would flag them for removal. Indeed, when parasites are demonstrable on a blood film the ones usually seen are in the ring stage, the initial erythrocyte infection where little hemoglobin breakdown has occurred.

It seems reasonable to assume that a person with an elevated level of natural band 3 specific antibodies would be better able to clear the parasite infected erythrocytes since antibody coating of the band 3 clusters should theoretically reduce their vascular adhesion. This would allow these infected cells to reach the spleen where both the band 3/IgG/C3b complex and the parasite antigens would cause them to be immunologically recognized and eliminated. Very importantly for the patient's survival, this would happen before the parasite matures and infects other erythrocytes. It would also be logical to assume that the level of band 3 specific antibodies would be elevated in the hemoglobinopathies. Unfortunately these levels have never been tested. However, these levels have been measured in malaria endemic areas and found to be elevated [19]. Children with this elevation were found to have a lower parasite load and a normal or slightly elevated hemoglobin. The demonstration of a normal hemoglobin level is important in that it shows that band 3 specific antibodies do not attack healthy erythrocytes. Interestingly, adults were found to have an even lower parasite load and their level of band 3 specific antibody was also lower. Presumably they had developed specific immunity to the various parasite antigens and the lower level of parasitemia that ensued reduced parasitic hemoglobin digestion and fewer band 3 clusters were formed.

A child who is three years old and lives in a malaria endemic area is a survivor who has developed a protective partial immunity in which a low level of parasitemia persists. If the child leaves the area for any length of time he will once again become susceptible. Indeed a low level of parasitemia almost seems necessary to maintain this immunity. The constant presentation of band 3 clusters on infected parasites may be a factor in this.

While this may be credible evidence for the ability of band 3 antibodies to provide a benefit in malaria, the support for band 3's involvement in both sickle crisis and its resolution comes from the consideration of Plasmodium falciparum malaria infection. The majority of deaths caused by malaria occur because of this parasite and this is a direct result of the vaso-occlusive pathology that occurs in the same vascular area as it does in sickle crisis, the post capillary venule. The reason for the Plasmodium falciparum parasite's lethal propensity is that it expresses a very adhesive parasite component on the erythrocytes surface called Plasmodium falciparum envelope membrane protein 1 (PfEMP1). This protein contains many adhesive loci that have both endothelial and erythrocyte receptors. Among these endothelial receptors are CD36, thrombospondin and VCAM-1. It is noteworthy that two of these are involved in the adhesion of band 3 clusters and reticulocytes. Adherence to the CD36 receptor is without question but the role of some of the other potential receptors is less clear. For example, adherence to thrombospondin is certain but it exhibits a low affinity and cannot support binding under flow conditions. In addition to causing the sequestering of infected erythrocytes to the endothelium, the ligand-receptor relationship between an infected erythrocyte and other erythrocytes results in the formation of red cell clusters called rosettes that may be responsible for the most serious complication in this disease, cerebral malaria.

Surprisingly, P. falciparum infections in people who have the sickle cell trait do not develop rosette formation, plus they have a greatly reduced incidence of cerebral malaria and other vaso-occlusive pathology. How could this mild asymptomatic genetic abnormality cause such a favorable response in this lethal disease? The hypothesis presented is that the accelerated breakdown of the sickle hemoglobin present in the erythrocytes of someone with the trait (approximately 40% of their hemoglobin is sickle) produces increased amounts of Heinz bodies and therefore has an enhanced immune response to band 3. That this single factor is significant enough to favorably modify the course of this severe malaria infection is remarkable. The fact that band 3 clusters and the malaria parasite's PfEMP-1adhesive molecule share some of the same receptors is undoubtedly significant. Here again, the band 3 levels in sickle trait have not been tested. The resemblance between the severe vaso-occlusive pathology of sickle cell disease and Plasmodium falciparum infection and their common denominator of band 3 clusters seems more than coincidental and suggests the possibility that anti-adhesive band 3 antibodies may have a dominant role in preventing and resolving the vaso-occlusive phenomenon in both these diseases.

Unfortunately, this is a hypothesis that is supported by circumstantial evidence. There is no question that the band 3 clusters on sickle cells are adhesive and that their peptides and antibodies against these peptides can prevent this adherence. However, this hypothesis is based on the premise that band 3 specific antibodies that result from premature breakdown of sickle hemoglobin protect against the vaso-occlusion of this disorder and unfortunately these antibodies have not been measured. Heinz body evaluation cannot be used to evaluate this hypothesis for two reasons. First, in a sickle cell patient in crisis these cells will be adherent to the endothelium. Second, in the sickle steady state, unless the spleen is dysfunctional, the anti-adhesive band 3/complement complex will prompt the spleen to remove those cells bearing Heinz bodies. In sickle disease they can sometimes be seen when the disease has advanced far enough for the spleen to become dysfunctional but this does not happen in sickle trait. Measurement of the level of these antibodies in both sickle disease and trait has not been done and this will remain a hypothesis until such measurements take place.

The favorable consequence of validating this hypothesis is the significant therapeutic potential that it suggests. Theoretically, an intravenous bolus of anti-adhesive band 3 peptides or of monoclonal band 3 specific antibodies may be able to terminate a crisis attack. An experiment that supports this concept used monkeys that were infected with P Falciparum. When these monkeys were infused with band 3 peptides, this resulted in the appearance of the mature forms of previously sequestered parasites in the peripheral circulation [20]. Even of greater importance is the possibility that a band 3 vaccine, administered on a regular schedule, may be able to prevent the vaso-occlusive pathology of sickle cell disease and perhaps even modulate the course of falciparum malaria.

DISCUSSION

In normal circumstances erythrocytes do not adhere to the vascular endothelium but this is not the case with sickle erythrocytes and those infected by malaria parasites. The following is a brief overview of the ones that do adhere and an attempt to connect this information with the sticky band 3 clusters. The presumption is that some of the adhesive concepts that are currently in the sickle cell literature describe the use of the same endothelial and erythrocyte receptors as those that react with the band 3 clusters. This is analogous to the adhesive PfEMP-1 molecule in falciparum malaria using the same CD36 and thrombospondin molecule as do the band 3 clusters. It is suggested that the band 3 antibody and the receptors it attaches to are pivotal in the vaso-occlusive processes of sickle cell disease.

Mechanically speaking the post capillary venule is the logical site for intra-vascular adhesion to take place. The circumference of this vessel is slightly larger than that of the capillary so the blood flow will be slower and the shear stress will be lower but the size of the vessel will still be small enough for circumferential contact by the erythrocytes. All of these factors contribute to the erythrocyte being better able to adhere to the vessel's wall. Except in unusual circumstances, any complete obstruction of blood flow in the area, other than briefly, would not seem to be compatible with the resolution of flow that usually occurs after a crisis attack. Presumably, the adhesive red cells that normally roll through this area will simply roll a great deal slower during a crisis. In the resolution of a vaso-occlusive event this will allow anti-adhesive humoral agents and non-adhesive red cells to slowly fill the vessel and ultimately allow full flow to resume.

Physiologically things are never normal in sickle cell disease. For instance, testing indicates that the shear stress is increased in the face of a normal arterial diameter and that the arterial musculature does not respond normally to 100% oxygen [21]. Another example, inflammation is a way of life in this disorder and it is continuously present with the C reactive protein being 12 times higher than normal [22]. The implication is that the vaso-occlusive process is an on going one and since, in the majority of time, a person with sickle cell anemia is not in crisis, the anti-vaso-occlusive forces must generally hold sway. The accelerated production of denatured sickle hemoglobin is also a continual process and presumably, the antibody response to the band 3 clusters will usually match the hemoglobin breakdown. When the antibody is consumed, the excess adhesive erythrocytes will become adherent but their excess will also stimulate increased production of band 3 antibody.

All sickle cells are not adhesive and their numbers appear to be dependent on the circumstances of systemic and local forces such as inflammation, hypoxia, stress and infection [22, 23]. Not only are the numbers of these cells dependent on external conditions, the expression of the adhesive molecules on these erythrocytes and their endothelial receptors are even more so. In comparing the adhesive qualities of different sickle erythrocytes, the stickiest is, without a doubt, the sickle reticulocyte. It has at least three adhesive molecules on its surface that are able to adhere to different sites and it is slightly larger than mature red cells so that these molecules will have greater circumferential contact with the endothelium. In sickle cell patients the reticulocyte count varies from five to fifteen percent which is certainly a large enough number for them to play a major role in sickle vaso-occlusion. On the opposite end of the sticky spectrum is the irreversibly sickled erythrocyte but its rigidity and irregular shape may be a significant factor that is needed to change the venules blood flow from slow flow to no flow.

The literature has essentially conceded the most and the least adhesive sickle erythrocytes but in-between is pretty much an unnamed void. Much of that void may be filled when the adhesive band 3 clusters receive further attention. The question of their adhesiveness is not in doubt but it will take the evaluation of the anti-adhesive effect of their natural antibodies to give them the status of major players in sickle crisis. The band 3 antibodies are open to investigation but determining the number of red cells displaying the band 3 clusters may be impossible. If these band 3 clusters are not immunologically recognized, their erythrocytes will adhere to the endothelium. If these antibodies cloak them, the spleen will remove them. Only in the absence of a spleen can these cluster bearing cells be counted and then, only those cloaked by antibody.

A consideration of some of the most investigated adhesive molecules on sickle erythrocytes and the endothelium is now in order. First, on the erythrocytes there are CD36 molecules, band 3 clusters, the alpha4beta1 molecule (VLA-4), the B-cell adhesion molecule/Lutheran (B-CAM/LU), the ICAM-4 molecule (LW gp), and antibody on the erythrocytes surface. Second, on the endothelium or the blood vessel wall there is the CD36 molecule, thrombospondin, the VCAM-1 molecule, the alpha(v)beta(3) molecule, laminin, fibronectin and the viral Fc receptors. Thirdly, in the plasma is thrombospondin and von Willebrand factor [8, 24].

This is not an all-inclusive list but it certainly contains many of the most significant participants in this sticky alphabet soup of ligands and receptors. Only 12 separate components are listed but two of these are present in multiple locations, CD36 on cell and endothelium, thrombospondin in plasma and vessel wall. To simplify this discussion these complementary molecules will be separated into 3 groups. They are the CD36-thrombospondin group, the VLA-4 group and the "other" group. The VLA-4 and "other" group will be briefly mentioned and the focus will be primarily on the CD36-thrombospondin group and the plasma proteins since they involve multiple adhesive components that can interact with the band 3 clusters and their antibody.

The "other" group includes the red cell ligands B-CAM/LU, ICAM-4 (LW gp), and surface immunoglobulins. The immunoglobulins theoretically adhere to viral Fc receptors on the endothelium and while their adhesive potential is obvious their contribution to the vaso-occlusive process is probably minor. The LWgp ligand is complementary to the VLA-4 ligand [25] and since both molecules are on erythrocytes they will be involved in cell to cell adhesion. The red cell's B-CAM/LU molecule adheres to laminin, a large polypeptide glycoprotein located on the basement membrane [26]. The location of laminin suggests that this coupling may only be active when the endothelium is disrupted. This group will play a role in the adhesive process but the degree of its involvement is uncertain.

The VLA-4 (alpha 4 beta 1) group would appear to have a higher level of vaso-occlusive involvement and play a more prominent role in crisis [24]. The VLA-4 molecule is present on sickle cell reticulocytes and forms complexes with 3 different molecules. As previously pointed out, it can adhere to the LWgp molecule on other erythrocytes for cell to cell adhesion. It also adheres to the endothelium by two different mechanisms. The first is direct adherence to the vascular cell adhesion molecule 1 (VCAM-1), a molecule that has variable expression on the vascular endothelium [24]. The VLA-4 molecule also adheres to the fibronectin molecule. Fibronectin is not present on the endothelium and is exposed to the plasma only when endothelial cells retract [27], an event that occurs in the presence of thrombin. Experimental evaluation of the VLA-4/fibronectin complex was carried out using phorbol ester to alter the endothelium [28] and it was found that this chemical increased adhesion of this complex 8 fold. These authors also found that interleuin-8, a chemokine released in response to bacterial or viral infections or other injurious agents, also increased adherence of sickle erythrocytes via fibronectin. Under the right conditions VLA-4 should be very active, adding to the already sticky state of the reticulocyte, sticking to other erythrocytes, and adhering to the endothelium by two different mechanisms.

Now for consideration of CD36 and thrombospondin: You may recall that band 3 clusters adhere to endothelium via both of these molecules and that this adhesion is blocked by band 3 peptides and by antibodies against these peptides. Thrombospondin has the ability to adhere to band 3 clusters and the CD36 molecule and it is secreted into the plasma both by activated platelets and the endothelium and under certain circumstances it is exposed on the vascular endothelium. Thrombospondin is therefore able to adhere to the very adhesive reticulocytes via the CD36 molecule and act as a bridge between it and the CD36 molecule that is present on the endothelium. Under conditions when thrombospondin is exposed on the endothelium it will adhere directly to reticulocytes. Except when thrombospondin is exposed on the endothelium, the adhesive connections made by thrombospondin to band 3 clusters and to the reticulocytes are made by bridging so they may not be very stable. Perhaps this is why the thrombospondin binding of falciparum malaria's adhesive PfEMP-1 exhibits a low affinity and cannot support binding under flow conditions. In view of this and in spite of all the connections that thrombospondin makes, it seems likely that it will play second fiddle to the stable direct adhesion of sickle band 3 clusters to the endothelial CD36 molecule.

The natural band 3 antibodies recognize the same areas on the band 3 clusters as do thrombospondin and the CD36 molecule. Because of this they are able to block both the adhesion of band 3 clusters to the endothelial thrombospondin and the CD36 molecule and they also block the interface between thrombospondin and CD36. This antibody therefore has the ability to block both the CD36 and the thrombospondin receptors of thrombospondin's reticulocyte bridge.

Whether a single band 3 antibody Fab region can recognize both CD36 and thrombospondin is not known, but the existence of 3 adhesive band 3 peptides suggests that multiple band 3 antibodies are more likely. It becomes obvious that a significant amount of the reticulocyte's adhesive ability will be abolished by the presence of this natural antibody (or antibodies). With the antibody's reduction of reticulocyte adhesion and its prevention of endothelial adhesion of sickle cells bearing band 3 clusters it is apparent that band 3 antibody may play a pivotal role in preventing and resolving vaso-occlusion in sickle cell disease.

Thrombospondin's interaction with von Willebrand factor gives it still another role to play in the vaso-occlusive action in sickle cell disease. Von Willebrand factor has been suggested as a bridging molecule between glycoprotein 1b-like molecules and integrin on sickle cells and similar receptors on endothelial cells [23]. The significance of this is brought into question because of the fact that von Willebrand factor has been to found to bind to thrombospondin and block that molecule's adherence to CD36 [29]. With the dominant place that thrombospondin appears to play in the vaso-occlusive process this suggests that the von Willebrand factor may act more like an anti-adhesive agent in this disease.

We obviously have many good pieces of this puzzle, and some of them seem to be coming together. Finding where band 3 fits in should certainly be a priority.

CONCLUSION

The hypothesis that is presented in this paper is that clusters of the band 3 molecule on sickle erythrocytes, whose hemoglobin has denatured prematurely, are recognized by natural band 3 specific antibodies that prevent endothelial adhesion of both these cells and reticulocytes. This hypothesis was conceived as a result of the observed benefit that sickle trait imparts to someone with a falciparum malaria infection and is based on the experimental demonstration of the adhesion of sickle cell band 3 clusters to endothelium via the CD36 and thrombospondin molecules and by the ability of band 3 peptides and antibodies against them to prevent this adhesion.

These same band 3 clusters are found on the surface of erythrocytes that are infected with malaria parasites and they also adhere to endothelial CD36 and thrombospondin and this adhesion is also blocked by band 3 specific peptides and antibodies. The most severe form of malaria caused by the Plasmodium falciparum parasite has an additional adhesive protein (PfEMP1) that adheres to these same receptors. A falciparum malaria infection results in a severe vaso-occlusive pathology that is almost identical to that in sickle cell crisis. When this type of malaria infection occurs in a patient with the sickle trait the vaso-occlusive process is eliminated or greatly diminished.

This prevention of vaso-occlusive pathology in malaria is presumed to occur because of the premature breakdown of sickle hemoglobin in sickle trait that causes an up regulation of the band 3 specific antibody production. This would result in a malaria infection being met by a pre-existing immune response. Because of the elimination of the severe vaso-occlusive pathology in this malaria infection, it is postulated that in sickle cell disease these antibodies may be a controlling factor in preventing and resolving a sickle crisis.

The therapeutic potential implicit in this hypothesis suggests the importance of further exploration of this concept. The demonstration that intravenous injection of band 3 peptides into a monkey infected with falciparum malaria caused the release into the general circulation of previously sequestered infected erythrocytes was very provocative.

In conclusion: the presumption is that when there is a relative deficiency of this band 3 specific antibody (too little of it or too many of the adhesive band 3 clusters), the vaso-occlusive process will begin. The concomitant antigenic stimulation caused by the relative excess of band 3 clusters will stimulate the immune production of the natural antibodies and attempt to reestablish blood flow. If this is so, the relative ratio between adhesive band 3 clusters and the band 3 specific antibodies is the defining variable that determines the state of vaso-occlusion in sickle cell disease.

REFERENCES

[1] Hebbel RP Adhesive interactions of sickle erythrocytes with endothelium. *J Clin Invest.* 1997 Dec 1;100(11 Suppl):S83-6. Review

[2] KayMM Generation of senescent cell antigen on old cells initiates IgG binding to a neoantigen. *Cell Mol Biol (Noisy-le-grand).* 1993 Mar;39(2):131-53. Review.

[3] Thevenin BJ, Crandall I, Ballas SK, Sherman IW, Shohet SB. Band 3 peptides block the adherence of sickle cells to endothelial cells in vitro. *Blood.* 1997 Nov 15;90(10):4172-9.

[4] Hornig R, Lutz HU. Band 3 protein clustering on human erythrocytes promotes binding of naturally occurring anti-band 3 and anti-spectrin antibodies. *Exp Gerontol.* 2000 Oct;35(8):1025-44.

[5] Liu SC, Yi SJ, Mehta JR, Nichols PE, Ballas SK, Yacono PW, Golan DE, Palek J. Red cell membrane remodeling in sickle cell anemia. Sequestration of membrane lipids and proteins in Heinz bodies. *J Clin Invest.* 1996 Jan 1;97(1):29-36.

[6] Yipp BG, Anand S, Schollaardt T, Patel KD, Looareesuwan S, Ho M. Synergism of multiple adhesion molecules in mediating cytoadherence of Plasmodium falciparum-

infected erythrocytes to microvascular endothelial cells under flow. *Blood*. 2000 Sep 15;96(6):2292-8.

[7] Crandall I, Guthrie N, Sherman IW. Plasmodium falciparum: naturally occurring rabbit immunoglobulins recognize human band 3 peptide motifs and malaria-infected red cells. *Exp Parasitol*. 1996 Jan;82(1):45-53.

[8] Thevenin BJ, Crandall I, Ballas SK, Sherman IW, Shohet SB. Band 3 peptides block the adherence of sickle cells to endothelial cells in vitro. *Blood*. 1997 Nov 15;90(10):4172-9.

[9] Rogers NJ, Targett GA, Hall BS. Plasmodium falciparum gametocyte adhesion to C32 cells via CD36 is inhibited by antibodies to modified band 3. *Infect Immun*. 1996 Oct;64(10):4261-8.

[10] Eda S, Lawler J, Sherman IW. Plasmodium falciparum-infected erythrocyte adhesion to the type 3 repeat domain of thrombospondin-1 is mediated by a modified band 3 protein. *Mol Biochem Parasitol*. 1999 May 25;100(2):195-205.

[11] Crandall I, Sherman IW. Antibodies to synthetic peptides based on band 3 motifs react specifically with Plasmodium falciparum (human malaria)-infected erythrocytes and block cytoadherence. *Parasitology*. 1994 May;108 (Pt 4):389-96.

[12] Brittain HA, Eckman JR, Swerlick RA, Howard RJ, Wick TM. Thrombospondin from activated platelets promotes sickle erythrocyte adherence to human microvascular endothelium under physiologic flow: a potential role for platelet activation in sickle cell vaso-occlusion. *Blood*. 1993 Apr 15;81(8):2137-43.

[13] Kramer RH, Fuh GM, Bensch KG, Karasek MA. Synthesis of extracellular matrix glycoproteins by cultured microvascular endothelial cells isolated from the dermis of neonatal and adult skin. *J Cell Physiol*. 1985 Apr;123(1):1-9.

[14] Lutz HU, Stringaro-Wipf G. Senescent red cell-bound IgG is attached to band 3 protein. *Biomed Biochim Acta*. 1983;42(11-12):S117-21

[15] Lutz HU, Flepp R, Stringaro-Wipf G. Naturally occurring autoantibodies to exoplasmic and cryptic regions of band 3 protein, the major integral membrane protein of human red blood cells. *J Immunol*. 1984 Nov;133(5):2610-8.

[16] Lutz HU, Nater M, Stammler P. Naturally occurring anti-band 3 antibodies have a unique affinity for C3. *Immunology*. 1993 Oct;80(2):191-6.

[17] Clegg JB, Weatherall DJ. Thalassemia and malaria: new insights into an old problem. *Proc Assoc Am Physicians*. 1999 Jul-Aug;111(4):278-82. Review.

[18] Ruwende C, Khoo SC, Snow RW, Yates SN, Kwiatkowski D, Gupta S, Warn P, Allsopp CE, Gilbert SC, Peschu N, et al. Natural selection of hemi- and heterozygotes for G6PD deficiency in Africa by resistance to severe malaria. *Nature*. 1995 Jul 20;376(6537):246-9.

[19] Hogh B, Petersen E, Crandall I, Gottschau A, Sherman IW. Immune responses to band 3 neoantigens on Plasmodium falciparum-infected erythrocytes in subjects living in an area of intense malaria transmission are associated with low parasite density and high hematocrit value. *Infect Immun*. 1994 Oct;62(10):4362-6.

[20] Crandall I, Collins WE, Gysin J, Sherman IW. Synthetic peptides based on motifs present in human band 3 protein inhibit cytoadherence/sequestration of the malaria

parasite Plasmodium falciparum. *Proc Natl Acad Sci U S A*. 1993 May 15;90(10):4703-7.

[21] Belhassen L. Pelle G, Sediame S, Bachir D, Carville C, Bucherer C, Lacombe C, Galacteros F, Adnot S. Endothelial dysfunction in patients with sickle cell disease is related to selective impairment of shear stress-mediated vasodilation. *Blood*. 2001 Mar 15;97(6):1584-9.

[22] Belcher JD, Marker PH, Weber JP, Hebbel RP, Vercellotti GM. Activated monocytes in sickle cell disease: potential role in the activation of vascular endothelium and vaso-occlusion. *Blood*. 2000 Oct 1;96(7):2451-9.

[23] Setty BN, Stuart MJ. Vascular cell adhesion molecule-1 is involved in mediating hypoxia-induced sickle red blood cell adherence to endothelium: potential role in sickle cell disease. *Blood* 1996 Sep 15;88(6):2311-20

[24] Wick TM, Eckman JR. Molecular basis of sickle cell-endothelial cell interactions. *Curr Opin Hematol* 1996 Mar;3(2):118-24

[25] Parsons SF, Spring FA, Chasis JA, Anstee DJ. Erythroid cell adhesion molecules Lutheran and LW in health and disease. *Baillieres Best Pract Res Clin Haematol* 1999 Dec;12(4):729-45

[26] Udani M, Zen Q, Cottman M, Leonard N, Jefferson S, Daymont C, Truskey G, Telen MJ. Basal cell adhesion molecule/lutheran protein. The receptor critical for sickle cell adhesion to laminin. *J Clin Invest* 1998 Jun 1;101(11):2550-8

[27] Manodori AB. Sickle erythrocytes adhere to fibronectin-thrombospondin-integrin complexes exposed by thrombin-induced endothelial cell contraction. *Microvasc Res* 2001 May;61(3):263-74

[28] Kumar A, Eckmam JR, Swerlick RA, Wick TM.Phorbol ester stimulation increases sickle erythrocyte adherence to endothelium: a novel pathway involving alpha 4 beta 1 integrin receptors on sickle reticulocytes and fibronectin. *Blood* 1996 Dec 1;88(11):4348-58

[29] Barabino GA, Wise RJ, Woodbury VA, Zhang B, Bridges KA, Hebbel RP, Lawler J, Ewenstein BM. Inhibition of sickle erythrocyte adhesion to immobilized thrombospondin by von Willebrand factor under dynamic flow conditions. *Blood* 1997 Apr 1;89(7):2560-7

In: Focus on Sickle Cell Research
Editor: Ralph L. Plasmar, pp. 113-124

ISBN 1-59033-920-7

Chapter VII

MULTIPLE MYELOMA IN SICKLE CELL SYNDROMES

Kaloterakis Andreas and Filiotou Anna
University of Athens School of Medicine,
Second Department of Medicine at Hippocration Hospital,
114 Vas Sophias Avenue, GR-11527, Athens, Greece

ABSTRACT

Multiple myeloma (MM) has rarely been reported in patients with sickle cell syndromes (SCS). We describe seven Greek sickle cell patients ranging in age from 42 to 65-years, five sickle cell-thalassaemia double heterozygotes, one sickle cell disease homozygote (HbSS), and one sickle cell heterozygote (SA), who developed MM (three M-IgGκ, one M-IgGλ, one M-IgAκ, one M-IgGκ.IgAκ (biclonal) and one Bence Jones-λ (BJ-λ). Two of these seven patients also developed amyloidosis (AL). Six of the seven cases represent the first documented association of MM with $HbS\beta^+$ thalassaemia or HbSA. Generalized bleeding diathesis, stroke, grand mal seizures, bone marrow necrosis and other complications of whole blood hyperviscosity syndrome due to serum hyperviscosity aggravated by sickle cell vaso-occlusion, were treated by plasmaphereses, exchange transfusions and/or blood transfusions. Due to the current availability of medical facilities, increased survival in patients with SCS may have an impact on the incidence of MM among such patients, if a link does exist between the two diseases. Six of our patients had chronic hemolysis, cholelithiasis - chronic billiary tract infection which may predispose one to MM; two of these patients progressed from monoclonal gammopathy of undetermined significance (MGUS) to MM. We believe that further confirmatory studies are required in order to define the relationship, if any, between SCS and MM.

Keywords: sickle cell syndrome, multiple myeloma, monoclonal gammopathy, amyloidosis (AL), hyperviscosity syndrome.

INTRODUCTION

Multiple myeloma (MM) in association with sickle cell syndromes (SCS) is considered to be rare; only five cases have been reported in detail in the literature: two black Jamaican females [1, 2], two black American males [3, 4] and one male from India [5]. Incomplete clinical information was provided in two more instances of MM [6, 7]. No such cases have been reported from either the Mediterranean countries or tropical Africa where a high prevalence of SCS exists [8].

We describe seven Greek patients with SCS (five with with HbSβ^+ thalassaemia, one with HbSS and one with HbSA), who developed MM. In two of these patients, amyloidosis (AL) was diagnosed. To our knowledge, all our cases but one (HbSS) represent the first reported association of MM with HbSβ^+ thalassaemia or HbSA.

CASE REPORTS

Case 1

A 56-year-old woman with confirmed HbSβ^+ thalassaemia and an IgAκ monoclonal gammopathy of undetermined significance (MGUS), diagnosed 12 years prior, was admitted in June 1987 because of weakness, bleeding diathesis, jaundice, blurred vision and hepatosplenomegaly. Laboratory investigation revealed IgAκ myeloma (Fig. 1, 2, Table I) and a serum relative viscosity (SRV) of 4.9 U (normal 1.4-1.8 U). Treatment involved plasmaphereses, exchange transfusions and six monthly courses of cyclophosphamide/ prednisone. Fifteen months later she was readmitted because of severe hyperviscosity syndrome (SRV 11.9 U) with bleeding diathesis, grand mal seizures and bone marrow necrosis (Fig.3). Following plasmaphereses and blood transfusions, she improved dramatically within four weeks but she died three months later in December 1989, during a grand mal crisis at home.

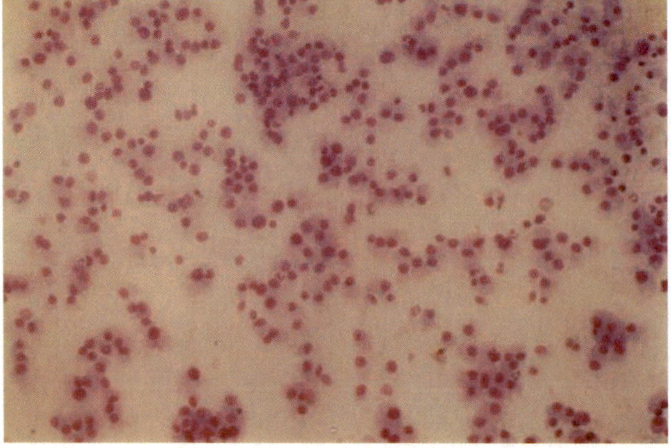

Fig.1. Case 1: Bone marrow aspiration. Infiltration by flaming plasma cells (X40).

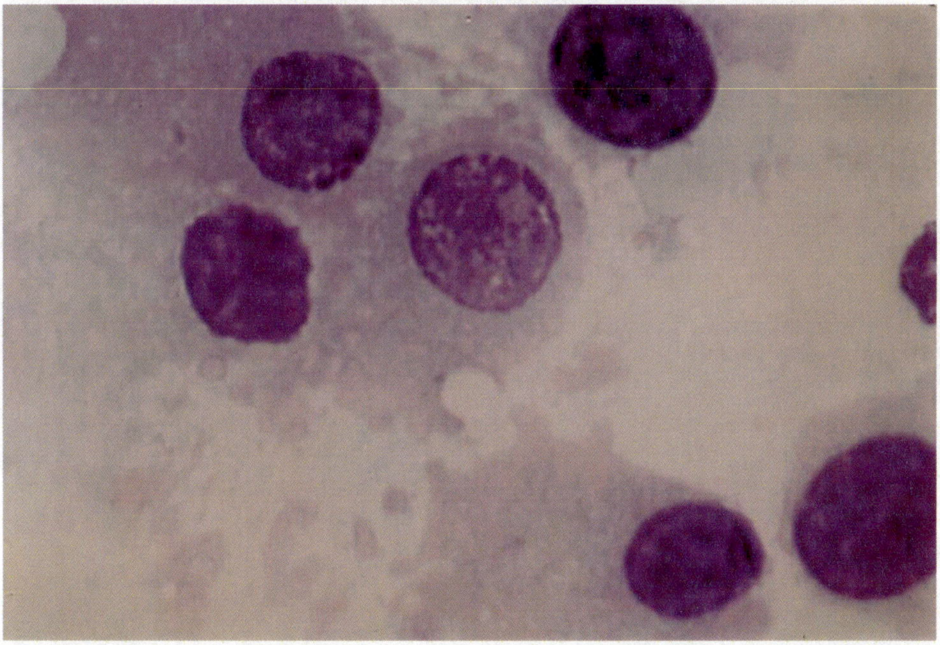

Fig. 2. Case 1: Detail of Fig.1 (X100)

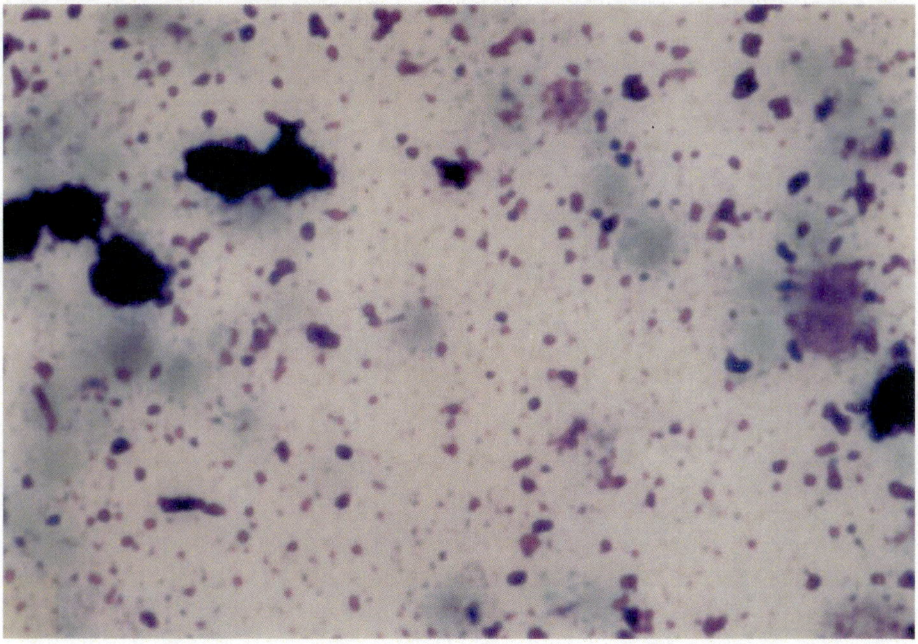

Fig. 3. Case 1: Extensive bone marrow necrosis after a severe hyperviscosity syndrome (X40).

Table I. Main laboratory data in seven Greek patients with Sickle Cell Syndrome (SCS) and Multiple Myeloma (MM)

	Age/ sex	Hb g/L	SCS pattern Hb electrophoretic analysis*	Serum M-protein g/L	Serum viscosity (normal 1.4-1.8)	Bone marrow plasma cell infiltration (%)	Case	Skeletal lesions	Gall-stones
1	56/F	72	HbSβ+ thalassaemia 10%A, 79%S, 6%F, 5%A2	IgAκ (48)	4.9 11.9	90	-	+	+
2	57/F	97	HbSβ+ thalassaemia 12%A, 76%S, 8%F, 4%A2	IgGκ (70)	4.3	60	+	+	+
3	55/F	120	HbSβ+ thalassaemia 6%A, 79%S, 12%F, 3%A2	IgGκ (65)	4.1	65	_	+	+
4	61/M	107	HbSβ+ thalassaemia 2%A, 78%S, 16%F, 4%A2	IgGκ (26)+IgAλ(14.7) (biclonal)	3.2	50	-	+	+
5	64/F	87	HbSA 63%A, 34%S, 1%F, 2%A2	Bence Jones-λ	1.7	70	+	+	_
6	65/M	56	HbSβ+ thalassaemia 20%A, 74%S, 1.8%F, 4.2%A2	IgGλ (26.6)	3.7	30	_	+	+
7	42/F	75	HbSS 88.2%S, 10%F, 1.8%A2	IgGκ (34)	not measured	35	_	+	+

* Sickle cell test positive in all seven cases

Case 2

A 57-year-old woman diagnosed with HbSβ^+ thalassaemia and an IgGκ MGUS seven years prior, was admitted in February 1991, because of weakness, jaundice, dyspnea, generalized edema, pleural and peritoneal effusions, hepatosplenomegaly and distended jugular veins. Laboratory investigation revealed an IgGκ myeloma (Table I). Echocardiography indicated restrictive cardiomyopathy. Amyloid deposits (permanganate resistant, Congo red positive) were found in the bone marrow and gingival biopsies. The patient was treated with diuretics, plasmaphereses, exchange transfusions and intermittent courses of melphalan/prednisone. Although the patient improved initially, she died five months later following a stroke, in July 1991.

Case 3

A 55-year-old woman with confirmed HbSβ^+ thalassaemia was admitted in March 1992, suffering from acute chest syndrome and repeated sickle cell crises and infections. Laboratory investigation showed an IgGκ myeloma (Fig. 4, Table I). Treatment involved exchange transfusions, plasmaphereses, antibiotics and two monthly courses of chemotherapy (melphalan/prednisone). The patient was lost to follow up. She was readmitted and died following a stroke in August 1992.

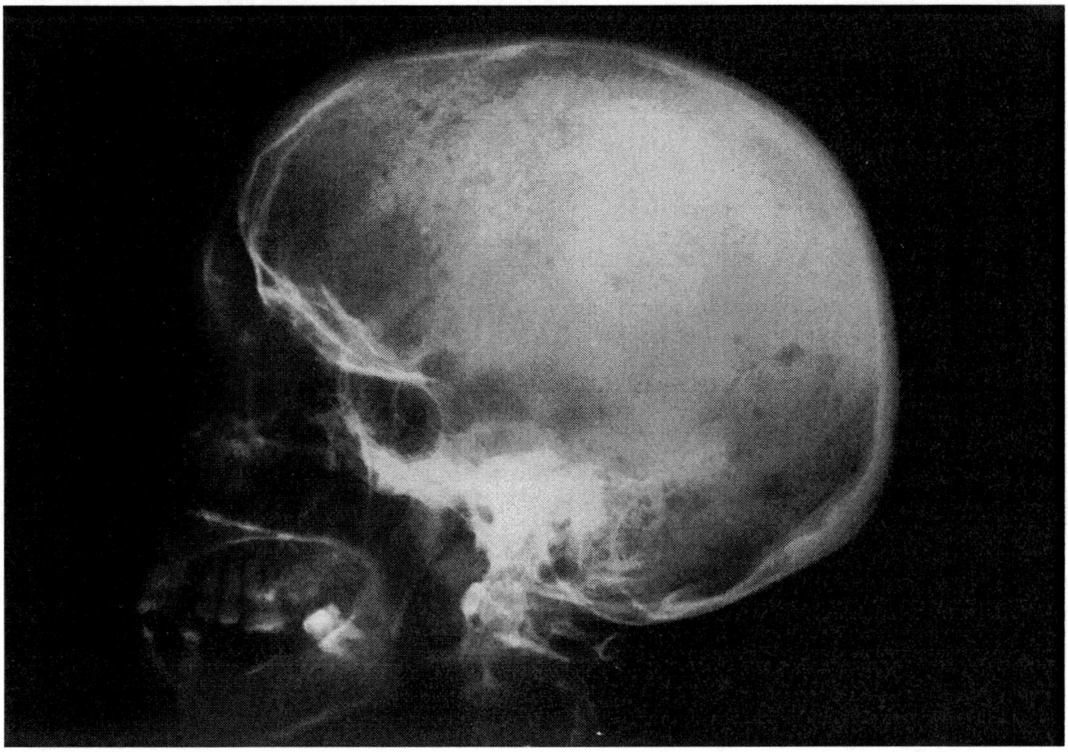

Fig. 4. Case 3: Multiple osteolytic lesions in the skull.

Case 4

A 61-year-old man was admitted in August 1992, because of a three-day history of fever, abdominal pain and diarrhea and was found to have hepatosplenomegaly. His past medical history was unremarkable. Laboratory investigation revealed HbSβ^+ thalassaemia and a biclonal (IgGκ.IgAκ) MM (Fig 5, Table I). On blood and stool cultures, salmonella enteritidis was detected. The patient was treated with parenteral fluids, antibiotics and plasmaphereses. He improved dramatically but he refused to undergo chemotherapy. He died with an acute chest syndrome, 36 months later, in August 1995.

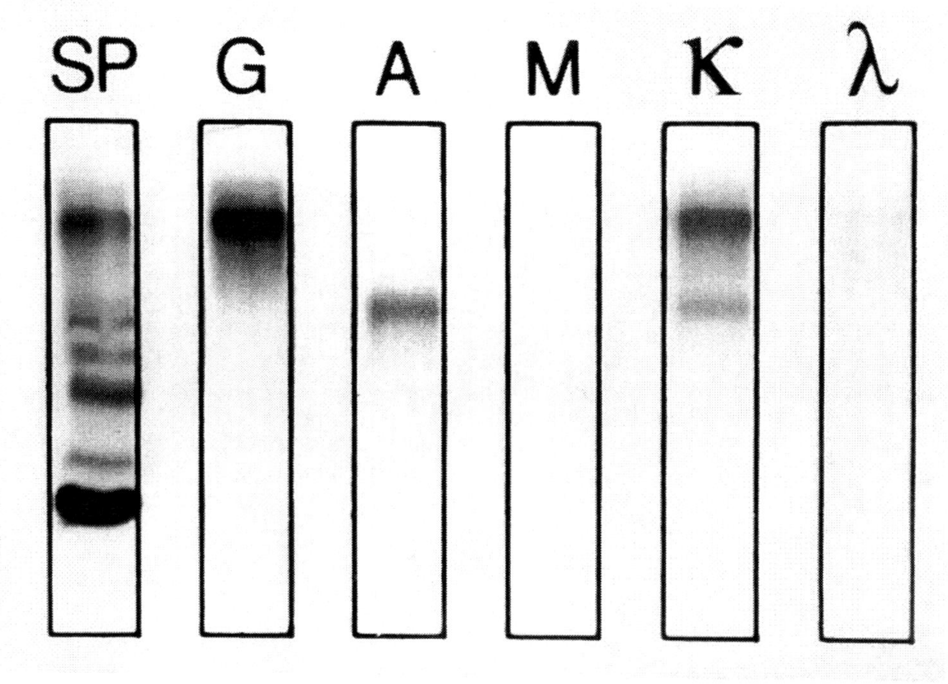

Fig. 5. Case 4: Serum protein immunofixation: biclonal gammopathy of M-IgGκ plus M-IgAκ type.

Case 5

A 64 year-old-woman with a history of asymptomatic haematuria, was admitted in February 1994 for resection of a laryngeal tumor. The tumor biopsy revealed a plasmocytoma. The patient developed azotaemia which rapidly progressed to anuria; serum creatinine was 12 mg/dL, uric acid 18 mg/dL and calcium 14.5 mg/dL. Laboratory investigation showed HbSA and BJ-λ MM (Table I). Treatment included haemodialysis, blood transfusions and two monthly courses of melphalan/prednisone. As of May 1994, the anuria persisted and the patient was put on continuous ambulatory peritoneal dialysis. In October 1994, she developed a severe orthostatic hypotension syndrome and remained bedridden. At that time the bone marrow and gingival biopsies revealed amyloid deposits (permanganate resistant, Congo red positive)(Fig. 6, 7). She died two months later, in December 1994.

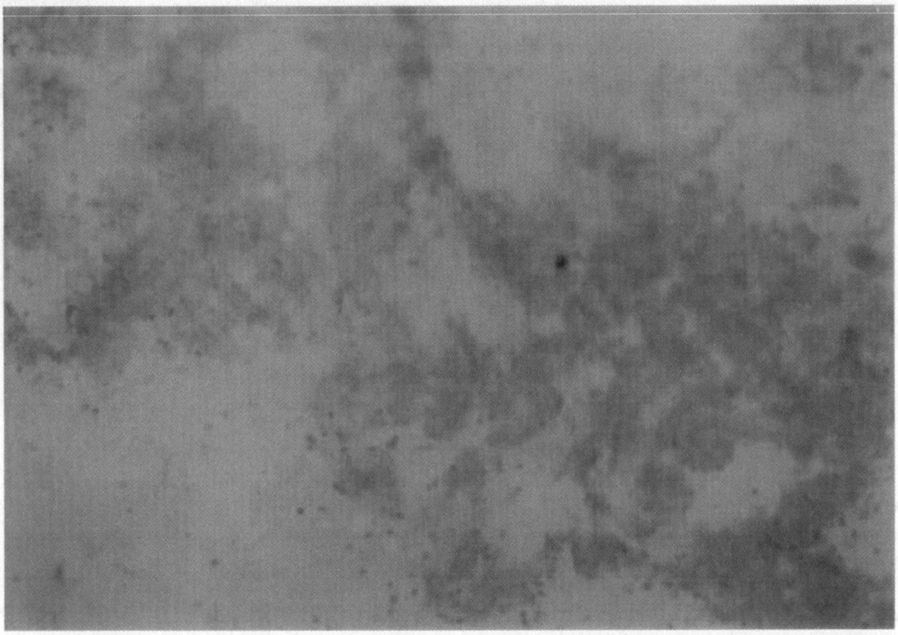

Fig. 6. Case 5: Bone marrow amyloid deposits stained with alkaline Congo-red. A: carrot red under usual light.

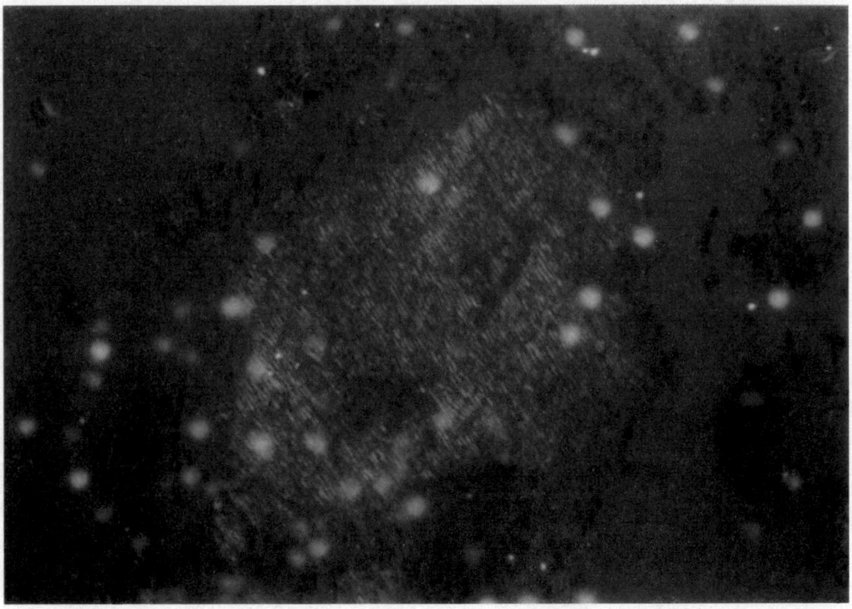

Fig. 7. Case 5: Bone marrow amyloid deposits. B: apple green under polarized light.

Case 6

A 65-year-old man, with confirmed HbSβ^+ thalassaemia and repeated episodes of asymptomatic haematuria, was admitted in January 1999 because of severe anaemia. Fourteen months prior, he had suffered from recurrent strokes which progressively resulted in spastic paraplegia, extrapyramidal and sensory abnormalities, bladder and bowel dysfunction as well as aphasia, ataxia, and dementia. Laboratory investigation revealed an IgGλ MM (Table I). Computed tomography (CT) and a magnetic resonance imaging (MRI) scan of the brain detected cerebral atrophy and numerous small areas compatible with old ischaemic infractions, extensively throughout the brain. In order to maintain HbS levels of < 30%, a chronic transfusion program was initiated and the patient remained stable. Six months later in June 1999, he died at home during a grand mal crisis.

Case 7

A 42 year old woman, with confirmed sickle cell anemia (HbSS), causing painful crises, chronic haemolysis, bilateral femoral head necrosis and cholelithiasis, was admitted because of severe anaemia (April 2000). Laboratory investigation revealed an IgGκ MM (Table I). The patient was treated by plasmaphereses, exchange transfusions and chemotherapy (Melphalan/prednisone) and she remains stable (February 2003).

DISCUSSION

We describe seven SCS cases (five HbSβ^+ thalassaemia, one HbSS and one HbSA) complicated by MM. Table I shows the main laboratory data.

Few case reports of SCS complicated by MM exist in the literature: three HbS homozygotes [1, 3, 5] and two HbS/HbC double heterozygotes [2, 4]. We note that two more cases are simply referred to in tables of data [6, 7].

All seven of our patients were of Greek origin whereas the cases reported by other authors were two black female from Jamaica [1, 2], a black American male from Washington, DC [3], another black male from San Francisco, CA [4] and a male from India [5]. These already documented patients were significantly younger than our patients who developed MM (mean ages 41 and 57 years, respectively).

Two out of seven of our patients presented with MGUS *(cases 1,2)* and progressed to MM twelve and seven years later, respectively. In the reported large series of monoclonal gammopathies, there have been no MGUS cases in association with SCS [9, 10, 11], thus, making our two cases unique.

In our patients with SCS and MM, the M-protein was IgG in four, (IgGκ in three, IgGλ in one), IgAκ in one, IgGκ.IGAκ (biclonal) in one and BJ-λ in one (Table I), thus encompassing a spectrum of various M-proteins; Of the previously reported patients with SCS and MM, four had an M-protein of the IgG type [1, 3, 4, 5] and one an M-protein of IgA type [2]. In addition, five out of seven of our patients with HbSβ^+ thalassaemia *(cases 1,2,3,4,6,7)* and one with HbSA *(case 5)* are the first to be described with coexistent MM.

The incidence of MM is 40 cases per 10^6 people per year and the incidence of biclonal myeloma is approximately 1% of the incidence of all myelomas [10, 11, 12]. In Greece, the total population is approximated at 10 million and the incidence of HbSβ^+ thalassaemia is approximately 0.8% [8]. Therefore, the coexistence of HbSβ^+ thalassaemia and MM in Greece must be extremely rare (one per 32 million), whereas in the USA the occurrence of MM in SCS is approximated at one per 25 million people [3].

In all but one of our cases (*case 5*: HbSA) the peripheral blood smear showed sickled forms, target cells, hypochromia and in addition marked rouleaux formation. Analogous red cell morphology was noted in three out of four SCS/MM patients reported by other authors [1, 3, 5].

The complications reported in the literature included hyperviscosity syndrome, hyperosmolar coma, disseminated intravascular coagulation, renal amyloidosis and acute renal failure [1, 3, 4, 5].

The clinical course of our patients varied: three patients had a mild clinical course prior to developing MM (*cases 4, 5, 7*) whereas the remaining four patients experienced a moderate to severe course. On developing MM, all of our HbSβ^+ thalassaemia or HbS/S patients suffered from vaso-occlusive crises and infections, while our patient with HbSA developed acute renal failure (ARF) after resection of a laryngeal plasmocytoma.

In the patients described in the literature, one with HbSS had a benign clinical course [1] and two with HbS.HbC were asymptomatic before developing MM [2, 4]; two patients with HbSS deteriorated on developing MM [3, 5].

Viscometry in a documented HbSS/MM patient revealed that the increased whole blood viscosity was due mainly to erythrocyte and M-protein interaction [3]. The dramatic clinical course in five of our patients patients with HbSβ^+ thalassaemia following the development of MM, may have been due to the whole blood hyperviscosity syndrome resulting from a synergistic effect of M-protein on deformed red sickled cells according to the literature [3, 13, 14, 15].

Complications such as bleeding diathesis, acute chest syndrome, stroke and bone marrow necrosis in our cases, were treated by plasmaphereses, exchange transfusions and blood transfusions. In SCS/MM cases, other authors utilized analogous modalities which seem to be the best measures for the acute severe clinical manifestations of SCS complicated by MM [13, 16, 17].

No clear conclusions with regard to the response to chemotherapy can be drawn, since the number of cases is sparse. However, we observed that one of our patients (case 4) and one case in the literature [1], both of whom did not undergo chemotherapy, achieved the longest survival.

The increased frequency and severity of infections in these patients may be due to myeloma immunodeficiency, to sickle cell-related asplenia [3, 13, 15], as well as to other factors such as tissue ischaemia and infarction [7].

In two of our patients, amyloid deposits were diagnosed by bone marrow (Fig 4,5) and gingival biopsies. In one patient *(case 2),* heart failure was due to cardiac amyloidosis and in the other *(case 5),* severe orthostatic syndrome could have been due to an amyloid autonomic neuropathy, according to the literature [18]. In one of the reported cases of MM in SCS [5], heart failure might also have been due to amyloidosis.

Following resection of a laryngeal plasmacytoma, one of our patients *(case 5)* developed ARF. ARF could be attributed to HbSA and BJ-λ protein in combination with other contributing factors such as hypercalcaemia, dehydration, and hyperuricaemia [18, 19].

Haematological malignancies seem to be very rare in SCS patients since such patients usually succumb before developing a malignancy. Although this may be pertinent to developing countries where patients with SCS seldom reach adulthood [8], in the Mediterranean countries where SCS usually takes a more benign course, no concurrent malignancy has been reported until now. However, a hypothesis for a protective role of SCS from malignancies can be validated: in black children with SCS, the incidence of Burkitt's lymphoma (Africa) and acute leukaemia (USA) does not differ from the incidence of these diseases in the general child population in the same areas [20, 21].The genetic difference among the several geographical types of SCS, however, may offer another explanation [22].

Our data on seven cases of MM in SCS patients over 42 years old (42-65), coupled with analogous data from Jamaica (two MM cases among 60 SCS patients over 30 years old) [6] and from the USA (one MM case among 209 cases over 20 years old) [7], suggest that as the survival of patients with SCS increases, the incidence of MM among them may also increase [1, 2, 6].

Although six out seven of our patients had gallstones, evidence that either the presence of gallstones or the chronic inflammatory process or the chronic haemolysis play a significant role in the development of MM does not exist; however we mention that an analogous pathogenetic mechanism is proposed for the development of monoclonal gammopathy not only in SCS but also in hereditary spherocytosis [5, 9, 23].

The major question is whether the incidence of MM is really increased in SCS. Although there is no clear indication or evidence for such an association, in this paper we report the first cases of MM occuring with HbSβ+thal, and also the first association of MM with HbSS and HbSA in Europe. We note that six of these patients (*cases 1,2,3,4,6,7*), have also been reported recently [24].

Our hospital is not a reference center for sickling syndromes and national registry data are not available, According a precise estimation on the incidence, the prevalence and survival for both diseases cannot be drawn; We only note that three of our patients were in their 60s, three in their 50s and one was 42 years of age, whereas MM is common in older age groups. On the other hand, as the rarity of MM in SCS in developing countries may be due to early death, increased survival and availability of medical facilities may increase the incidence of it.

In order to assess the true incidence of MM in SCS and /or to clarify whether an association between the two diseases is real or it merely constitutes a coexistence, further follow up studies in a large number of older patients with sickle cell syndromes are required.

REFERENCES

[1] Talerman, A., Serjeant, G., & Milner, P. Normal pregnancy in a patient with MM and sickle cell anemia. *West Indian Medical Journal*, **20,** 97-100 (1971).

[2] Nicoleau, A., Kaplan, B., Balzora, JD. Hemoglobin SC and Multiple Myeloma. *Am J Hematol,* **60**, 250-1 (1999).

[3] Anderson, I.S., Yeung, K., Hillman, D. & Lessin, L. Multiple myeloma in a patient with sickle cell anemia. Interacting effects on blood viscosity. *American Journal of Medicine,* **59,** 568-574 (1975).

[4] Stricker, R., Linker, C., Crowley, T. & Embury, S. Hematological malignancy in sickle cell disease: Report of four cases and review of the literature. *American Journal of Hematology,* **21,** 223-230 (1986).

[5] Sarma, P.S.A., Viswanathan, K.A. & Mukherjee, M.M. Multiple myeloma in a patient with sickle cell anaemia. *Journal of the Association of Physisicians of India*, **34,** 877-878(1986)

[6] Serjeant, G.R., Richards, R., Barbor, P., & Milner, P. Relative benign sickle cell anemia in 60 patients over 30 in the West Indies. *British Medical Journal* **3**, 86-89 (1968).

[7] Platt, O.S., Brambilla, D.J., Rosse, W.F., Milner, P.F., Castro, O., Steinberg, M.H. & Klug P.P. Mortality in sickle cell disease. Life expectancy and risk factors for early death. *New England Journal of Medicine,* **330,** 1639-1644 (1994).

[8] Loukopoulos, D. Hemoglobin variants and thalassemia in Greece. In *Hemoglobin variants in human populations* (ed. by W. Winter), Vol. 1. pp. 166-172 (1987). CRC Press Incorporated, Florida.

[9] Isobe, T. & Osserman, E. Pathologic conditions associated with plasma cell dyscrasias. A study of 806 cases. *Annals of the New York Academy of Sciences* **190,** 507-518 (1971).

[10] Kyle, R., Robinson, R. & Katzmann, J. The clinical aspects of biclonal gammopathy. Review of 57 cases. *American Journal of Medicine,* **71,** 999-1008 (1981).

[11] Smith, I., Barlogie, B. & Alexanian, R. Biclonal and hypodiploid Multiple Myeloma. *American Journal of Medicine,* **80,** 841-843 (1986).

[12] Waldenstrom, J. *Multiple myeloma: Diagnosis and treatment.* Crune & Straton, New York. (1970)

[13] Somer, T. (The viscosity of blood, plasma and serum in paraproteinemias *Acta Medica Scandinavica,* **190,** (Suppl 456) (1966).

[14] Schechter, A., Noguchi, C. & Rodgers, G. Sickle cell disease. In *The molecular basis of blood diseases* (ed. by G. Stamatoyannopoulos, A. Nienhuis, P. Leder and P. Majerus) pp. 179-818. W.B. Saunders Company, London (1987)

[15] Kaul, D.K., Fabry, M.E. & Nagel, R.L. Microvascular sites and characteristics of sickle cell adhesion to vascular endothelium in shear flow conditions: pathophysiological implications. *Proceedings of the National Academy of Sciences of the United States of America,* **86,** 3356-3360 (1989).

[16] Davies-Jones, G., Preston, F. & Timperley, W. Myelomatosis and the hyperviscosity syndrome. *Neurological complications in clinical haematology* pp. 83-95. Blackwell Scientific Publications, London (1980).

[17] Davies-Jones, G., Preston, F. & Timperley, W. Sickle cell anemia. *Neurological complications in clinical haematology pp17-25.* Blackwell Scientific Publications, London (1980).

[18] Kyle, R.A. & Greip, P.R. Amyloidosis (AL). Clinical and laboratory features in 224 cases. *Mayo Clinic Proceedings,* **58,** 665-676 (1983).

[19] Buckalew, V. & Someren, A. Renal manifestations of sickle cell disease. *Archives of Internal Medicine,* **133,** 660-669 (1974).

[20] Pike, M.C., Morrow, R., Kisuule, A. & Maffigirri, J. Burkitt's lymphoma and sickle cell trait. *British Journal of preventive and Social Medicine*, **24,** 39-41 (1970).

[21] Jackson, R.E. & Short, B.J. Frequency and prognosis of coexisting sickle cell disease and acute leukemia in children. *Clinical Pediatrics,* **11,** 183-85 (1972).

[22] Konstantopoulos, K., Vulliamy, T., Swirsky, D., Reeves, JD., Kaeda, J., Luzzatto L. DNA haplotypes in Africans and West Indians with sickle cell anaemia or SC disease. Gene Geogr **10(1):**19-24 (1996)

[23] Schaffer, A., Miller, B., Lester, E., Bowers, T. & Jacob, H. Monoclonal Gammopathy in hereditary spherocytosis: a possible pathogenetic relation. *Annals of Internal Medicine,* **88,** 45-46 (1978).

[24] Kaloterakis, A., Filiotou, A., Konstantopoulos, K., Rombos, Y., Bossinakou, I., Hadziyannis, S. Multiple myeloma in sickle cell syndromes. *Haematologia*, 31, 153-159 (2001).

In: Focus on Sickle Cell Research
Editor: Ralph L. Plasmar, pp. 125-130

ISBN 1-59033-920-7

Chapter VIII

SICKLE CELL HEMOGLOBINOPATHY AND SUDDEN DEATH

G. Lorin de la Grandmaison*

Department of Pathology and Forensic Medicine, Raymond Poincaré Hospital, University R. Descartes, Paris-Ouest, 104 Bd Raymond Poincaré, F-92380 Garches, France

ABSTRACT

Although rare, sudden death is the most serious complication of sickle cell trait. Sickle cell trait has a substantially increased age-dependent risk of exercice-related sudden death. Sudden death may occur in susceptible persons when poor physical conditioning, dehydration, heat stresses or hypoxic states precipitate sickling of the abnormal erythrocytes. Most of the death mechanisms are related to the biological consequences of diffuse microvascular occlusion due to sickling, although a significant number of such sudden deaths remain unexplained after thorough autopsy. Rare mechanisms encountered include acute splenic sequestration. The main pathological findings include widespread intravascular sickling, but the exact cause of death is not always explained after a complete autopsy. Morphological findings are only indicative of the possible mechanism of death and do not prove it. A complete autopsy with systematic histologic examination, hemoglobin electrophoresis, vitreous electrolytes, urine myoglobin, microbiological studies and DNA analysis should be evaluated in any unexplained sudden death in a young African-American patient.

Keywords: Sickle cell trait, sickle cell disease, sudden death, autopsy

* Correspondence: Docteur Geoffroy Lorin de la Grandmaison, Service d'Anatomie Pathologique et de Médecine Légale, Hôpital Raymond Poincaré, 104 Boulevard Raymond Poincaré, 92380 GARCHES, FRANCE, Phone: 33-1-47-10-76-84, Fax: 33-1-47-10-76-83, E-mail: glorin@club-internet.fr

1. Introduction

Sudden death has become increasingly recognized as an important clinical feature of both homozygous or heterozygous sickle cell disease. The sickle cell trait carriers are generally asymptomatic or have little clinical problems compared to sickle cell anemia [1]. They develop painful crisis linked with vaso-occlusion only in case of severe anoxia. In some cases this hemoglobinopathy is revealed by sudden death. The exact nature of its cause has remained unexplained. The heterozygous sickle cell disease of low morbidity (sickle cell trait) is very common among black people and could favor death in hypoxic conditions. It has been found to be a risk factor of exercise-related sudden death [2]. This risk may be as high as 0.3 case per 1,000 persons [2]. Although rare, sudden death is the most serious complication of sickle cell trait. Studies suggest that this condition may occur in susceptible persons where poor physical conditioning, dehydration, heat stress or hypoxic states precipitate sickling of the abnormal erythrocytes [3].

2. Death Mechanisms Involved in Sickling

The chain of events leading to sudden death is initiated by conditions that shift the oxygenation curve to the right [3]. Sickling phenomenon by abnormal hemoglobin S polymerization is favored by many factors, including increase of intracellular hemoglobin S concentration, severity of blood deoxygenation, acidosis and red blood increase of 2,3-diphosphoglycerate concentration [1]. Consequently, metabolic acidosis related to exertion and hyperthermia (which shift the hemoglobin saturation curve to the right, displacing more oxygen from haemoglobin S), increased osmolality and dehydration (which increases the concentration of haemoglobin S) and severe hypoxaemia (haemoglobin oxygen saturation below 20% causes major sickling of erythrocytes in sickle cell trait), all favor the sickling [3, 4]. Then, the sickling of the erythrocytes interferes with the microcirculatory blood flow, resulting in vascular occlusion, which increases capillary time transit and causes further hypoxia [3]. The prolonged deprivation of oxygen and nutrients results in rhabdomyolysis with resultant leakage of myoglobin into the circulation. Poor physical conditioning is associated with an increased risk for exercice-induced myoglobinuria and clinical rhabdomyolosis. Myoglobin-induced renal tubular injury due to rhabdomyolysis associated with dehydration, hypervolaemia and acidosis may cause acute renal failure [3,4]. Sickling also leads to endothelial damage, which may cause vasoconstriction, disseminated intravascular coagulation and local tissue damage. Cardiac effects include acute ischemia and arrhythmias. Fatalities with autopsy-proven massive fat and bone marrow emboli have been described in patients with both sickle cell-hemoglobin C and sickle cell β^{+} - thalassemia [5].

For individuals who suddenly died with sickled erythrocytes, as in other examples of sudden death, lethal cardiac instability may be the final common pathway [6]. Cardiovascular autonomic nervous dysfunction has been also suggested as a possible risk factor for sudden death in sickle cell disease [7]. Other cardiac effects might include acute ischemia associated with arrhythmia. Myocardial microvascular occlusion by sickled erythrocytes could also induce a fatal arrhythmia triggered by ischemia [8]. Rare mechanisms such as acute splenic sequestration may be encountered [9]. Indeed, this disorder is usually associated with children with homozygous and rarely heterozygous sickle cell syndromes [5]. Acute splenic sequestration crisis is rarely reported in patients with sickle-hemoglobin C disease except in conjunction with exposure to high-altitude conditions where the partial pressure of oxygen is decreased [9]. The pathophysiology of acute splenic sequestration crisis is poorly understood, although it has been noted that most affected patients have preexisting splenomegaly [9]. This phenomen could be due to the obstruction of the venous outflow of a distensible spleen by sickle red cells [10] and fatalities may occur as a result of anemia, hypoxemia, hypovolemia and sepsis [10].

It must be stressed that between 12% and 26% of the patients with sickle cell anemia who died had unexplained deaths [11]. In a series of 74 autopsied patients, 22% died of unknown cause [11].

3. Postmortem Diagnosis in Case of Sudden Death with Sickling

The discovery of the sickle cell trait may be fortuitous at postmortem and initially carried out by histology. Sickle cells are erythrocytes that have a somewhat elongate shape and very sharply pointed ends. It is the latter feature that best distinguishes this type of cell. No normal red cell has needle-sharp pointed ends, no matter how deformed it becomes, but red cells from patients with the sickle cell trait do have this feature, particularly in severe oxygen deprivation. It can be assumed that any patient in the agonal state experiences terminal hypoxemia. However, the mere finding of sickle cells, even in a large number of organs, does not indicate that the patient had sickle cell disease, or that he or she died of the disease. Crosby pointed out that the presence of sickle cells in the vessels of people with the sickle trait is an expected postmortem finding [12]. Morphological criteria used to detect sickle states at autopsy are as described by Thoma and McCormick [13]:

- Crises: Characteristic pooling of blood around splenic follicles; packing of liver sinusoids and glomerular capillaries with massed sickle cells; distension and plugging of vessels in all other tissue sections with massed sickle cells.
- Past activity: Old vascular thrombi, especially in lungs, spleen or brain; hemosiderin deposits in spleen, liver and bone marrow; scarred, atrophic spleen.
- Terminal sicklemia: Presence of sickle cells in vessels but absence of the other changes noted above.

Shock lesions can be found with disseminated intravascular coagulation. Immunohistochemistry can show renal tubular myoglobin cast in case of rhabdomyolysis [14]. In case of acute cardiac ischemia due to myocardial microvascular occlusion by sickled erythrocytes, immunohistochemistry can also detect earlier ischemic myocardial lesions [15, 16]. Visceral infarcts are rare, more frequent when they are found in the spleen, in the lung, in the brain and in the medullary renal tissue where they can provoke hematuria [17]. These visceral infarcts are considered to be due to AS hemoglobinopathy since fewer than 1% of the controls without AS hemoglobinopathy have such infarcts [12]. Hemorrhage due to disseminated intravascular coagulation may be found. Pulmonary hypertension changes are frequently found in patients with sickle cell hemoglobinopathy who suddenly died [18].

A complete autopsy with systematic histologic examination, hemoglobin electrophoresis, vitreous electrolytes, urine myoglobin, microbiological studies and DNA analysis should be evaluated. Prudent forensic practice would include these studies in any unexplained sudden death in a young African-American patient. The differential diagnosis of sudden death during exertion includes pulmonary embolism, acute cardiac events, anaphylaxis and heat stroke [3].

Exposure to hypoxia of endogenous origin such as asthma attack may produce a variety of clinical abnormalities of sufficient severity to threaten the life of the patients with sickle cell trait [17] and this disorder must be viewed as a potentially fatal disorder [19]. Although the estimated frequency of asthma and heterozygous sickle cell disease among the young black population is relatively high, the diagnosis of such associations is very rarely reported in the literature [20-22].

In case of sudden death within a history of sickle cell trait, morphological findings are only indicative of the possible mechanism of death and do not prove it. If intense and diffuse intravascular sickling is found without other obvious causes of death, it could be considered as the contributory cause of death. The postmortem findings of Mac Cormick [23] based on 120 autopsies of subjects suffering from sickle cell trait showed that in 12.5% of the cases, the disease was a contributing factor in the death.

The interpretation of the findings is a little different in case of sudden infant death syndrome (SIDS). Indeed, pediatric hematologists believe it highly improbable that an infant under 6 months would or could die of sickle cell disease because his/her relative levels of residual fetal haemoglobin are so high [24]. Even the very first clinical manifestations of the disease do not usually appear until the latter part of the first year [25]. Consequently, the autopsy observation of moderate numbers of sickle cells in an infant who succumbed to SIDS, especially in the first six months of life, probably indicates only that the baby had sickle cell trait [24].

4. Conclusion

Although rare, sudden death is the most serious potential complication of sickle cell trait. The main pathological findings include widespread intravascular sickling, but the exact cause of death is not always explained after a complete autopsy. People with sickle cell trait, especially athletes, should be taught that maintenance of adequate hydration and avoidance of both high-altitude training sites and substances that may promote dehydration, such as alcohol, caffeine and diuretics, can help prevent sickle cell trait-associated collapse and sudden death during exertion [3].

References

[1] Embury S. The clinical pathophysiology of sickle cell disease. *Ann Rev Med* 1986;37:36.

[2] Kark JA, Posey DM, Schumacher HR, Ruehle CJ. Sickle-cell trait as a risk factor for sudden death in physical training. *N Engl J Med* 1987;317(13):781-7.

[3] Kerle KK, Nishimura KD. Exertional collapse and sudden death associated with sickle cell trait. *Am Family Physician* 1996;54(1):237-240.

[4] Browne RJ. Sickle cell trait and sudden death. *Sports Med* 1994;18(6):373-4.

[5] Hutchins KD, Ballas SK, Phatak D, Natarajan GA. Sudden unexpected death in a patient with splenic sequestration and sickle cell-β^+-Thalassemia syndrome. *J Forensic Sci* 2001;46(2):412-4.

[6] James TN, Riddick L, Massing GK. Sickle cells and sudden death: morphological abnormalities of the cardiac conduction system. *J Lab Clin Med* 1994;124(4):507-20.

[7] Romero Mestre JC, Hernandez A, Agramonte O, Hernandez P. Cardiovascular autonomic dysfunction in sickle cell anemia: a possible risk factor for sudden death? *Clin Autonom Res* 1997;7(3):121-5.

[8] Wirthwein DP, Spotswood SD, Barnard JJ, Prahlow JA. Death due to microvascular occlusion in sickle-cell trait following physical exertion. *J Forensic Sci* 2001;46:399-401.

[9] Michel JB, Hernandez JA, Buchanan GR. A fatal case of acute splenic sequestration in a 53-year-old woman with sickle-hemoglobin C disease. *Am J Med* 1992;92:97-100.

[10] Shurin SB. Disorders of the spleen. In Handin RI, Lux SE, Stossel TP, editors. *Blood: principles and practice of hematology*. Philadelphia:J.B. Lippincott Company, 1995.

[11] Charache S. Sickle cells and sudden death. *J Lab Clin Med* 1994;124(4):473-4.

[12] Sears DA. The morbidity of sickle cell trait. A review of the literature. *Am J Med* 1978;64:1021-1036.

[13] Jones SR, Binder RA, Donowho EM Jr. Sudden death in sickle-cell trait. *N Engl J Med* 1970 Feb 5;282(6):323-5.

[14] Karger K, Teige K. Fatal malignant hyperthermia – delayed onset and atypical course. *Forensic Sci Int* 2002;129(3):187-190.

[15] Edston E, Kawa K. Immunohistochemical detection of early myocardial infarction. An evaluation of antibodies against the terminal complement complex (C5b-9). *Int J Legal Med* 1995;108:27-30.

[16] Piercecchi-Marti MD, Lepidi H, Leonetti G, Vire O, Cianfarani F, Pelissier JF. Immunostaining by complement C9: a tool for early diagnosis of myocardial infarction and application in forensic medicine. *J Forensic Sci* 2001;46(2):328-334.

[17] Levin WC. Asymptomatic sickle-cell-trait. *Blood* 1958;13:904-7.

[18] Haque AK, Gokhale S, Rampy BA, Adegboyega P, Duarte A, Saldana MJ. Pulmonary hypertension in sickle cell hemoglobinopathy: a clinicopathologic study of 20 cases. *Hum Pathol* 2002;33(10):1037-1043.

[19] Wirthwein DP, Spotswood SD, Barnard JJ, Prahlow JA. Death due to microvascular occlusion in sickle-cell trait following physical exertion. *J Forensic Sci* 2001 Mar;46(2):399-401

[20] Johnson K, Stastny JF, Rucknagel DL. Fat embolism syndrome associated with asthma and sickle cell-β^+-thalassemia. *Am J Hematology* 1994;46:354-7.

[21] Thogmarin JR. Sudden death in police pursuit. *J Forensic Sci* 1998;43:1228-31.

[22] Lorin de la Grandmaison G, Paraire F. Postmortem revelation of sickle cell disease following fatal episode of acute bronchial asthma. *Forensic Sci Int* 2002;126:48-52.

[23] Mac Cormick WF. The pathology of sickle cell trait. *Am J Med Sci* 1961;241:329-36.

[24] Valdès-Dapena M. et al. *Histopathology atlas for the sudden infant death syndrome.* AFIP, Washington, 1993.

[25] Pearson HA. Sickle cell hemogloninopathies, in Chapter 15: *Diseases of the blood: Hemolytic anemias due to hemoglobinopathies.* In: Behrman RE, Vaughan VC, eds. Nelson Textbooks of Pediatrics, 13th ed. Philadelphia: W.B. Saunders Co., 1987, pp. 1049-51.

In: Focus on Sickle Cell Research
Editor: Ralph L. Plasmar, pp. 131-136 ISBN 1-59033-920-7

Chapter IX

GLOBAL LEFT VENTRICULAR PERFORMANCE IN SICKLE CELL ANEMIA DURING CHILDHOOD AS DETERMINED BY ECHOCARDIOGRAPHY

Mohamed A. Seliem*
Division of Pediatric Cardiology
Aramco Dhahran Health Center
Dhahran 31311
Saudi Arabia

INTRODUCTION

In Sickle Cell Anemia, one of the chronic anemias of childhood, there is a two-fold burden imposed on the cardiovascular system, namely the hemodynamic effect of the anemia and the influence of the myocardial insult caused by the sickling process.

The increase in the preload and afterload caused by the anemia will eventually result in left ventricular hypertrophy and dilatation. Development of congestive heart failure in children and young adults is usually related to co-existing complications of the disease and not due to the anemia itself. Echocardiography has been well utilized for assessment of left ventricular performance in patients with severe anemia.

* Correspondence: Mohamed A. Seliem, MD, Consultant Pediatric Cardiologist, Dhahran Health Center, Dhahran 31311, Saudi Arabia, Tel: 00966-878-1009, Fax:00966-877-3792, E-MAIL: Mohamed. Seliem@aramco.com.sa

OBJECTIVE OF CURRENT STUDY [1]

To evaluate prospectively the left ventricular performance, both systolic and diastolic, in young patients with Sickle Cell Disease using comprehensive echocardiographic imaging including automated border detection.

METHODS

Twenty-six patients with Sickle Cell Disease underwent an echocardiographic examination including M-mode, 2D, Doppler and Automated Border Detection. All patients were admitted to the hospital for treatment of acute vaso-occlusive crises and underwent their cardiac evaluation immediately before their discharge from the hospital after complete recovery. None of these patients was receiving intravenous fluids at the time of the echocardiographic examination. All patients were matched for age, sex, weight and height with twenty normal controls (Table I). All patients were below 13 years of age. The study was approved by the institutional Public Relations and Medical Support Services Division.

RESULTS: TABLE I, II.

All patients were significantly anemic when compared with normals ($P<0.0001$), Table I. The left ventricular systolic performance was preserved. Both M-mode derived percentage of shortening fraction (SF%) and Automated Border Detection derived ejection fraction (EF%) and emptying rates were normal. The left ventricular geometry (2D imaging), showed increased muscle mass. This was mainly due to increased wall thickness ($P<0.02$) and mild dilatation (although ventricular dimensions did not reach statistical significance). The left ventricular diastolic filling (Doppler Mitral inflow dynamics), Fig. 1, showed increased flow in late diastole (A-wave), Normal E-wave velocity, lower E/A ratio and shortened diastolic time (DT). The left ventricular volumetric parameters (Automated Border Detection imaging), Fig. 2, showed significantly dilated ventricles while the filling rates were normal (Table II).

Table 1. Demographic Data on Patients and Controls

#	Parameter		SCD Patients	Controls
1.	**N**		26	20
2.	**Age (years):**			
	mean ± SD		10.2 ± 2.6	9 ± 2.7
	range		5 - 14	3 - 13.2
	95% CI		9.1 - 11.2	7.2 - 10.7
3.	**Sex:**			
	Male		19	5
	Female		7	8
4.	**Weight (Kg):**			
	Mean ± SD		26.9 ± 7.7	26.7 ± 6.7
	Range		12.7 ± 47.5	19 - 38
	95% CI		24 - 30	22.6 - 30.8
5.	**Height (cm):**			
	mean ± SD		130.5 ± 16.1	128.8 ± 15.9
	range		100 - 165	112 - 157
	95% CI		123 - 138	119 - 138
6.	**BSA (M^2):**			
	mean ± SD		0.98 ± 0.2	1 ± 0.2
	range		0.6 - 1.48	0.8 - 1.3
	95% CI		- 1.1	- 1.1
7.	**Hg (g)***			
	mean±SD		8.9±1.5	12±1
	range		7-13	10-13
	95% CI		8-9.5	11-12.5
8.	**Hct(%)***			
	mean±SD		26.6±4.7	35±2.6
	range		18-38	29-37
	95% CI		25-29	33-36.5

* P is < 0.0001 when SCD patients were compared with normal controls.

Table 2. Echocardiographic Parameters of Patients and Controls

LV Parameter		SCD Patients n=26	Normals n=20
(A)	M-Mode:		
	End Diastolic Dimension {EDD} (mm/M²)	4.6 ± 0.9	4.2 ± 0.6
	End Systolic Dimension {ESD} (mm/M²)	2.7 ± 0.6	2.5 ± 0.4
	Inter-Ventricular Septum {IVS} (mm/M²)	0.8 ± 0.2†	0.6 ± 0.1
	Posterior Wall {PW} (mm/M²)	0.6 ± 0.1†	0.5 ± 0.07
	Shorting Fraction (SF%)	40 ± 4.5%	39 ± 5%
	Left Ventricular muscle mass {LVMM} g/M²	79 ± 22†	56 ± 8.9
(B)	Doppler:		
	E-Wave (cm/s)	113 ± 17	113 ± 17
	A-Wave (cm/s)	76 ± 19†	60 ± 10
	E/A ratio	1.6 ± 0.4†	1.95 ± 0.5
	Deceleration Time [DT] (msec)	118 ± 52†	177 ± 90
	Diastolic Filling Period [DFP] (msec)	276 ± 67†	364 ± 120
(C)	Automated Border:		
	End Diastolic Volume {EDV} (ml/M²)	45 ± 9†	36 ± 7.3
	End Systolic Volume {ESV} (ml/M²)	20 ± 6†	15 ± 3.8
	Ejection Fraction (EF%)	54 ± 7.8%	58 ± 6%
	Peak Filling Rate. EDV (PFR.EDV)	4.7 ± 0.8	4.6 ± 0.9
	Peak Emptying Rate. EDV (PER.EDV)	4 ± 0.7	3.9 ± 0.4
	Time-to-Peak Filling Rate (TPFR) {msec}	122 ± 44	124 ± 32
(D)	R-R Interval (msec)	732 ± 76	732 ± 127
	Blood Pressure (mm Hg):		
	Systolic	106 ± 9	
	Diastolic	63 ± 6	
	Mean	77 ± 7	

† =P≤ 0.02 compared with controls.

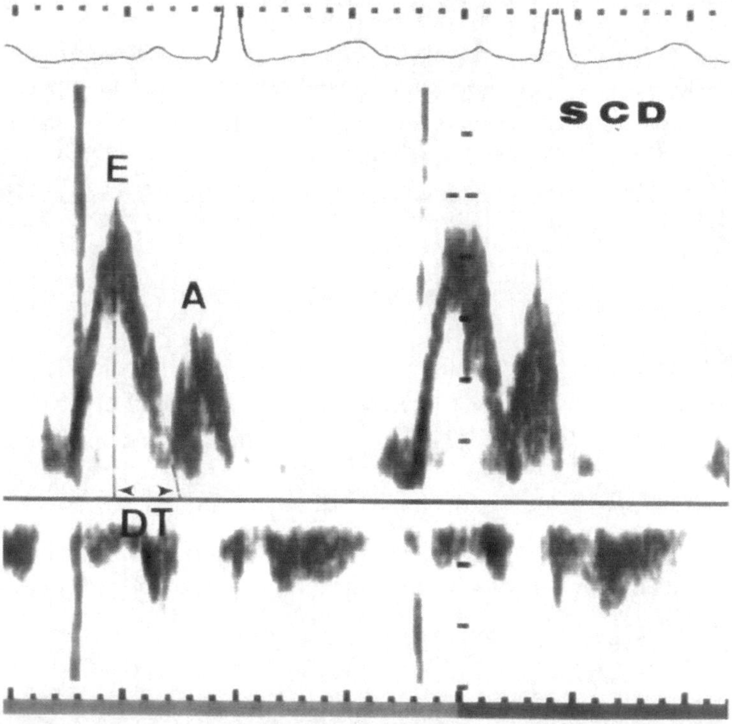

Figure 1: Mitral flow Doppler signal from a patient with sickle cell disease (SCD) showing increased flow in late diastole (A-wave) with decreased E/A ratio, and shorter deceleration time (DT).

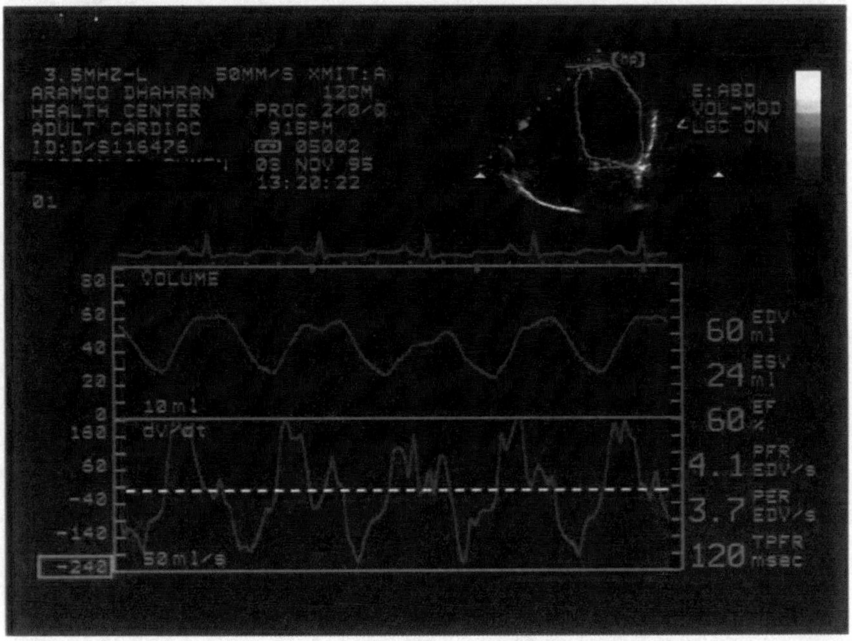

Figure 2: Waveform recording of acoustic quantification of the left ventricle of a patient with SCD Abbreviations are as in text.

CONCLUSION

The left ventricular systolic performance is well preserved in young patients with chronic anemia due to Sickle Cell Disease. There is, however, left ventricular hypertrophy and measurable abnormalities in the diastolic filling detected by Doppler. Such changes do not fit a specific cardiomyopathy pattern i.e. delayed relaxation vs. restrictive physiology.

SUMMARY

This study documented the presence of early, non-specific diastolic abnormalities in young patients with Sickle Cell Disease. Such diastolic abnormalities can be detected very early in the course of the chronic disease provided that all available echocardiographic modalities are used in a complementary fashion. No single echocardiographic imaging modality is sensitive enough to detect these early and subtle changes. Serial follow up of these young subjects therefore, is a fundamental part of their overall medical care to address any diastolic abnormality before development of systolic dysfunction which is usually a late sequale of the disease.

REFERENCE

[1] Seliem, MA, Al-Saad, HI, Bou-Holaigah, IH, Khan MN, Pabileo MR. Left Ventricular Diastolic Dysfunction in Congenital Chronic Anemias During Childhood as Determined by Comprehensive Echocardiographic Imaging including Acoustic Quantification. *Eur. J. Echocardiography* 2002, 3; 103-110.

In: Focus on Sickle Cell Research
Editor: Ralph L. Plasmar, pp. 137-155

ISBN 1-59033-920-7

Chapter X

SICKLE CELL DISEASE: LABORATORY INVESTIGATIONS AND HEMOGLOBIN STUDY

Henri Wajcman*

INSERM U468 and Department of Biochemistry, Hôpital H. Mondor,
94010 Créteil, France

ABSTRACT

The diagnosis of any sickle cell disease syndrome is based on the unambiguous identification of the Hb S mutation. Electrophoretic tests are usually the first that are performed. A much better resolution is obtained with isoelectric focusing than with the more conventional cellulose acetate electrophoresis at alkaline pH. In some laboratories the first test which is performed is now cation exchange HPLC. The diagnosis of Hb S should never be accepted if not confirmed by a second test, more specific of this Hb, such as the solubility test or electrophoresis on agar in citrate buffer.

The laboratory should also evaluate the other factors interacting with Hb S, such as Hb F level, sickle cell restriction haplotype, association with α-thalassemia or other α or β globin gene variants. It should also evaluate other cellular factors and, in case of symptomatic heterozygous patients, help in the understanding of the underlying mechanisms.

Key words: sickle cell disease, HbS, electrophoresis, HPLC, biological diagnosis

* Corresponding author: Dr H.Wajcman, INSERM U468, Hôpital Henri Mondor, 51 avenue du Maréchal de Lattre de Tassigny, 94010 Créteil Cédex, France, Tel: 01 49 81 35 78 Fax: 01 48 99 33 45, e-mail: henri.wajcman@im3.inserm.fr

INTRODUCTION

The diagnosis of any genetic form of sickle cell disease must be based on the unambiguous identification of the Hb S mutation. Laboratory findings are usually the only way to identify heterozygous carriers (Hb A/Hb S), which usually are clinically and hematologically silent. In the case of a major sickle cell syndrome the laboratory tests will recognize if the patient is homozygous for the mutant hemoglobin (Hb S/Hb S), which is the most frequent situation, or if the patient is compound heterozygous for Hb S and another Hb abnormality. Classical associations, which may lead to a sickle cell disease include the simultaneous presence of the Hb S mutation and of a β-thalassemia gene in trans, or of some Hb variants. Among those, the more frequent are Hb D-Punjab [β121(GH4) Glu →Gln] and Hb O-Arab [β121(GH4) Glu →Lys], which stabilize the Hb S polymers, or Hb C [β6(A3) Glu →Lys], which dehydrates the erythrocyte and enhances sickling [1]. The laboratory tests may also bring some valuable elements to evaluate a clinical prognosis.

In the case of individuals who are apparently heterozygous for Hb S; which displays some clinical features characteristic of sickle cell disease; the laboratory will have to demonstrate the presence of an additional red cell abnormality, which may facilitate the sickling process. This could result from an additional electrophoretically neutral mutation carried by the other allele or by the Hb S gene itself; as it has been reported in Hb S-Antilles [2]; in which the replacement of the β 23Val by an Ile leads to a further stabilization of the Hb S polymer. Another possibility could be the association with a pyruvate kinase deficiency, which by blocking some steps of the erythrocyte metabolic pathway, increases the intra-erythrocytic 2,3-diphosphoglycerate (2,3-DPG) concentration and thus the fraction of Hb S deoxygenated [3]. A membrane defect increasing or favoring the RBC dehydration would also favor sickling

An electrophoretic study is usually the first step done for the diagnosis of Hb S. Cellulose acetate electrophoresis (CAE), because of its simplicity, is still among the more frequently used techniques for Hb screening. Its resolution is nevertheless below that of isoelectric focusing (IEF), which therefore is considered by many laboratories as the method of choice. Nowadays, an increasing number of laboratories prefer to use cation exchange HPLC as the first test since it is an almost fully automated method.

A single positive result is always insufficient to establish definitively the diagnosis of Hb S. It always needs to be confirmed either by a functional test showing the decreased solubility of deoxygenated Hb S or by a electrophoresis on agar gel, which specifically explores the region structurally modified in this Hb. Molecular biology tests using restriction enzymes could be required in some cases.

In any major sickle cell disease syndrome, laboratory investigations should not be solely restricted to the identification of Hb S: they must also evaluate other genetic factors, which may modify the clinical expression of the disease. Among them are the β-gene restriction haplotypes, the level of expression of HbF, the presence of an associated α-thalassemia, or even of another erythrocyte abnormality.

In sickle cell anemia the laboratory needs to control the consequences of the disease on the RBC but also on other organs, such as the kidney, liver, lungs, and heart...aspects which concern various chapters of medicine that stay largely outside of the scope of this paper.

IDENTIFICATION OF HB S

Electrophoresis at Alkaline pH and Isoelectric Focusing

Using moving boundary electrophoresis, Pauling et al. discovered Hb S in 1949 [4]. Sickle cell disease was then revealed to result from the presence of an abnormal Hb differing in its electric charge from normal adult hemoglobin. It was only about 10 years later that Ingram [5] brought to light the explanation of this historical finding. He demonstrated that Hb S resulted from a replacement by a glutamic acid of the valine at position 6 of the β chain, leading to two additional positive charges in the Hb tetramer. This substitution raises the isoelectric point of Hb from 6.95 to 7.25.

Electrophoresis, a technique consisting of the migration of electrically charged molecules under an applied electric field, became, thus, the method of choice to analyze mutated Hbs. Hb variants were first studied by zone electrophoresis on paper and starch gel. In the years that followed, cellulose acetate strips and cellulose acetate thin layer plates, which were easier to use and had a correct resolution power, became available [6-8]. In these techniques, at pH 8.5 the Hb molecule carries an overall negative charge, and any variant differing in charge is easily separated. Under these conditions, Hb S migrates slower than Hb A towards the anode, as shown schematically in figure 1.

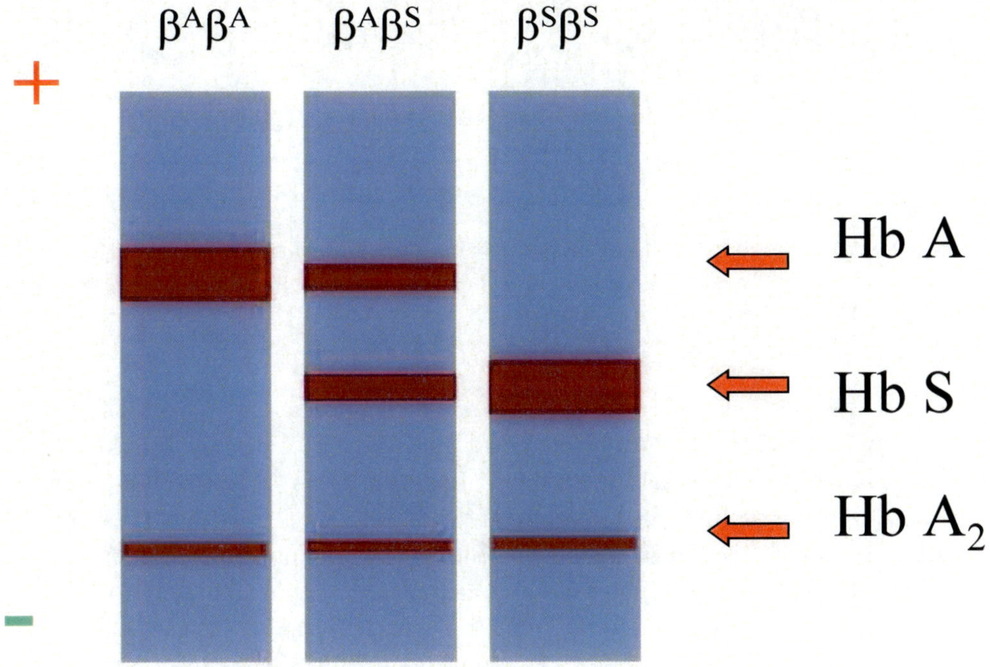

Figure 1: Schematic view of the electrophoretic migration of Hb S, compared to Hb A, at alkaline pH.

Nevertheless, when using this kind of electrophoresis at alkaline pH, Hb S cannot always be differentiated from other variants with an identical difference in charge, which display a very similar mobility. As shown in figure 2, Hb D-Punjab; that may be observed in some populations where Hb S exists; migrates as Hb S on cellulose acetate electrophoresis. By this method it is not possible to discriminate Hb C from Hb E, but while the association of Hb S with Hb C is frequent and cause a sickle cell syndrome, that with Hb E is rare, and is very mild.

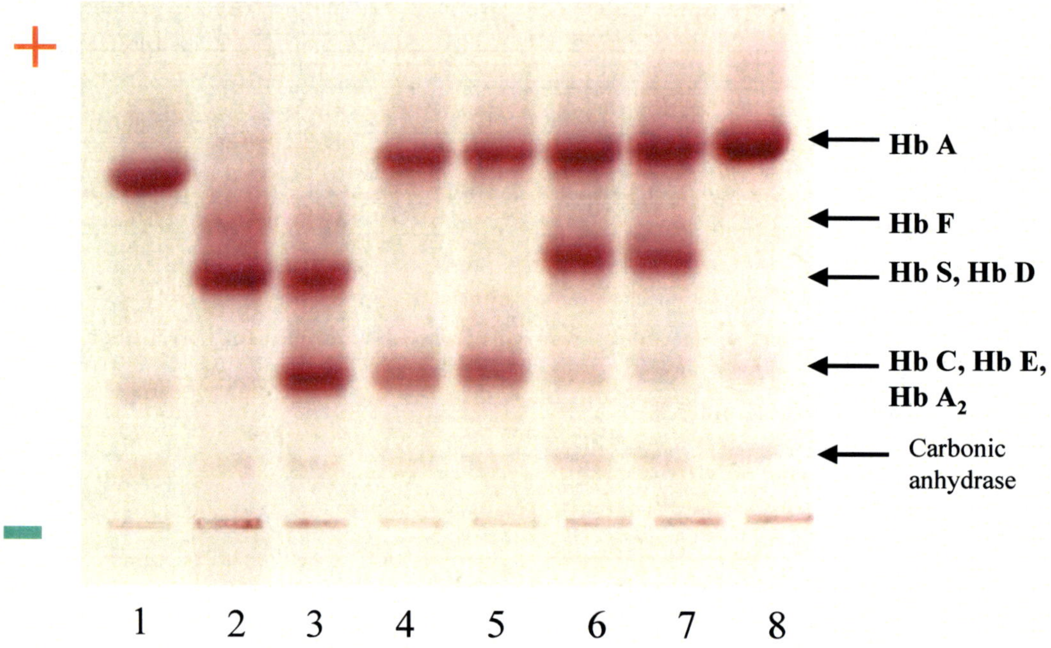

Figure 2: Cellulose acetate electrophoresis. In this technique it is difficult to distinguish Hb S from Hb D-Punjab, and Hb C from Hb E, both migrating at the position of Hb A_2. (1) β thalassemia trait with increased level of Hb A_2; (2) Hb S/ Hb D-Punjab; (3) Hb S/Hb C; (4) Hb A/ Hb E; (5) Hb A/Hb C; (6) Hb A/ Hb D-Punjab; (7) Hb A/Hb S; (8) normal control

The poor resolution between variants having an identical charge is one of the reasons why, in our opinion, CAE should no longer be used for Hb screening. IEF in agarose (or polyacrylamide) gel should be selected instead, despite that this technique being more labor-intensive and time-consuming that the previous one. In IEF, a pH gradient is established by carrier ampholytes submitted to an electric current with the Hb molecule migrating across this gradient until it reaches the position where its net charge is zero (isoelectric point). It will then concentrate in a sharp band. Variants having isoelectric points differing by a 0.05 pH unit are discriminated by in this method. Two mutants with identical global electric charges, but which display some three dimensional differences leading to slight modifications in the exposure of charged groups, may thus be distinguished [9-11]. Through this technique, Hb D-Punjab is separated from Hb S, and Hb C from Hb E as observed in figure 3.

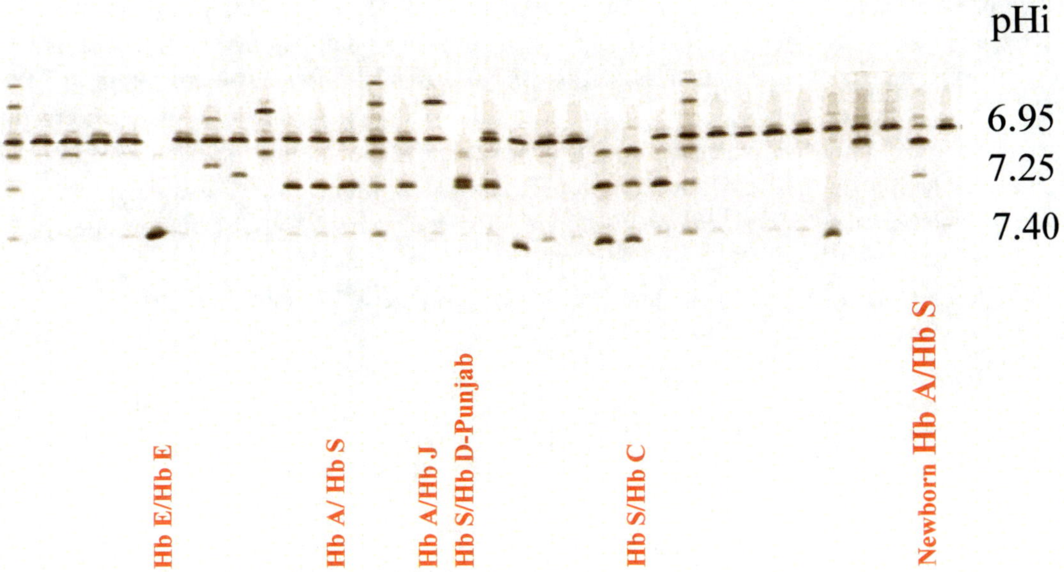

Figure 3: Isoelectric focusing on an agarose gel plate. In this system Hb S separates from Hb D-Punjab and Hb E migrates at the position of Hb A_2 while Hb C is below.

Another reason to use IEF as the initial step for the characterization of Hb variants is the facility offered by this method to handle simultaneously and comparatively a large number of samples. As an example, in neonatal screening for sickle cell disease or for epidemiological studies, up to 90 samples may be analyzed on a single plate and, in a single glance, any abnormal line will be easily recognized.

In the case of a patient who has only Hb S as major Hb component, IEF will not be able to prove if he is really homozygous for this Hb or if he is compound heterozygous for Hb S and a β^0 thalassemia. A familial study and a hematological determination of the RBC indices are always necessary and additional molecular biology investigations may be required.

It also needs to be mentioned that neither electrophoresis nor IEF allow an accurate determination of the percentage of Hb fractions when they are expressed below 10%. In these electrophoretic methods the measurements have to be performed by densitometric scanning which has poor precision and accuracy, especially for fractions such as HbF and HbA_2 or the adult Hbs in a sample from a newborn.

Citrate Agar Electrophoresis

This method was introduced for Hb study some forty years ago [12]. It is not sensitive primarily to the charge of the mutated residue, but to structural modifications of positively charged regions of the Hb molecule interacting with the agaropectin contained in the gel [13]. These regions are usually those interacting physiologically with anions. Position β6; where the structural abnormality of Hb S or Hb C are located; is close to one of these regions and leads therefore to highly specific profiles when modified. Agar plates are available from several manufacturers (Helena Laboratories, Beaumont, TX) or may be home made. In the

Paragon kit (Beckman), maleate buffer is used instead of citrate buffer. In this type of electrophoresis, a good reproducibility may be difficult to obtain from one run to another. Several experimental factors, such as slight differences in the ionic strength or pH of the electrophoretic buffer, may be responsible for this. Defects in reproducibility may also result from storage conditions of the agar plate, or of variation in the volume and Hb concentration of the sample applied. The amount of agaropectin present in the gel may also vary from one batch to another; the highest amount is found in crude agar; while all the agaropectin is removed from the agarose gels used for IEF. A typical citrate agar gel electrophoresis is shown in figure 4: Hb S displays a characteristic mobility between Hb A and Hb C.

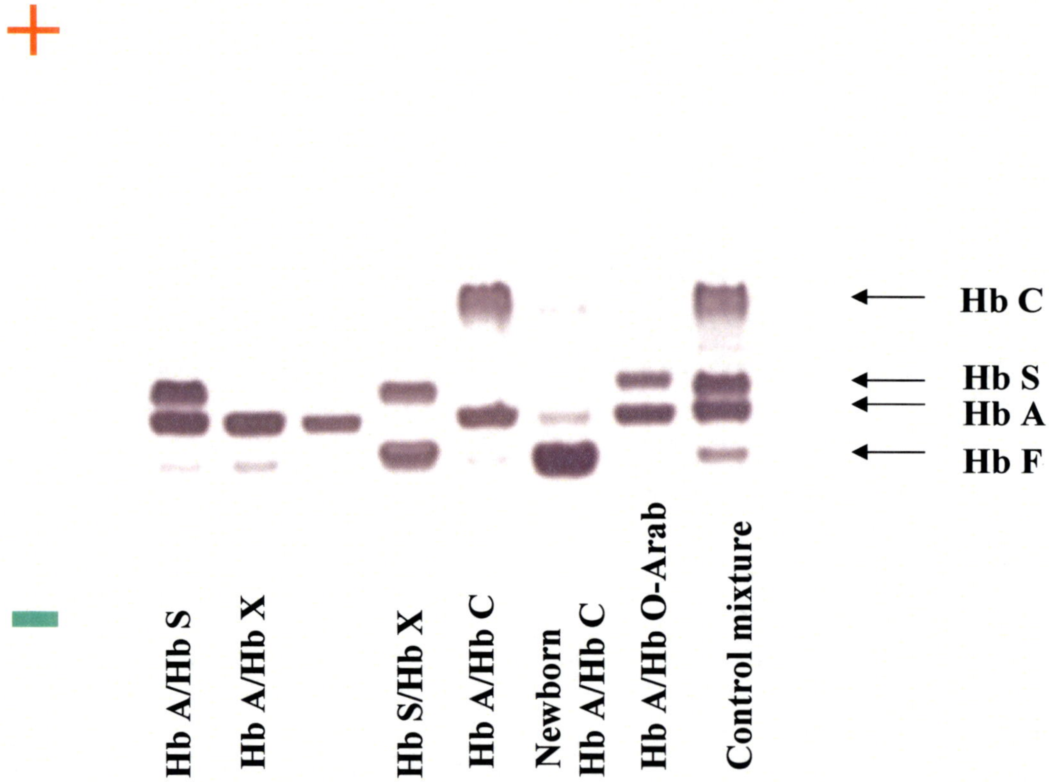

Figure 4: Electrophoresis on agar gel in citrate buffer.

Cation-Exchange HPLC Separation of HbS

Cation-exchange (CE) HPLC is considered by many laboratories as the method of choice to quantify the various normal and abnormal Hb fractions [14-16]. This is the method of reference for measuring glycated Hb for the monitoring of diabetes mellitus. It is also generally used for measurements of the levels of HbA_2, HbF and of several abnormal Hbs. According to some authors, this method could replace electrophoretic techniques in the primary screening of Hbs of clinical significance such as Hb S. Automated apparatus, such as the Bio-Rad Variant Hemoglobin Testing System (Bio-Rad Laboratories, Hercules, CA) have been developed for large series measurements. This apparatus uses double wavelength detection (415 and 690 nm) and an elution program named "β Thalassemia Short", which, in 5-6 minutes, determines an area percentage for Hb A_2 and Hb F and provides qualitative determinations of a few abnormal hemoglobins. Presumptive identification of the most commonly occurring variants (Hb S, Hb C, Hb E, and Hb D-Punjab) is made using the retention time windows named "S-Window," "D-Window," "A_2-Window," and "C-Window," which have been specified by the manufacturer. Hb S, is nevertheless, not the only variant which elutes in the Hb S window and when a variant is observed eluting in this position; unless the Hb S is known in the proband's family; then additional tests always need to be performed to confirm the real identity of the variant. A few CE-HPLC elution patterns involving Hb S are shown in figure 5. Longer elution programs may result in an even better resolution.

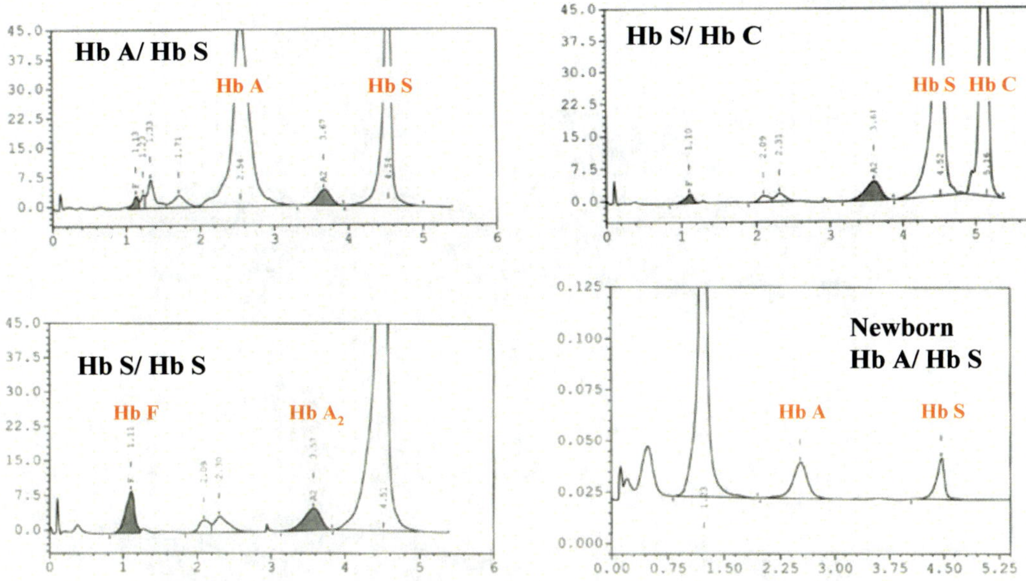

Figure 5: Cation exchange HPLC analysis using the Biorad Variant II system.

The measurement of Hb A_2, using CE-HPLC is complicated in individuals with Hb S because this fraction may be falsely increased by the presence of Hb S adducts, particularly those produced by in-vitro aging.

When a dedicated machine is not available for Hb analysis, alternative techniques may be used, which are suitable for conventional HPLC equipment. Several anion exchange and cation exchange HPLC columns may be used for Hb separation; some are silica based and others are synthetic polymers. Some of these methods have been standardized for several years [14-16]. Use of PolyCat A (Poly LC, Columbia, MD) is one of the more popular methods for Hb separations [16].

The Itano test

In 1949, before that the structural abnormality of Hb S was identified, Itano described a test characteristic of sickle cell disease [17]. This test is still used when nothing else is available. It is not able to differentiate between homozygous and heterozygous carriers and is only positive if the amount of Hb S in the cell is sufficient to induce sickling. In this test a drop of blood is sealed between a cover slip and a microscope slide and the decline in oxygen tension due to oxidative processes in the blood cells leads to transformation of discocytes into sickled cells.

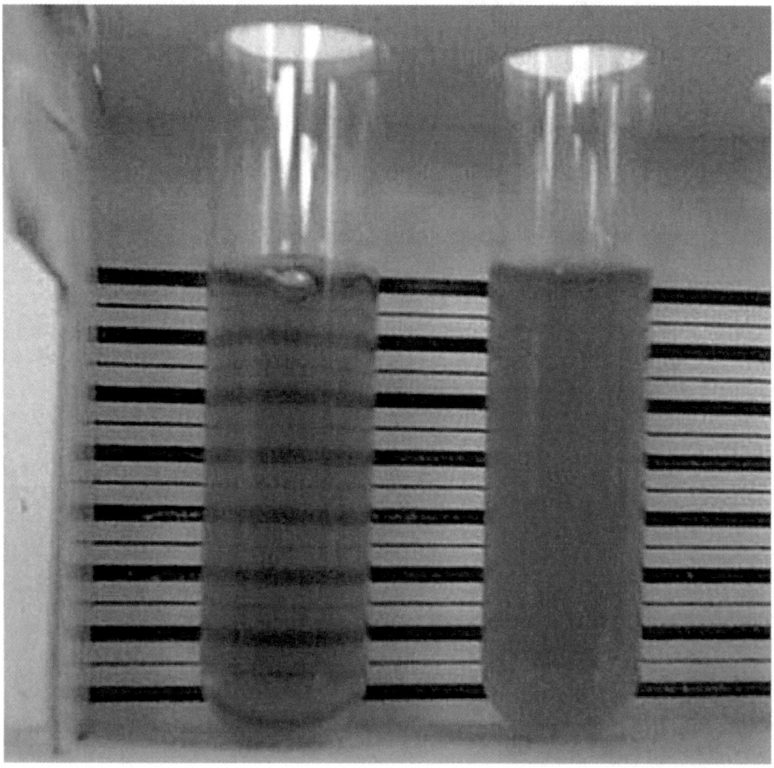

A B

Figure 6: Solubility test. In the normal sample (A) the black lines behind the tubes are visible but not (B) when Hb S precipitates.

Solubility Test

When a solution of Hb S in a concentrated phosphate buffer (2.8 M, pH 6.8), is deoxygenated by the addition of sodium hydrosulfite a heavy precipitate forms rapidly [18]. This reaction is highly specific for Hb S and is therefore one of the best tests in proving the β 6 Glu →Val mutation. This test, as well as the cellular Itano test, does not always allow for a discrimination between an homozygous and an heterozygous situation because of several factors; such as the level of Hb S and that of Hb F, interacting with the result. For this obvious reason, this test cannot be used in situations where Hb S is only present as a minor fraction, as in newborns. Figure 6 shows the result obtained in a normal control and in a patient with Hb S.

Molecular Biology Tests

Molecular biology tests using restricted nuclease enzymes may also be used for the diagnosis of Hb S on a DNA extracted from white blood cells [19]. The most classical method is PCR amplification of a fragment of DNA, containing the first exon of the β chain and digesting it with a specific restriction enzyme. The resulting fragments are then analyzed by polyacrylamide gel electrophoresis. The A→T mutation, responsible for Hb S, destroys a site specifically recognized by Dde I, Mnl I, Mst II or any of their isoschyzomers. Other methods may be used for identification of the Hb S mutation such as ARMS; in which a modified primer is employed for PCR; or a DNA hybridization with a specific probe.

A Few Pitfalls in the Diagnosis of Hb S

The possibility of falsely identifying as Hb S another slow moving Hb variant decreases considerably by multiplying the number of tests, each exploring a different property of the abnormal protein. Several mutants exist, which migrate as Hb S on IEF or CAE, or which elute as Hb S on a cation exchange HPLC. But, those, which migrate as Hb S in electrophoresis, may behave differently in chromatography. Thus, using together an electrophoretic and a chromatographic test will lead to a very high probability of diagnosis for Hb S. To ascertain this diagnosis, a solubility test or a citrate agar gel electrophoresis, which are both highly specific for Hb S, should be run. As a rule, further biochemical studies should always be performed when there is a discrepancy between the Hb pattern and the clinical or biological presentation.

It has, nevertheless, been mentioned that a few variants may mimic Hb S through several tests. One of the most striking examples is that of Hb G-Makassar; in which the substitution concerns the same residue as in Hb S; replaced in this case by an alanine [20]. Cellulose acetate, IEF or citrate agar electrophoresis patterns of Hb S and Hb G-Makassar are identical; solubility of Hb G-Makassar is also slightly decreased. Molecular biology tests are unclear since the same nucleotide is modified in both variants. The existence of a normal hematological and clinical presentation in an apparently homozygous individual should always suggest that the patient is not really homozygous for Hb S. Another variant needs, thus, to be looked for. When technically available, an electrospray mass spectrometry measurement should be performed; the molecular weight of the β globin chain may then demonstrate the presence or not of a β^S chain. The mass of the β^S chain is 15096.3 Da (versus 15126.3 Da for the β^A chain) but any other Glu→Val substitution would lead to the same mass shift. In the case of Hb G-Makassar the Glu→Ala change decreases the mass by 58 Da. Another possible way to demonstrate this mutation would be DNA sequencing. Up to now,

Hb G-Makassar has only been described in populations of S-E Asia where Hb S is very scarce, but with the mixing of populations today, cases associating these two variants have some chance to occur.

Another pitfall which is observed in neonatal screening concerns Hb Hope [β136(H14) Gly.→Asp] [21]. This variant is found in the same populations as Hb S and focuses nearly at the same position of the acetylated fetal Hb. Thus, a newborn baby, who is compound heterozygous for Hb S and Hb Hope will have no Hb A and Hb S is apparently the only adult Hb observed on the gel. A correct diagnosis will arise from CE-HPLC showing a peak of Hb Hope eluting, with the Bio-Rad Variant, in the P2 window, which is very close to Hb F. Confirmation of the diagnosis requires a family study.

FACTORS MODIFYING THE PRESENTATION OF SICKLE CELL DISEASE

Hb F

The level of Hb F is among the more important factors for the prognosis of a patient with sickle cell anemia. It has been established that a level of Hb F above 10%, partly inhibits the sickling process by interfering with the Hb S polymerization. An increase of Hb F is one of the rationals of treatment with hydroxyurea.

This Hb is not equally distributed among the RBC but is restricted to a subpopulation of cells, called "F-cells" [22], which derive by differential survival from F-reticulocytes. In a sickle cell patient the mean RBC life span is 20 days, compared to 120 for a normal subject, with there being large differences between these cells according to the amount of Hb F they contain.

Several methods may be used to determine the level of Hb F; the two most popular being resistance to alkali denaturation (RAD) and cation exchange HPLC.

Historically, the first method used was the measurement of the percentage of Hb resistant to alkali denaturation as described by Singer et al. [23]. This technique was later on modified by Betke et al. [24] by Pembrey et al. [25] and is well codified [26]. This is a reliable, easy to perform method, which has an acceptable accuracy and reproducibility in the clinically relevant range (1 to 12%) of Hb F [27]. Measurements of Hb F levels by RAD is based on the observation that there is a difference between Hb A and Hb F in susceptibility to alkali denaturation. As suggested by Perutz [28], this effect results from a difference between Hb A and Hb F in the number of groups localized in the $\alpha_1\beta_1$ contact that could be ionized around pH =12.

In the method of Betke, the Hb is first converted into cyanmetHb to avoid, in some patients (smokers), erroneous values due to presence of HbCO, which is more resistant to alkali denaturation than oxyHb. Two minutes after the reaction with NaOH 1.2N, the denaturation process is stopped by adding a saturated solution of ammonium sulfate. This reagent stops denaturation by lowering the pH and, simultaneously precipitates the denatured Hbs. After filtration or centrifugation, the soluble HbF is measured at 419 or 540 nm. The level of Hb F is expressed as the percentage of alkali resistant Hb on total Hb. This technique is accurate for Hb F levels in the range between 1 and 12 %. The kinetics and the stoechiometry of the reaction must be carefully controlled since kinetic studies of Hb A and Hb F have shown that Hb A is fully precipitated in 2 min. while only 10% of Hb F is precipitated during this time. This method is therefore very sensitive to very small variations in the experimental procedures and lead always to about a 10% underestimation of the Hb F levels. Such a technique is therefore difficult to use for a large series of samples and is now largely replaced by cation exchange HPLC, using apparatus such as the Bio-Rad Variant Hb analyzer. Chromatography allows an accurate measurement of levels of Hb F as low as 0.5% and, unlike the RAD tests, has no upper limits. It should be pointed out that RAD measures together both the Hb F and its acetylated fraction, while chromatographic methods usually only measures the Hb F, since Hb F_{Ac} is eluted as a distinct peak. The percentage of Hb F_{Ac} corresponds to 8% of total Hb F.

Hb F is a mixture of two molecular species ($\alpha_2{}^G\gamma_2$ and $\alpha_2{}^A\gamma_2$) which differ by having at position 136 of their γ-chains either a glycine or an alanine, encoded by the $^G\gamma$ and $^A\gamma$ gene, respectively [29]. During the switch from the fetal to the adult Hb pattern there is a quantitative change in the γ-chain composition. The $^G\gamma$: $^A\gamma$ globin ratio normally 70:30 at the time of birth, when Hb F is the major component, is usually 40:60 in the trace amounts of Hb F which remain in the adult. Determination of the $^G\gamma$: $^A\gamma$ globin ratio is of interest in several circumstances such as molecular characterization of hereditary persistence of fetal Hb (HPFH), haplotype linked Hb F composition in thalassemias, control of the expression of HbF in sickle cell disease or during therapeutic trials (hydroxyurea, arginine butyrate etc.) stimulating Hb F synthesis [30]. Reversed phase HPLC is one of the methods of choice for the measurement of the $^G\gamma$: $^A\gamma$ globin ratio. Several techniques using different columns and elution programs have been described [31-32].

β Gene Cluster Haplotypes

From genetic and epidemiological studies it appears that the sickle mutation emerged independently in at least five populations. This is supported by the observation that, in each of these populations, carriers of Hb S have a few functionally neutral mutations, which are in disequilibrium linkage, both between them and with the pathological mutation [33-34]. These mutations are located within the non-translated regions of the β gene cluster and are specifically recognized by a few restriction enzymes; they are indicated as "-" when not cleaved and by "+" when cleaved. The specific association of these neutral mutations is named haplotype. Thus, the Hb S mutation is found in five major haplotypes, which correspond to populations from Senegal, Benin and Cameroon in West Africa, Bantou speaking peoples in Central Africa, and Arabo-Indians (Fig. 7). Besides these major haplotypes, numerous "atypical" haplotypes have been observed which may result from recombinations between the previous ones. According to several studies, haplotypes may have some prognosis value since some of those are in disequilibrium linkage with factors controlling the expression of Hb F. For example, the Senegalese and Arabo-Indian haplotypes are frequently linked to an increased expression of Hb F, and always with a dominant expression of the $^G\gamma$ chain. In contrast, the Cameroon haplotype is in linkage disequilibrium with a polymorphism of the $^A\gamma$ chain, which consists in the presence of a Thr instead of an Ile at position γ75 ($^{A}\gamma^{T}$). It is also linked to a 4nt deletion, which likely is responsible for the low level of expression of the γ genes carried by this chromosome [35]. RP-HPLC elution patterns of the γ globin chains, typical of the different haplotypes, are shown in figure 8.

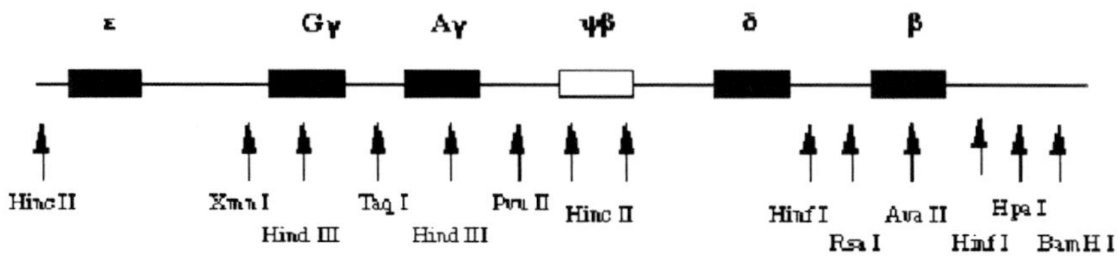

Haplotypes Hb S	HincII	XmnI	HindIII	TaqI	HindIII	PvuII	HincII	HincII	HinfI	RsaI	AvaII	HinfI	HpaI	BamHI
Bénin	-	-	-	-	-	+	-	+	-	-	+	+	-	+
Bantou	-	-	+	+	-	+	-	-	-	+	+	+	+	+
Sénégal	-	+	+	+	-	+	+	+	+	-	+	+	+	+
Arabo-Ind	+	+	+	+	-	+	+	+	-	+	+	-	+	-
Cameroon	-	-	+	+	+	+	-	+	+	-	+	-	+	-

Figure 7: The five main β cluster haplotypes observed in patients with Hb S.

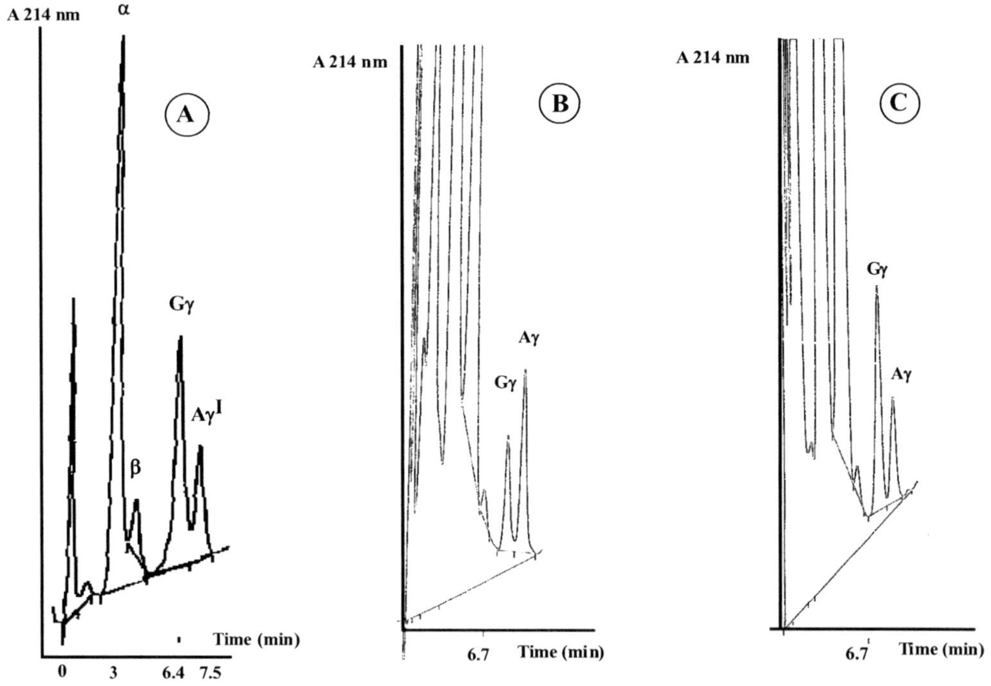

Figure 8: Reversed phase HPLC elution pattern of the region where the γ chains are eluted. (A) normal newborn, (B) sickle cell patient with an "adult" expression of Hb F, (C) sickle cell patient with a Senegalese haplotype and a fetal mode of expression of Hb F.

Association with an α-Thalassemia

In African populations, the α-thalassemia due to the 3.7 kb deletion is frequent. In some regions this abnormality is found in a large percentage of the population [36-37]. This deletion results from a crossing over that affected the two α genes yielding a recombinant gene, which remains under the control of the promotor region of the α2 gene. The overall biosynthesis of the α chain is only very mildly affected in the heterozygous carrier of an $\alpha^{-3.7kb}$ gene, with an α/β biosynthetic ratio near 0.9 [38]. This mutation is, thus, perfectly well tolerated and the only abnormal features are a MCV and a MCH at the bottom or just below normal values in heterozygotes. In homozygotes the RBC indices and the biosynthetic ratio are more clearly affected.

In relation to a preferential association of α chains to normal β chains during the tetramer assembly, the percentage of Hb S is decreased in Hb A/Hb S individuals carrying α-thalassemias. Classically, when the four α genes are present, the level of Hb S is around 40%; in individuals heterozygous for an $\alpha^{-3.7kb}$ deletion it is of about 30-35%; and it falls to 25-30% for homozygous carriers.

In patients with sickle cell disease some complications have been described to occur more specifically when an α-thalassemia is associated with and this is why these defects have to be looked for.

Up until recently, the presence of an α–thalassemia was only suspected from indirect arguments; such as the red cell indices or the level of Hb S expressed in a Hb A/Hb S individual. Today molecular techniques are available [39], such as by gap-PCR which permits an easy diagnosis of this deletion as shown in figure 9.

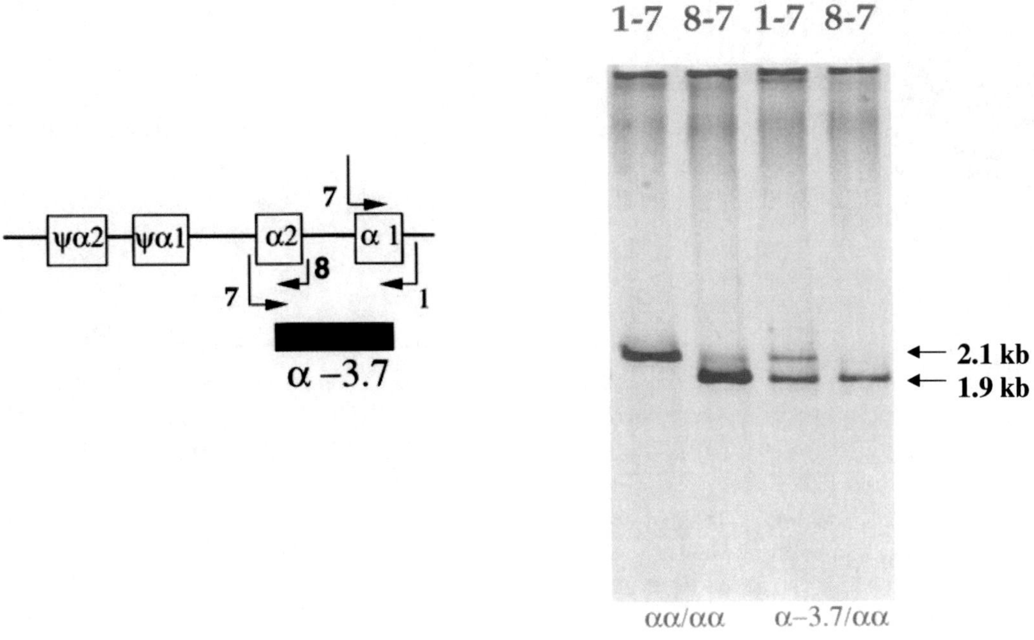

Figure 9: PCR design for identification of the fragments resulting from the $\alpha^{-3.7\ kb}$ thalassemic deletion.

CELLULAR EFFECTS

RBC Density Profile

Heterogeneity is one of the main characteristics of the RBCs of a patient with sickle cell disease. This is demonstrated by the distribution of any of the RBC indices. One of the most interesting to consider is the Hb concentration; since sickling is accompanied by dehydration of the cell; in which increasing its Hb concentration favors sickling. Cells; which have experienced several episodes of sickling became smaller than those which have not; their Hb concentration may reach 40 g/dL or even higher and these cells became irreversibly sickled. An interesting approach to this problem consists of studying the distribution of the RBC population according to the density of the cells. In a normal individual erythrocytes are distributed according to a narrow gaussian curve centered on a density of 1.096. In a sickle cell patient, the RBC population is often heterogeneous. Typically, three groups of cells are observed. The first corresponds to young cells with a density lower than normal resulting from stimulation of the erythropoiesis. On the other side of the distribution are these rigid, irreversibly sickled cells, who's density is above 1.120.

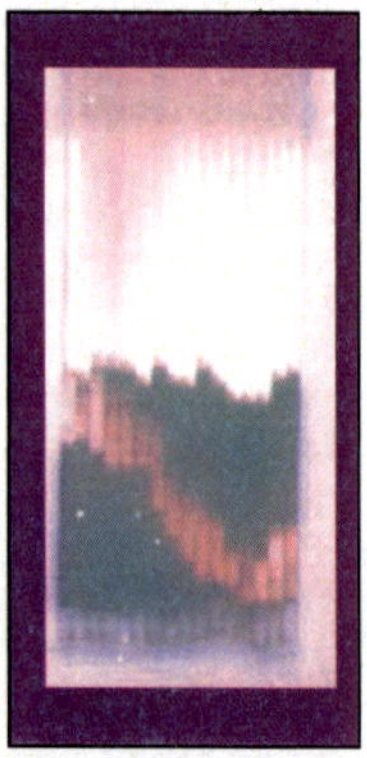

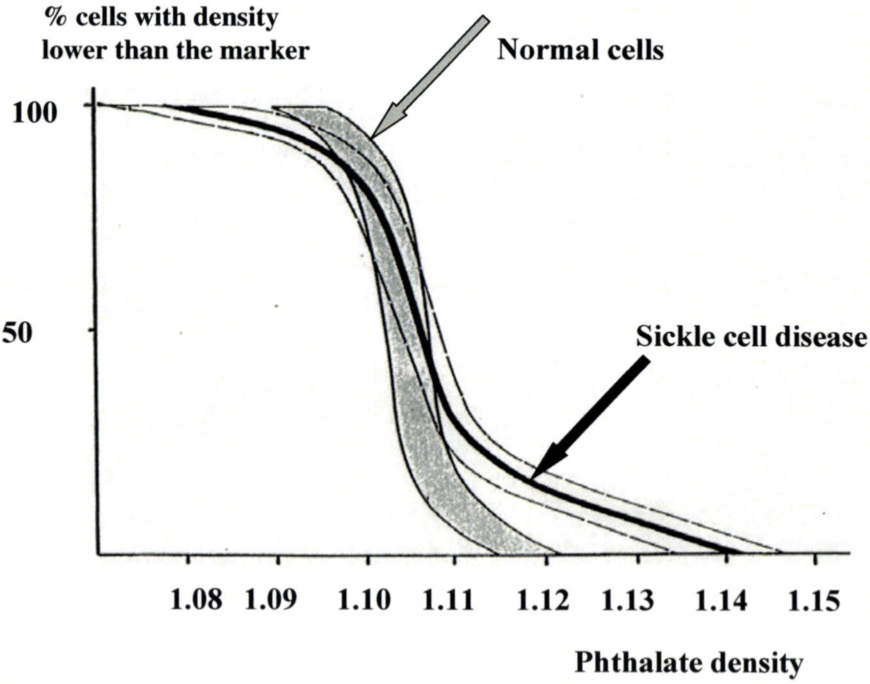

Figure 10: Phatalate density gradient. (A) microhematocrit tubes containing each a drop of phtalate marker, (B) profil obtained for a patient with sickle cell disease as compared to a normal control.

Danon and Marikovsky [40] described in 1974 a simple and practical method to study the density profile of a RBC population. By performing on the same sample a series of micro hematocrits; with in each tube a drop of a different mixture of phthalate esters as a density marker; it is possible to study the distribution of the cells according to their density. In each tube the percentage of cells having a density below that of the marker is measured (Figure 10). The presence of an α- thalassemia shifts the distribution profile towards a lower density, but much less than a β-thalassemia would do. Conversely, the cell distribution is displaced towards a higher density in an individual who is compound heterozygous for Hb S and Hb C. This profile is explained by the effect of Hb C on trans membrane ionic exchanges causing cell dehydration.

Oxygen Binding Properties of RBCs

Oxygen affinity of a RBC suspension is characterized by the P_{50}. This parameter corresponds to the partial pressure of oxygen at which the hemoglobin is half-saturated. This depends upon several factors, including the type of Hb, the temperature, the pH (Bohr effect) and the intra-cellular 2,3-DPG concentration. From the experimental plot of the HbO_2 percentage versus pO_2, the interaction between heme groups; known as the Hill coefficient or n_{50}; may be obtained. Several methods are available to study the oxygen binding properties; the most convenient is a continuous recording method using the Hemox Analyzer [41]. Pure Hb S has the same binding properties as Hb A, and a Hb A/ Hb S subject does not differ from a normal control. But because of anemia and increased 2,3-DPG concentration, the oxygen affinity of the RBC of a patient with sickle cell disease is decreased.

In addition, in a RBC suspension of a patient homozygous for sickle cell disease, the polymerization of Hb S modifies some properties. The main abnormal feature is a hysteresis of the oxygen equilibrium curve between the deoxygenation and the reoxygenation curves. In the reoxygenation experiment the amount of polymerized Hb at the beginning of the recording is larger than in the deoxygenation curve, which results in a further shift to the right of the curve [3, 41]. Further evidence of the presence of these polymers was observed in the cooperativity profiles which show the variation of "n" according to the level of oxygen saturation: for homozygous SS red cells, an increased n_{MAX} value is observed, which can be higher than the theoretical limit for normal Hb cooperative behavior (n_{MAX}=3), indicating that an aggregation process is present during oxygen binding.

SYMPTOMATIC HETEROZYGOUS PATIENTS

The general rule for a heterozygous Hb A/ Hb S individual is to be clinically and hematologically normal. The only consequence of this finding should be to offer genetic counseling and to recommend avoiding extreme physical conditions that may lead to oxygen desaturation of the blood.

In a few rare cases, a discrepancy exists between the result of biological tests showing an Hb A/ Hb S heterozygous state and a clinical presentation showing some typical features of sickle cell disease. In such a patient, further biochemical studies are required to demonstrate that the variant is not a mutant, carrying on the same allele the mutation of Hb S and a neutral additional one which favor polymerization as in the case of Hb S-Antilles. Usually, such a situation could be easily demonstrated by performing electrophoretic or chromatographic studies under other experimental conditions. In some cases a structural study of the Hb molecule may be required to control the abnormality. Another situation may be encountered in which the clinical presentation is that of a sickle cell disease but the electrophoretic study shows a variant with a mobility differing from that of Hb S. This has been observed in the case of Hb S-Oman [42], a very slow moving Hb in which the abnormal allele carries the mutation of Hb S and that of Hb O-Arab which enhance sickling. Usually these variants which lead to a sickle cell syndrome and have on the same gene the mutation of Hb S and an additional one will show a positive solubility test.

Other mechanisms than an additional Hb abnormality may cause such a clinical situation. We observed a case of a Hb A/ Hb S patient, who carried a severe pyruvate kinase deficiency. His intra-erythrocytic 2,3 DPG was twice the norm and, thus, the amount of deoxyHb in the cell was increased to a level favoring sickling [3].

ACKNOWLEDGMENTS

We acknowledge the important contribution of all the staff of the Hemoglobin Laboratory of the Hospital Henri Mondor (Créteil, France) in establishing the strategy here developed.

REFERENCES

[1] Nagel RL, Steinberg MH: Genetics of the β^S gene: origins, genetic epidemiology, and epistasis in sickle cell anemia. pp. 711-755. In: *Disorders of Hemoglobin*, Eds MH Steinberg, BG Forget, DR Higgs et RL Nagel, Cambridge University Press, Cambridge, GB, 2001.

[2] Monplaisir N, Merault G, Poyart C, Rhoda MD, Craescu C, Vidaud M, Galacteros F, Blouquit Y, Rosa J: Hb S Antilles ($\alpha_2 \beta_2$ 6 Glu $\rightarrow$ Val, 23 Val $\rightarrow$ Ile): A new variant with lower solubility than Hb S and producing sickle cell disease in heterozygotes. *Proc. Natl. Acad. Sci. USA* 1986, 83, 9363-9367.

[3] Cohen-Solal M, Prehu C, Wajcman H, Poyart C, Bardakdjian-Michau J, Kister J, Prome D, Valentin C, Bachir D, Galacteros F: A New sickle cell disease phenotype associating HbS trait, severe pyruvate kinase deficiency (PK Conakry), and an α2 globin gene variant (Hb Conakry). *Brit. J. Haematol.* 1998, 103, 950-956.

[4] Pauling L, Itano HA, Singer SJ, Wells IC: Sickle cell anemia: a molecular disease. *Science* 1949, 110, 543-548.

[5] Ingram VM: Gene mutations in human hæmoglobin: the chemical difference between normal and sickle cell hæmoglobin. *Nature* 1957, 180, 326 - 328

[6] Lehmann H, Huntsmann RG: *Man's haemoglobin*.- North Holland Publ. Co. édit. Oxford, Amsterdam, 1974.

[7] Huisman THJ, Jonxis JHP: *The Hemoglobinopathies Techniques of Identifcation, Clinical and Biochemical Analysis,* Volume 6, Marcel Dekker, Inc., New York, NY, 1977.

[8] Huisman THJ.: Introduction and review of standard methodology for the detection of hemoglobin abnormalities. In: *The Hemoglobinopathies*, edited by T.H.J., Methods in Hematology, Volume 15, page 1, Churchill Livingstone, Edinburgh, 1986.

[9] Righetti PG: *Isoelectric focusing: Theory, Methodology and Applications*, Elsevier, Amsterdam, 1983.

[10] Basset P, Beuzard Y, Garel MC, Rosa J: Isoelectric focusing of human hemoglobin: its application to screening, to the characterization of 70 variants, and to the study of modified fractions of normal hemoglobin. *Blood* 1978, 51, 971-982.

[11] Righetti PG, Gianaza E, Bianchi-Bosisio A, Cossu, G: Conventional isoelectric focusing and immobilized pH gradients for hemoglobin separation and identification. In: *The Hemoglobinopathies*, edited by T.H.J. Huisman, Methods in Hematology, Volume 15, page 47, Churchill Livingstone, Edinburgh, 1 986.

[12] Schneider RG, Barwick RC: Hemoglobin mobility in citrate agar electrophoresis. Its relationship to anion binding. *Hemoglobin* 1982, 6, 199-208

[13] Winter WP, Yodh J: Interaction of human hemoglobin and its variants with agar. *Science*. 1983, 221, 175-178.

[14] Kutlar A, Kutlar F, Wilson JB, Headlee ME, Huisman THJ: Quantitation of hemoglobin components by high-performance cation-exchange liquid chromatography: its use in diagnosis and in the assessment of cellular distribution of hemoglobin variants. *Am. J. Hematol.* 1984; 17, 39-53.

[15] Ou CN, Rognerud CL: Rapid analysis of hemoglobin variants by cation-exchange HPLC. *Clin Chem* 1993; 39:820-4.

[16] Riou J, Godart C, Hurtrel D, Mathis M, Bimet C, Bardakdjian-Michau J, Préhu C, Wajcman H, Galactéros F: Evaluation of cation-exchange high-performance liquid-chromatography for presumptive identification of hemoglobin variants. J. *Clin. Chem.* 1997, 43, 34-39.

[17] Itano HA., Pauling L: A rapid diagnostic test for sickle cell anemia, Blood, 1949; 4: 66-68.

[18] Greenberg MS, Harvey HA, Morgan C: A simple and inexpensive screening test for sickle hemoglobin. *N. Engl. J. Med.* 1972, 286, 1143.

[19] Old JM: DNA-based diagnosis of the hemoglobin disorders. pp 941-957. In: *Disorders of Hemoglobin*, Eds MH Steinberg, BG Forget, DR Higgs et RL Nagel, Cambridge University Press, Cambridge, GB, 2001.

[20] Préhu C, Godart C, Riou J, Promé D, Somchai S, Siripakorn S, Yavamal S, Wannee S, Chartchai M, Wajcman H:. Hb Makassar (β6 Glu$\rightarrow$Ala) A False Positive Diagnosis For HbS., ASH (New Orleans 1999). *Blood* 1999/ 94 suppl 1, (abst 875), 200a.

[21] Huisman THJ, Carver, MFH, Efremov GD: *A syllabus of human hemoglobin variants*, 2nd edition. The sickle cell anemia foundation. Augusta, GA, 1998. (http://globin.cse.psu.edu)

[22] Boyer SH, Belding TK, Margolet L, Noyes AN: Fetal hemoglobin restriction to a few erythrocytes (F cells) in normal human adults, *Science* 1975, 188, 361-363.

[23] Singer K, Chernoff AI, Singer L: Studies on abnormal hemoglobins. I. Their demonstration in sickle cell anemia and other hematologic disorders by means of alkali denaturation. *Blood* 1951, 6, 413-427.

[24] Betke K, Marti HR, Schlicht I: Estimation of small percentage of foetal haemoglobin. *Nature* 1959, 184, 1877-1878.

[25] Pembrey ME, McWade P, Weatherall DJ: Reliable routine estimation of small amounts of foetal haemoglobin by alkali denaturation. *J. Clin. Pathol.* 1972, 25:738-740.

[26] National Committee for Clinical Laboratory Standards. Quantitative measurement of fetal hemoglobin using the alkali denaturation method; Approved Guideline. *NCCLS publication H13-A*. Villanova, Pa.: NCCLS; 1989.

[27] Préhu C, Ducrocq R, Godart C, Riou J, Galactéros F: Determination of Hb F levels: the routine methods. *Hemoglobin* 1998, 22, 459-467.

[28] Perutz MF: Mechanism of denaturation of haemoglobin by alkali. *Nature* 1974, 247, 341-344.

[29] Schroeder WA, Huisman TH., Shelton, J.R., Shelton, J.B., Kleihauer, E.F., Dozy, A.M., and Robberson, B. Evidence for multiple structural genes for the γ chain of human fetal hemoglobin. *Proc. Natl. Acad. Sci. U. S. A.* 1968, 60, 537-544.

[30] Wajcman H, Galacteros F, Hanichi A, Yapo A, Prehu C. Hb F in the adult: could its composition discriminate normal from abnormal fetal globin gene expression? C.R. Acad. Sci. Paris, *Sciences de la vie/Life sciences* 2000, 323, 975-981.

[31] Shelton JB, Shelton JR, Schroeder WA: High-performance liquid-chromatographic separation of globin chains on a large-pore C_4 column. *J. Liq.Chromatogr.* 1984, 7, 1969-1977.

[32] Wajcman H, Ducrocq R, Riou J, Mathis M, Godart C, Préhu C, Galacteros F: Perfusion chromatography on reversed-phase column allows fast analysis of human globin chains. *Anal Biochem.* 1996, 237, 80-87.

[33] Powars DR: Beta S-gene-cluster haplotypes in sickle cell anemia. Clinical and hematologic features *Hematol Oncol Clin North Am* 1991, 5, 475-493

[34] Labie D, Pagnier J, Lapoumeroulie C, Rouabhi F, Dunda-Belkhodja O, Chardin P, Beldjord C, Wajcman H, Fabry ME, Nagel RL: Common haplotype dependency of high $^{G}\gamma$ globin gene expression and high F levels in β thalassemia and sickle cell anemia patients. *Proc. Natl. Acad. Sci. USA* 1985, 82, 2111-2114.

[35] Beldjord C, Ducrocq R, Nadifi S, Lapoumeroulie C, Elion J, Labie D: A haplotype-linked four base pair deletion upstream of the $^{A}\gamma$ globin gene coincides with decreased gene expression, *Hum. Genet.* 1992, 89, 625-628.

[36] Higgs DR, Aldridge BE, Lamb J: The interaction of α-thalassemia and homozygous sickle cell disease. *New Engl J Med* 1982, 306, 1441-1446.

[37] Segbena AY, Prehu C, Wajcman H, Bardakdjian-Michau J, Messie K, Feteke L, Vovor A, David M, Feingold J, Galacteros F: Hemoglobins in Togolese newborns: Hb S, Hb C, Hb Bart's, and alpha-globin gene status. *Am J Hematol.* 1998, 59, 208-13.

[38] Bowden DK, Hill AV, Higgs DR, Oppenheimer SJ, Weatherall DJ, Clegg JB: Different hematologic phenotypes are associated with the leftward (-alpha 4.2) and rightward (-alpha 3.7) alpha+-thalassemia deletions. *J Clin Invest.* 1987, 79, 39-43.

[39] Dode C, Krishnamoorthy R, Lamb J, Rochette J: Rapid analysis of $\alpha^{-3.7}$and $\alpha^{anti3.7}$ triplication by enzymatic amplification analysis. *Br J Haematol* 1992, 82, 105-111.

[40] Danon D, Marikowsky Y: Determination of density distribution of red cell population. *J. Lab. Clin. Med.* 1974, 64, 668-674.

[41] Kister J, Wajcman H: Oxygen Equilibrium Measurements of Human Red Blood Cells. In *Hemoglobin Disorders, Molecular Methods and Protocols* Ed.Nagel, R.L. Humana Press, Series: Methods in Molecular Medicine vol. 82 Totowa, NJ USA, 2003, pp 49-64

[42] Nagel RL, Daar S, Romero JR, Suzuka SM, Gravell D, Bouhassira E, Schwartz RS, Fabry ME, Krishnamoorthy R: HbS-Oman heterozygote: a new dominant sickle syndrome. *Blood.* 1998, 92:4375-4382.

In: Focus on Sickle Cell Research
Editor: Ralph L. Plasmar, pp. 157-166
ISBN 1-59033-920-7

Chapter XI

RENAL MEDULLARY CARCINOMA: THE SEVENTH SICKLE CELL NEPHROPATHY

*Ali Nawaz Khan**
Department of Diagnostic Imaging
North Manchester General Hospital, Crumpsall, Manchester M86RB UK

Many renal abnormalities are known to occur in association with sickle cell anemia and the related hemoglobinopathies. The abnormalities reported include impaired ability to concentrate urine, defects in urinary acidification and potassium excretion, and supranormal proximal tubular function. An extremely aggressive malignant epithelial neoplasm of the kidney in association with a sickle cell trait has recently been described and named renal medullary carcinoma (RMC). These tumors predominantly affect young patients of African descent with sickle cell trait. The tumor carries a poor prognosis and all patients reported so far have been metastatic at surgery. Surgery, radiotherapy and chemotherapy do not appear to alter the course of the disease. The survival time is very short. Presentation is usually with haematuria, abdominal pain and weight loss. Fifty-five patients have been reported from the USA, the majority being African/Americans. The reports have mostly appeared in pathology journals. Imaging plays an important role in the diagnosis of renal neoplasms. On review of the imaging findings reported in the radiological journals, it becomes apparent that it is possible for a radiologist to suggest a specific diagnosis in the appropriate demographic and clinical setting. It is expected that a high index of suspicion in the appropriate clinical setting may lead to earlier diagnosis, treatment and survival of patients. We describe a patient with renal medullary carcinoma on whom the full range of imaging was undertaken in RMC.

* Correspondence: Dr. Ali Nawaz Khan, FRCS, FRCP, FRCR Consultant Radiologist, Department of diagnostic imaging, North Manchester General Hospital, Crumpsall, Manchester M86RB UK. Tel. 44 161 7202270 / 720 2260, Fax. 44 161 720 2262 e-mail +

RENAL ABNORMALITIES IN SICKLE CELL DISEASE

Sickle cell disease causes microvascular occlusion, which is manifested in most organ systems. The genitourinary tract is most commonly affected, resulting in hematuria, urinary tract infection and priapism but other more serious sequelae have been identified. A variety of renal abnormalities have been reported in patients with sickle cell anemia and associated hemoglobinopathies [1-4]. There is impairment of urinary concentration and potassium excretion and defective urinary acidification. The proximal tubules are in a condition of "overdrive", with increased sodium and phosphorus reabsorption and greater creatinine and uric acid secretion perhaps owing to a compensatory mechanism. Mild tubular acidosis may be present. Hematuria commonly occurs as a consequence of red blood cell sickling in the renal medulla and papillary necrosis. Nephropathy in patients with sickle cell disease can be manifested by proteinuria and, more rarely, nephrotic syndrome. Chronic renal failure, although not common, may ensue. The "hyperfunctioning" proximal tubules manifests by increased secretion of creatinine and by reabsorption of phosphorus and beta(2)-microglobulin. Young patients with sickle cell disease (SCD) have supranormal renal hemodynamics with elevations in both effective renal plasma flow and glomerular filtration rate. These parameters decrease with age as well as following the administration of prostaglandin inhibitors [2].

Hematuria is a common finding in patients with all forms of sickle cell disease and its variants as well as with sickle cell trait. In most cases the etiology of the hematuria turns out to be benign. However, there does appear to be an increased association between SCD and RMC. Therefore, those SCD patients who present with hematuria should initially undergo a thorough evaluation in order to exclude this aggressive neoplasm.

Renal function may be affected mildly or end stage renal failure may ensue. Patients with sickle cell disease are at increased risk for urinary tract infection. Priapism is a painful complication of sickle cell disease and challenging to treat and prevent. Testicular infarction has also been noted. Heightened awareness of the genitourinary complications of sickle cell disease may prevent end stage disease, including renal failure and impotence.

Proteinuria, hypertension, and increasing anemia predict end-stage renal disease. While end-stage renal disease can be managed by dialysis and/or renal transplantation, there may be an increased rate of complications in renal transplant recipients with SCD [2]. Papillary necrosis may occur due to medullary ischemia and infarction. Erythropoietin levels are usually lower than expected for their degree of anemia and decrease further as renal function deteriorates. An abnormal balance of renal prostaglandins may be responsible for some of the changes in sickle cell nephropathy. Acute renal failure is a component of the acute multiorgan failure syndrome. End stage renal failure may be slowed by adequate control of hypertension and proteinuria. However, the prevention of the renal complications of SCD will require a cure for this genetic disorder.

RMC is an unusual highly aggressive renal tumor recently classified as a distinct clinopathologic entity [5]. In 1995 Davis et al. from the Armed Forces Institute of Pathology, United States, described this hitherto unrecognised renal pelvic tumour, proposing the term renal medullary carcinoma. Their study was based on a 22-year review of 34 patients with an extremely aggressive tumour of the renal pelvis of these 32 were associated with sickle cell trait (SCT) and one with haemoglobin SC disease [5]. Where race was documented, they were all African-Americans aged between 11-39 years. Between the ages of 11-24 years, males predominated by 3:1, while beyond the age of 24 there was no gender predilection. Consequently issues have been raised that RMC has a genetic basis [5, 6]. Davis et al. postulated that there might be a link between renal papillary necrosis commonly seen in sickle cell patient group and RMC, with the likely origin of the tumor within the calyceal epithelium of the renal papilla. Davis et al. [5] called the tumour "the seventh sickle cell nephropathy" an addition to those described by Berman in 1974 i.e. gross haematuria, papillary necrosis, nephrotic syndrome, renal infarction, inability to concentrate urine and susceptibility to bacterial infections [1].

The diagnosis and management of sickle cell disease have advanced rapidly with a significant increase in the life expectancy of affected patients and recognition of a greater number of genitourinary complications. New forms of therapy for sickle cell disease, such as hydroxyurea, may prevent these complications in the future [3].

Renal Medullary Carcinoma

The primary tumour is located within the renal pelvis with satellite tumours within the renal cortex and renal pelvic soft tissues. All reported patients show extensive vascular and lymph node invasion at presentation. The mean survival after surgery was 15 weeks [5]. The most common presenting symptoms are gross hematuria, flank pain, and weight loss. At the time of diagnosis, approximately two-thirds of the patients already have metastatic disease to lymph nodes, adrenal, peritoneum, retroperitoneum, and in some case, to the liver and lungs and bones. Available follow-up data reveal a dismal prognosis. All patients died of disease with a mean interval of 15 weeks [5].

To date 56 patients with RMC have been reported in the medical literature [5-32]. All but three [18, 23, 25] were Americans, and 51 of the 53 were African-Americans. All but two were sickle trait positive. There have been only two white patients, one 31-year old woman and the other a 13-year old girl, both sickle cell negative [5, 10]. The presenting symptoms are usually haematuria, abdominal pain and weight loss. The occurrence of unilateral gross haematuria is a well-known complication of sickle cell trait [33]. Curiously it occurs in the same age group as RMC (i.e15-39) years. For reasons unknown, spontaneous bleeding is said to occur in the majority of patients from the left kidney. Seventy per cent of reported RMC cases however have occurred on the right. It is apparent that RMC should be included in the differential diagnosis of haematuria in patients with SCT.

Pathology of RMC

On naked eye examination RMC characteristically shows a predominant tumor mass occupying the renal medulla. Previously these tumors were classed as variants of renal pelvic carcinomas as the microscopic features of the tumor are consistent with a poorly differentiated carcinoma, closely mimicking carcinomas arising from transitional epithelium. Some of these tumors were thought to be Bellini duct carcinomas. However, the only feature that RMC shares with Bellini duct carcinoma are its medullary location the microscopic features of these tumors are otherwise quite distinct. Sickled erythrocytes can be readily demonstrated in tissue sections. The architecture of the tumor is variable including gland-like areas with intra- and extracytoplasmic material resembling mucin with hematoxylin and eosin stain. The tumor cells frequently contain PAS-diastase positive intracellular mucin. The tumors are immunohistologically positive for cytokeratin, EMA, and in some cases, CEA. In this particular case, the cells also demonstrate positive staining for BER-EP4, and weak reaction with S-100. They are negative for B72.3, QBEND, vimentin, actin, desmin, placental alkaline phosphatase, AFP, and HCG. The material is negative with periodic acid-Schiff and mucicarmine stains, and may stain only weakly with Alcian Blue, and be positive using antibodies against peanut agglutinin. Tumor cells stain positively with antibodies to epithelial membrane antigen, cytokeratin, vimentin, and Ulex europaeus lectin. The luminal face of tumor cells stain with peanut agglutinin. Stains using antibodies against carcinoembryonic antigen and alpha-fetoprotein are negative. The ultra structure of the tumor cells is characterized by short microvilli lining the luminal surface and lateral complex infoldings of adjacent plasma membranes [34]. Sickle cell trait is present in almost all patients with renal medullary carcinoma.

Only one case with positive urine cytology for RMC has been reported. Further positive cases might be expected given the central location of the tumour in the renal pelvis [29].

Course of Disease

RMC is a highly chemotherapy-resistant tumor. Average survival after diagnosis is 15 weeks; the longest survival reported in the literature is 12 months from diagnosis.

There are a few reports of longer survival: Stahlschmidt J [22] describe a child with RMC who was treated with multiagent chemotherapy, followed by abdominal radiotherapy. The child obtained complete radiological remission following chemotherapy, although he later relapsed and died of progressive disease despite further attempts at treatment with chemotherapy. The authors suggest that although there are no previous reports of response of this tumour to chemotherapy, this case illustrate that treatment of this disease is justified.

Pirich LM, and associates [23] describe a 12-year-old boy with sickle cell trait and metastatic renal medullary carcinoma. After surgical resection of the primary tumor, he received chemotherapy with methotrexate, vinblastine, doxorubicin, and cisplatin. The carcinoma progressed after a 6-month period of stable disease. At that time, he received chemotherapy including ifosfamide, etoposide, carboplatin, and topotecan. The patient died of progressive disease 15 months from diagnosis. The patient's tumor in this report showed no progression while he was receiving methotrexate, vinblastine, doxorubicin, and cisplatin, but eventually became refractory to these and other cytotoxic agents.

Differential Diagnosis of RMC

Differential diagnosis from other centrally placed tumors. Transitional cell carcinoma (TCC) may invade the renal parenchyma and perinephric tissues but TCC is seldom as aggressive as RMC, tends to present early, and has no association with SCT. TCC and sarcomatoid or undifferentiated renal cell carcinoma may invade the renal pelvis. Renal lymphoma is characterized by multiple homogeneous masses, often with associated adenopathy [19]. Metastases to the kidney from a squamous cell carcinoma may also cause an infiltrative pattern, but the clinical setting is different [35]. Wilm's tumors and renal cell carcinomas are unusual in the 11-39 age group, moreover, their growth pattern is different in that they grow by expansion, producing well-defined tumor as compared to the infiltrative invasive growth of RMC [6, 9]. Our patient had neurofibromatosis, which to our knowledge is not associated with malignant renal tumours although NF1 is associated with genetic transmission of other tumors. Renal pelvic neurofibroma has been reported as a well-defined tumour, with a non-invasive behaviour [37]. Collecting duct carcinoma of the kidney is a rare neoplasm that arises from the medullary collecting ducts. It has an aggressive clinical course and patients usually present with metastatic disease and may closely mimic RMC by its location, histology and clinical course. Like with RMC therapeutic approaches apart from surgery have been unrewarding. Yip D et al. [36] have described a case of collecting duct carcinoma in a 61-year-old black female who exhibited the sickle cell trait. Histopathology revealed a high-grade tubular carcinoma with marked desmoplasia, adjacent dysplastic collecting ducts and positive immunohistochemical staining for high and low molecular weight cytokeratins and epithelial membrane antigen. The association of collecting duct carcinoma with sickle cell trait has not been previously reported. The authors postulate that collecting duct carcinoma and RMC may be part of the same spectrum of renal malignancies. CDC usually affects adults. It is grossly multicystic or partially cystic, the latter are not primary features of the tumour and are usually secondary to necrosis and have no association with SCT [13].

The concept of collecting duct carcinoma (CDC) as a distinct entity is now well established. They are rare neoplasms and constitute about 0.4 to 2% of renal cell carcinomas (RCC). On the cut surface, they are generally firm, white or grey and poorly circumscribed and may resemble RMC. CDC is characterized by a variety of cytological and microscopic appearances. There is often desmoplastic stromal reaction around the tumor and atypical hyperplastic changes or carcinoma in situ in the adjacent medullary collecting ducts. Histological distinction from papillary RCCs is most important, because both tumors share some structural and histochemical features, and in the past there has been confusion in the diagnostic criteria for CDCs. There have been few studies on chromosomal abnormalities of CDCs but consistent abnormalities have not been identified, a recent study using microsatellite analysis has shown a high frequency (60%) of LOH in 1q32.1-32.2. Further studies are needed to elucidate the genetic characteristics of CDCs and to determine the relationship or difference between CDCs and RMC [32, 38, 39].

In the pediatric age group RMC may also be mimicked by a variety of tumors. Wilm's tumor is distinguished by vascular invasion and displacement of structures and is bilateral in approximately 10% of cases and can be differentiated by their imaging and clinical characteristics. Nephroblastomatosis occurs most often in neonates and is characterized by multiple bilateral subcapsular masses, often associated with Wilms tumors. Clear cell sarcoma is characterised by frequent skeletal metastases, and the rhabdoid tumor is frequently associated with brain neoplasms. Renal cell carcinoma is unusual in children except in association with von Hippel-Lindau syndrome and typically occurs in the 2nd decade. Mesoblastic nephroma is solid tumor that primarily affects the neonate. Multilocular cystic renal tumor is suggested by a large mass with multiple cysts and little solid tissue. Angiomyolipoma frequently contains fat and often associated with tuberous sclerosis in the pediatric age group and the tumors may be multiple. Ossifying renal tumor of infancy is differentiated from mesoblastic nephroma by the presence of ossified elements. Metanephric adenoma lacks any specific features but is always well defined.

IMAGING OF RMC

Hemoglobin electrophoresis, intravenous pyelography, and CT should be performed in young black patients with hematuria [26].

On review of the imaging findings reported in the radiological journals, it becomes apparent that it is possible for a radiologist to suggest a specific diagnosis of RMC. The tumors generally show a diffusely echogenic heterogenous echo-texture on US. RMCs arise centrally in the kidney, exhibit infiltrative growth pattern, and invade the renal sinus. RMC has a characteristic appearance on CT scans. The tumour arises deep within the renal medulla and infiltrates the renal pelvis and sinus. The collecting system of the kidney is compressed rather than obstructed and the reniform outline of the kidney is preserved although focal hydronephrosis may occur. On contrast enhanced CT and MR images the tumor enhances poorly. In most patients there is extension of the disease into the surrounding organs and tissues often associated with lymphadenopathy at the time of diagnosis. Distant metastases to the liver and lung parenchyma are also commonly seen. Metastatic disease to bone has been reported in a few cases. Angiography depicts hypovascularity. These radiologic features, together with demographic and clinical information, may point to a specific diagnosis of renal medullary carcinoma.

A normal ultrasound and intravenous urogram have been reported in a sickle cell positive child who presented with haematuria, in whom a tumour was subsequently demonstrated on US, CT and angiography two months latter [13]. This probably reflects the rapidity of RMC growth.

CASE REPORT

We present a case of a 29 –year old man of Afro-Caribbean descent who carried a sickle cell trait and was profoundly deaf as a result of NF II. On the present occasion he was admitted to our hospital with a six-week history of abdominal pain, nausea and vomiting and weight loss. The patient was self-medicating with aspirin for pain relief. Clinical examination revealed an emaciated young man, deaf, depressed and in obvious distress. Multiple café au lait spots were noted over the body and a neurofibroma was visible and could be palpated over the dorsal surface of the left forearm. There was voluntary guarding of the abdomen but no peritonism or masses were elicited. Neurological deafness was confirmed but other systemic examination failed to reveal any abnormality. The laboratory results showed a WBC count of 9.4, (N=4-11x 10 7/L) haemoglobin 6.8 (N= 13.0-18.0 g/Dl), PCV 0.233 (N= 0.4-

0.54), MCV 60 (N=80-100fl), MCH 17.5 (N=27-32 p g) plasma viscosity 400, total protein > 110 μ mol/L (N=3-22) albumin 31 G/L (35-48), bilirubin 7 m mols (3-22) alkaline phosphatase 251(38-126), alanintransferase 2(21-72), γ GT 150 (N= up to 72) LDH 652 (N= up to 620) and IgG 43.7 (N= 6.8 – 17.0). Hemoglobin electrophoresis confirmed the presence of a sickle cell trait. A chest x-ray showed an elevated left hemidiaphragm but no other abnormality while a plain abdominal radiograph gave a vague impression of a soft tissue mass in the left hypochondrium. Ultrasonography revealed a 13 cm heterogeneous left renal mass centrally located within the renal pelvis, which was growing outwards towards the renal cortex involving most of the renal tissue. There was associated focal hydronephrosis at the upper and lower poles of the kidney. Color Doppler interrogation of the left renal pedicle showed a normal left renal vascular pedicle, a patent inferior vena cava and no flow through the renal mass. But the application of power Doppler revealed minor peritumoral vascularity. Both unenhanced and enhanced CT scans of the abdomen were obtained confirming the presence of a large solid mass, with low attenuation areas presumed to be necrotic, arising from the left renal pelvis, correlating with heterogeneous contrast enhancement. A solid lobulated mass, thought to be lymphadenopathy, was noted medial to and above the left kidney. Digital subtraction renal angiography showed a mainly large avascular left renal mass centrally placed extending outwards from the renal pelvis. A few tiny ectatic vessels surrounding the tumour were noted. The renal vein was confirmed to be patent. MRI scans were obtained, which showed a large centrally located left renal tumor that was associated with caliectasis, both at the upper and lower renal poles but not pelviectasis. MRI interrogation included T1, T2 and STIR sequences obtained in axial and coronal planes. Associated extensive necrosis and para-aortic lymphadenopathy was noted. The aorta was displaced to the right; the inferior vena cava appeared patent with no tumour extension. An isotope renogram showed a relative function L: R =19:81%. Ultrasound-guided 18-gauge needle biopsies of the renal mass were obtained, which revealed mostly necrotic tissue with a few malignant cells, which could not be typed. A left nephrectomy was performed. The tumour was seen to be infiltrating the perirenal fat, and several metastatic lymph nodes were removed. The pathological specimen was reported as showing a large kidney 16.0 x 14.0 x 11.0cm weighing 1279 grams. The overall reniform shape was preserved. On section there was large centrally placed tumour (11.5 x 11.0 x 13.0cm) involving the renal pelvis and growing outwards infiltrating the renal cortex. The lower pole of the kidney showed caliectasis. Several satellite smaller tumours were seen in the renal cortex. The tumour had penetrated the capsule. There was involvement of the vascular pedicle on naked eye examination.

Microscopically the tumour showed extensive necrosis but had a reticular, micropapillary pattern with infiltrate of polymorphonuclear leukocytes. P. A. S. stains were negative for mucin and glycogen. Satellite tumour nodules were present in the renal cortex. There was no desmoplastic reaction. The tumour involved the vascular pedicle and extrarenal lymph nodes. The microcytic hypochromic anaemia was secondary to chronic blood loss from severe gastritis (diagnosed on gastroscopy) and anaemia of chronic disease in the later stages of the disease process. The patient's macroscopic hematuria exacerbated the anaemia. The elevated plasma viscosity, protein levels and immunoglobulins were due to an acute phase response to underlying malignancy. The underlying cause for the mildly deranged liver function tests was not fully explained. There was no macroscopic evidence of liver metastases on imaging or laparotomy. However the patient was having omeprazole for gastritis and opiates, which are both known to cause deranged liver function tests. During his admission there was no deterioration in his liver function tests. The patient died 11 months after surgery. No chemotherapy was given to the patient.

CONCLUSION

All patients with sickle cell anemia and the related hemoglobinopathies presenting with hematuria should be screened thoroughly and the presence of RMC excluded. It is also important to realise that RMC can occur outside the USA. SCT occurs frequently in tropical Africa with a gene incidence of up to 40% in some tribes. It occurs in their descendants in the USA, South America and the West Indies with a gene incidence of 7% [40]. The possibility of RMC should be considered in the south Mediterranean, southern Arabia and India where SCT is prevalent. A preoperative diagnosis is possible within the present knowledge base of clinical, demographic and diagnostic imaging findings. With better understanding of RMC, it is possible that earlier diagnosis may result in more effective therapy.

REFERENCES

[1] Berman LB Sickle cell nephropathy. *JAMA* 1974; 228: 1279

[2] Ataga KI, Orringer EP. Renal abnormalities in sickle cell disease. *Am J Hematol.* 2000;63(4):205-11.

[3] Bruno D, Wigfall DR, Zimmerman SA, Rosoff PM, Wiener JS. Genitourinary complications of sickle cell disease. *J Urol.* 2001;166(3):803-11.

[4] de Santis Feltran L, de Abreu Carvalhaes JT, Sesso R. Renal complications of sickle cell disease: managing for optimal outcomes. *Paediatr Drugs.* 2002; 4(1):29-36.

[5] Davis CJ, Mostofi FK, Isabell A, et al. Renal medullary carcinoma: The seventh sickle cell nephropathy. *The American Journal of Surgical Pathology.* 1995; 19: 1-11.

[6] Davidson AJ, Choyke PL, Hartman DS, et al. Renal medullary carcinoma associated with sickle cell trait: radiologic findings. *Radiology* 1995; 195: 83-85

[7] Avery RA, Harris JE, Davis CJ JR et al. Renal medullary carcinoma: clinical and therapeutic aspects of a newly described tumor. *Cancer* 1996; 78: 128-132.

[8] Hartman DS, Davidson AJ, Davis CJ JR, et al. Infiltrative growth in the kidney revisited. CT-Sonographic-Pathologic correlation *AJR* 1988; 150: 1061-1064.

[9] Hartman DS, Davis CJ, Goldman SM, et al. Renal lymphoma: radiologic-pathologic correlation of 21 cases *Radiology* 1981; 144: 759-766.

[10] Kalyanpur A, Schwarts DS, Fields JM, et al. Renal medulla carcinoma in a white adolescent. *AJR* 1997; 169: 1037-1038.

[11] Herring JC, Schmetz MA, Digan AB, et al. Renal medullary carcinoma: a recently described highly aggressive renal tumour in young black patients. *J Urol* 1997; 157: 2246-2247.

[12] Figenshau RS, Basler JW, Ritter JH, et al. Renal medullary carcinoma. *Journal Urology* 1998; 159: 711-713.

[13] Wesche WA, Wilmas J, Khare V, et al. Renal medullary carcinoma: A potential sickle cell nephropathy of children and adolescents. *Pediatric Pathology and Laboratory Medicine.* 1998; 18: 97-113.

[14] Adsay NV, deRoux SJ, Sakr W, et al. Cancer as a marker of genetic medical disease: an unusual case of medullary carcinoma of the kidney. *Am. J Surg. Pathol.* 1998; 22: 260-264

[15] Larsen DM, Gilstad CW, Manson GW, et al. Renal medullary carcinoma: report of a case with positive urinary cytology. *Diagnostic Cytopathology* 1998; 18: 276-279.

[16] Friedrihs P, Lassen P, Canby E, et al. Renal medullary carcinoma and sickle cell trait. *Journal of Urology* 1997; 157: 1349.

[17] Swartz MA, Karth J, Schneider DT, Rodriguez R, Beckwith JB, Perlman EJ. Renal medullary carcinoma: clinical, pathologic, immunohistochemical, and genetic analysis with pathogenetic implications. *Urology*. 2002 60(6):1083-9.

[18] Khan A, Thomas N, Costello B, Jobling L, deKretser D, Broadfield E, O'Shea S. Renal medullary carcinoma: sonographic, computed tomography, magnetic resonance and angiographic findings. *Eur J Radiol.* 2000; 35(1): 1-7.

[19] Lowe LH, Isuani BH, Heller RM, Stein SM, Johnson JE, Navarro OM, Hernanz-Schulman M. Pediatric renal masses: Wilms tumor and beyond. *Radiographics*. 2000; 20(6):1585-603.

[20] Selby DM, Simon C, Foley JP, Thompson IM, Baddour RT. Renal medullary carcinoma: can early diagnosis lead to long-term survival? *J Urol.* 2000 Apr;163(4):1238.

[21] Qi J, Shen PU, Rezuke WN, Currier AA, Westfall PK, Mandavilli SR. Fine needle aspiration cytology diagnosis of renal medullary carcinoma: a case report. *Acta Cytol.* 2001; 45(5):735-9.

[22] Stahlschmidt J, Cullinane C, Roberts P, Picton SV. Renal medullary carcinoma: prolonged remission with chemotherapy, immunohistochemical characterisation and evidence of bcr/abl rearrangement. *Med Pediatr Oncol.* 1999; 33(6):551-7.

[23] Pirich LM, Chou P, Walterhouse DO. Prolonged survival of a patient with sickle cell trait and metastatic renal medullary carcinoma. *J Pediatr Hematol Oncol.* 1999 Jan-Feb; 21(1):67-9.

[24] Desai S, Kulkarni JN. Renal medullary carcinoma. *J Urol.* 1999 May; 161(5):1581.

[25] Chatelain D, de Pinieux G, Slama J, Couturier J, Le Charpentier M, Vielh P, Thirouard D, Vieillefond A. [Renal medullary carcinoma, a new clinico-pathological entity. Immunohistochemical, ultrastructural, flow cytometric and cytogenetic study of a case] *Ann Pathol.* 1999; 19(4):320-4. French.

[26] Warren KE, Gidvani-Diaz V, Duval-Arnould B. Renal medullary carcinoma in an adolescent with sickle cell trait. *Pediatrics*. 1999 Feb;103(2):E22. Review.

[27] Pickhardt PJ. Renal medullary carcinoma: an aggressive neoplasm in patients with sickle cell trait. *Abdom Imaging*. 1998;23(5):531-2.

[28] Coogan CL, McKiel CF Jr, Flanagan MJ, Bormes TP, Matkov TG. Renal medullary carcinoma in patients with sickle cell trait. *Urology*. 1998 Jun;51(6):1049-50. Review.

[29] Larson DM, Gilstad CW, Manson GW, Henry MR. Renal medullary carcinoma: report of a case with positive urinary cytology. *Diagn Cytopathol.* 1998 Apr;18(4):276-9.

[30] Bohni B. [A case from practice (203). Bilateral renal medullary carcinoma with persistent microhematuria, right-sided nephroptosis without obstruction. Status following hysterectomy for uterine myomatosis] *Schweiz Rundsch Med Prax.* 1990 Dec 11;79(50):1580-1. *German Urology.* 2002 Dec;60(6):1083-9.

[31] Hoenig JD, Husain AN, Waters BW. Pathologic quiz case: gross hematuria in a 20-year-old black woman with sickle cell trait. Renal medullary carcinoma. *Arch Pathol Lab Med.* 2002 May;126(5):627-9.

[32] Dimashkieh H, Choe J, Mutema G. Renal medullary carcinoma: a report of 2 cases and review of the literature. Arch Pathol Lab Med. 2003; 127 (3) 135-8. Review.

[33] Crone RI, Jefferson SC, Piloggi VJ et al. Gross hematurias in sickle cell trait. *Arch Intern Med.* 1957; 100: 597-603

[34] Wesche WA, Wilimas J, Khare V, Parham DM. Renal medullary carcinoma: a potential sickle cell nephropathy of children and adolescents. *Pediatr Pathol Lab Med.* 1998 Jan-Feb;18(1):97-113. Review.

[35] Mitnick JS, Bosniak MA, Rotherberg M et al. Metastatic neoplasms to the kidney studied by computed tomography and sonography *J Comput. Tomogr.*1985; 9: 43-49

[36] Yip D, Steer C, al-Nawab M, van der Walt J, Harper P. Collecting duct carcinoma of the kidney associated with the sickle cell trait. *Int J Clin Pract.* 2001 Jul-Aug;55(6):415-7.

[37] Cheong LL, Khan AN, and Bisset RAL, Sonographic features of a renal pelvic neurofibroma. *Journal Clinical Ultrasound* 1990; 18: 129-131

[38] Kuroda N, Toi M, Hiroi M, Enzan H. Review of collecting duct carcinoma with focus on clinical and pathobiological aspects. *Histol Histopathol.* 2002 17(4):1329-34. Review.

[39] Srigley JR, Eble JN. Collecting duct carcinoma of kidney. *Semin Diagn Pathol.* 1998 Feb;15(1):54-67. Review.

[40] The hemoglobinopathies. In: Reeder MM, Palmer PS, ed. *The radiology of tropical diseases.* Baltimore: Williams & Wilkins, 1981: 723-748.

In: Focus on Sickle Cell Research
Editor: Ralph L. Plasmar, pp. 167-191
ISBN 1-59033-920-7

Chapter XII

SICKLE CELL DISEASE: INTRODUCING A DISTINCT ELASTIC TISSUE DEFECT ASSOCIATED WITH INHERITED HEMOLYTIC SYNDROMES

Athanasios Aessopos and Dimitrios Farmakis
First Dept. of Medicine, University of Athens Medical School,
Laiko Hospital, Athens, Greece

ABSTRACT

The development of a diffuse elastic tissue defect, presenting a clinical and histopathological resemblance to Pseudoxanthoma Elasticum (PXE), was initially observed in sickle cell disease in late 1950s and subsequently encountered with a notable frequency in other hemoglobinopathies, including β-thalassemia and sickle thalassemia. This association is currently a well-established one and elastic tissue injury represents one of the most prevalent co-morbid abnormalities encountered in thalassemia and sickle cell disease. The clinical syndrome consists of skin, ocular and cardiovascular manifestations and is age-dependent, with a generally late clinical onset, after the second decade of life, while subclinical pathological abnormalities have been encountered even in childhood. In contrast to the inherited PXE, this defect is believed to be acquired and potentially related to the consequences of the primary disease. The clinical severity in hemoglobinopathies is variable and a number of complications, sometimes serious, have been related to the ocular and cardiovascular elastic tissue defects in these patients. The high occurrence of the hemoglobionopathy-associated PXE-like syndrome, the wide clinical spectrum of its manifestations and the severity of some of the related complications underscore the significance of a multidisciplinary approach and of an increased awareness for its early detection. On the other hand, this entity introduces a novel pathogenetic aspect of PXE and research on the field may provide new insights into the pathogenesis of elastic tissue injury.

INTRODUCTION

Over the past decades, a significant amelioration of survival has been achieved in patients with hemoglobinopathies owing to the introduction of novel therapeutic modalities, the orthologic application of traditional treatments and the systematic and multi-disciplinary follow-up of patients. The prolongation of life expectancy and the closer follow-up have brought to light new, previously unknown manifestations that have broadened the clinical spectrum of hemoglobionopathies. In this context, a set of clinical and pathology findings similar to those observed in pseudoxanthoma elasticum (PXE) has been described. [1] Sickle cell disease (SCD) was the first hemoglobinopathy to be associated with clinical manifestations that were later proved to be related to a systemic elastic tissue defect. More specifically, in 1957 Goodman noticed the presence of angioid streaks (AS) in patients with SCD and later on found that one of the first cases of PXE described in the literature concerned a negro woman with SCD. [2, 3] In 1960, Geeraets and Guerry observed a close relationship of AS and PXE skin lesions with SCD and suggested the presence of an underlying systemic elastic tissue degeneration in these patients. [4, 5] Since then, an increasing number of investigators have been involved in this field and the solid body of evidence that has already been accumulated still keeps growing. What is currently thought to be a close correlation, however, was an obscure coexistence until recently. During the last few years, systematic studies of groups of patients followed the initial sporadic observations hence establishing the correlation between inherited hemoglobin disorders and a diffuse elastic tissue defect. A thorough review of the up-to-date knowledge and the corresponding clinical implications, with a focus on the sickling syndromes, is presented in this Chapter.

PSEUDOXANTHOMA ELASTICUM: AN OVERVIEW

Pseudoxanthoma elasticum is a rare inherited disorder of connective tissue, with a prevalence ranging between 1:70,000 and 1:160,000 in the general population. [3, 6] It was first described in 1881 by Rigal and was offered this name in 1896 by Darier. [7, 8] Pseudoxanthoma elasticum is characterized by a diffuse degenerative disorders of elastic fibers. [3, 6] The elastic fibers represent an important component of the connective tissue, being responsible for its elastic properties.

The age that the inherited disorders of elastic tissue become clinically evident varies widely; the reported average age of clinical onset is 13 years. [9] As the degeneration of elastic tissue is diffuse, the phenotypic expression of PXE is quite broad, resulting from the injury of organs that are rich in elastic fibers; cutaneous, ocular and vascular manifestations are the most common. Histopathology of affected skin consists of swollen, irregularly clumped and multiply fragmented elastic fibers in the middle and deep reticular dermis, followed by secondary calcium deposition with a positive von Kossa stain. [3, 6, 10] Vascular changes involve degeneration of the elastic lamina of the arterial wall, often with calcium deposition. [11]

Skin changes appear usually during the second decade of life. [3] They develop mainly at flexural areas, such as the neck, axillae, antecubital and popliteal fossae, inguinal areas and the periumbilical region. [3, 6, 9, 10] The typical lesions are small yellowish papules or larger coalescent plaques with an appearance similar to that of plucked chicken skin. [3, 6, 10] More severe abnormalities include hanging, redundant skin folds. [9, 10] In some of the cases, a more subtle macular form develops that is difficult to be recognized and requires careful inspection. [10] Except for the skin, mucous membranes may also be affected, most often in the inner aspect of the lower lip. [9]

Angioid streaks, a fundoscopical finding, represent the typical ocular manifestations of PXE. Their presentation is variable; AS are predominantly bilateral but usually asymmetrical in the two eyes and they appear as dark-red, brownish-red or gray bands or lines, with a varying width, resembling cracks in an old painting. They lie underneath the retinal vessels, originate from a white or pinkish ring around the optic disk and extend in a radiating fashion towards the periphery. [4, 12, 13] The earliest form is known as "peau d'orange". The end stage condition includes disciform macular degeneration, helicoid peripapillary atrophy and/or diffuse choroidal sclerosis. [13] Diagnosis of AS may be confirmed by fluorescent angiography.

Angioid streaks were first described by Doyne in 1889 as a result of eye trauma and were given this name by Knapp in 1892. [14, 15] Forty years later, in 1929, Grönblad and Strandberg noticed in 3 patients the coexistence of AS with skin changes typical of those reported earlier in PXE and they proposed that AS were probably part of a systemic degeneration of elastic tissue; [16, 17] the combination of cutaneous lesions and AS was named the Grönblad-Strandberg Syndrome. A decade later, a pathology study showed that the responsible lesion was located underneath the retina in the membrane of Bruch and that AS represented ruptures of the elastic fibers in the elastic lamina of this membrane. [18, 19] Subsequently, AS were reported in association with several other systemic conditions besides PXE, including Paget's disease of the bone, Marfan's syndrome, Ehlers-Danlos syndrome and hemoglobinopathies. [12, 20-22] Nowadays, AS are considered a manifestation of a systemic disorder of connective tissue, even if such disorder cannot be identified at the time that AS are diagnosed. [12, 13] Angioid streaks along with macular hemorrhage have also been frequently noted after local trauma, as well as in association with eye inflammation or myopia. [4, 13]

In PXE, AS are present in about 80% of cases while in a large series of patients with AS, 50% also had PXE on diagnosis. [12, 13, 23] Angioid streaks may also develop in the absence of typical cutaneous lesions and may be for years the only clinical manifestation of PXE. [3, 24] They usually appear during the third or fourth decade of life, later than skin manifestations in most of the cases. [10] Angioid streaks are usually asymptomatic. The development however of subretinal neovascularisation with macular involvement, resulting in haemorrhage and scarring in the course of the disease may lead to impairment of visual acuity. [13] Light coagulation is not recommended for prevention, but may be used for the treatment of neovascularisation foci. [22] As neovascularisation tends to relapse after photocoagulation, a close follow-up is needed.

The coexistence of arterial involvement in patients with PXE was initially noticed by Plang in 1891 and subsequently by other investigators in cases with AS. [4] Following the description of the Grönblad-Strandberg syndrome in 1929, several reports of intracranial aneurysms, gastrointestinal hemorrhages and lower extremity artery calcification and occlusion in patients with this syndrome were published. [4] Vascular disorders in PXE affect mainly gastrointestinal, cerebral, coronary, renal and extremity arteries; [3, 6, 10, 24, 25] both hemorrhagic and ischemic complications have been reported. The most common manifestations include gastric, intestinal and cerebral hemorrhages, early coronary artery disease, arterial hypertension due to renal artery stenosis and intermittent claudication. [3, 6, 10, 24, 25] Manifestations may appear quite early, even in childhood; indeed, PXE-associated coronary artery disease presents typically with premature myocardial infarction in adolescents or young adults. Furthermore, restrictive cardiomyopathy has also been reported, while elastic tissue defects of the placenta have been implicated in the development of obstetrical complications seen in women with PXE. [26-32]

Reports on the inheritance of PXE had been conflicting, describing both autosomal dominant and autosomal recessive patterns; [33, 34] most of the cases however appear to be sporadic. [6] Recent studies have mapped the PXE locus to chromosome 16p13.1. [35-38] The responsible mutation is believed to affect the MRP6 gene that encodes a cellular trans-membrane protein, associated with multi-drug resistance. [39, 40] MRP6 is a member of the ABC (ATP binding cassette) transporters super-family and its specific biological function is currently unknown.

Elastic Tissue Defects in Sickle Cell Disease and Other Hemoglobinopathies

The development of AS in patient with SCD was initially noticed in 1957. [2] The remarkably high occurrence of AS encountered by subsequent studies leaded to the early establishment of an association between the two entities. The observed frequency of AS in SCD ranges widely between 1% and 22%. [41-48] Moreover, the development of AS in SCD found to be age-dependant; the average age of appearance was 25 years and the highest prevalence (22%) was reported in a group of patients older than 40 years. [42]

Goodman et al. in 1957 and Paton in 1959 were the first to notice the presence of AS in cases with SCD. [2, 49] Following these sporadic observations, Geeraets and Guerry studied systematically a series of 69 patients with SCD and found that AS were present in 5 cases (6%), aged 11 to 30 years; one of these 5 patients, aged 26 years, also had skin changes in the left side of the neck, typical of PXE. [4] The authors commented that the 6% incidence of AS in their patient group could not be coincidental, given the rarity of AS in the general population; thus, they suggested a relationship between AS and SCD. Histopathology examination of the membranes of Bruch was performed during autopsy in one of the AS-positive patients. Elastic tissue stains (Verhoeff's and orcein) showed that large areas of the membrane of Bruch were completely devoid of elastic fibers and that the Bruch's layer was separated from the basal layer of pigment epithelium in some of the sections. Iron stains performed to test the previously proposed pathogenetic role of iron in AS, proved negative for iron deposition; calcium stain (von Kossa's) could not be performed due to technical reasons. The authors also proposed a causative relationship between SCD and AS, based on the theory presented by Hagedoorn in 1939 in non-SCD patients, according to which AS result from the nutritional damage of elastic fibers in the membrane of Bruch. [19] Actually, nutrition may even be more impaired in SCD, due to the stasis and occlusion occurring in choriocapillaries and the effect of low oxygen tension. [4] Besides introducing the relationship between AS and SCD, Geeraets and Guerry were also the first to consider AS as a potential manifestation of a generalized elastic tissue disorder in SCD, commenting that the occurrence of PXE skin lesions in only one of AS-positive cases might have been higher but not clinically demonstrable. Having encountered the significantly high prevalence of 6% of AS and the coexistence of AS with skin lesions typical of the Grönblad-Strandberg syndrome in one patient, the two investigators proceeded to an autopsy study of 16 consecutive SCD patients. [5] Elastic tissue stains in two of these patients, aged 43 and 46 years, respectively, who both died in sickling crisis, revealed that the arterial wall of medium-sized arteries in multiple organs was characterized by histopathological alterations identical to those observed in PXE.

In the subsequent years, the study of AS in SCD was continued and a number of large patient series were published. The clinical and histopathological pursue of an underlying elastic tissue defect was also continued, but the initial enthusiasm of Geeraets and Guerry was treated by considerable skepticism in 1970s. In 1972, Paton reported a 1.33% incidence of AS in patients with SCD. [20] Skin biopsies performed in two of these cases proved negative for an elastic tissue defect and the author postulated that a generalized elastic tissue degeneration is highly unlikely in SCD. Condon and Sergeant described in 1976 the ocular findings in 60 Jamaican patients with homozygous sickle cell anemia aged over 40 years. [42] Angioid streaks were present in 13 of 60 patients (22%); the prevalence of AS was 27% in cases older than 45 years and 14% in cases aged 40-45 years. These data indicated a close correlation of AS with increasing age in SCD. In contrast to the impressively high occurrence of AS, clinical evidence of PXE were not found in any of the 60 patients of this group. In the same year, Napgal et al. published their clinical and histopathological observations in a large series of 356 patients with various forms of SCD. [41] The group comprised 162 patients with homozygous sickle cell anemia, 101 with sickle cell-hemoglobin C disease, 49 with sickle cell trait, 34 with sickle thalassemia, 8 with hemoglobin C trait and 2 with homozygous hemoglobin C disease. Angioid streaks were present in 5 of 356 patients (1.4%), all American negroes, aged 36 to 49 years (4 of 5 cases aged over 40 years); 3 of them had homozygous sickle cell anemia, one had sickle cell-hemoglobin C disease and one sickle thalassemia. Skin biopsies performed in all 5 AS-positive patients did not show any evidence of elastic tissue alterations. The authors suggested that the occurrence of AS in SCD ranged in general between 1% and 2% and agreed with the absence of a diffuse elastic tissue defect in SCD proposed earlier by Paton. Five years later, in 1981, Hamilton et al. reported on the ocular abnormalities in another large series of 242 Jamaican patients with homozygous sickle cell disease. [43] In this group, 21 patients (8.7%) were found to have AS. Skin biopsies in AS-positive cases proved again negative for disorders of elastic tissue.

The etiology of AS in SCD remained for many years obscure. The fact that the causative relationship between AS and a systemic degenerative disorder of elastic tissue, suggested by Geeraets and Guerry in 1960, was strongly questioned by subsequent investigators leaded to the consideration that AS were pathophysiologically related to the main disease. [21, 41, 43] In this context, different pathogenetic mechanisms were recruited to explain the association between the two entities. Vascular obstruction in the choriocapillary circulation caused by sickling was proposed early by Paton. [49] Patients with posterior cilliary vessel obstruction however was later found to lack evidence of AS. [50] According to another theory, chronic hemolysis leads to iron deposition in the membrane of Bruch, which in turn causes degeneration of the elastic fibers. [20] Neither hemochromatosis nor hemosiderosis, however, have been associated with AS. At the same time, a recent histochemical and light and electron microscopic study of two eyes in a patient with homozygous sickle cell anemia and AS demonstrated absence of iron deposition in the membrane of Bruch; in contrast, heavy calcification was present, a typical feature of PXE histopathology. [51]

In contrast to the above data, three different studies of ocular abnormalities in SCD, published in 1978, 1985 and 1994, respectively, reported absence of AS in patients with SCD. More specifically, Majekodunmi et al. studied 124 Nigerian patients with homozygous sickle cell anemia without ocular symptoms. [48] In order of frequency, ocular findings included conjunctival vessel anomalies, tortuosity of the major retinal vessels and chorioretinal scars. Angioid streaks however were not observed. In another series of 50 Nigerian cases with homozygous SCD, similar ocular abnormalities were found in 90% of cases while AS were totally absent. [47] Finally, another 50-patient series with SCD were assessed with full ocular examination, including fundus fluorescein angiography. Retinopathy was present but AS were not seen in any of the cases. [46]

The issue of a diffuse elastic tissue defect in SCD emerged for a second time in 1985 due to the two papers published by Lippman et al. The investigators started by investigating echocardiographically the occurrence of mitral valve prolapse in 57 patients with SCD, aged 10 to 59 years (mean 28 years); 46 of them had homozygous sickle cell anemia and 11 sickle cell-hemoglobin C disease. [52] Mitral valve prolapse was present in 14 of 57 patients (25%); this incidence was at least four times higher than the 5% reported in the general adult population and the 3% observed in the authors' control group, consisted of patients with chronic anemia of end-stage renal disease. According to the authors, such a high incidence of mitral valve prolapse could not be explained on the basis of chronic anemia or of any concomitant cardiac abnormality. The investigators hypothesized that a coexistent connective tissue defect is probably related to mitral valve prolapse in SCD. Indeed, it is known that mitral valve prolapse is a frequent clinical finding in patients with connective tissue disorders such as Marfan's syndrome, Ehlers-Danlos syndrome, osteogenesis imperfecta and PXE. [53-56] At the same time, histopathology studies revealed elastic tissue abnormalities in the mitral valves of patients with mitral valve prolapse undergoing mitral valve replacement. [57, 58] To test the above hypothesis, the same investigators analyzed skin biopsies taken from 32 SCD patients, 11 of whom had mitral prolapse. [59] Biopsies were taken from scapular skin areas and were examined both histopathologically and biochemically with sophisticated and computerized techniques for evaluation of elastic tissue. They found that an increased elastic fiber concentration was associated with the presence of mitral prolapse in these patients. Combining the results of the above tests, the authors concluded that a spectrum of elastic tissue disorders rather than a specific collagen defect is present in SCD and that this feature predisposes to mitral valve prolapse. However, the high incidence of mitral valve prolapse in SCD, described by Lippman et al., was later questioned. An echocardiographic-Doppler study in 40 adult patients with SCD showed that valvular structures were normal and the authors postulated that no association with a myxomatous valvular degeneration or mitral valve prolapse existed in SCD. [60]

Bearing in mind the above, it becomes clear that data regarding the presence of an elastic tissue defect in SCD had been conflicting until 1990s. At that time, the attention of investigators was attracted by elastic tissue defects occurring in another hemoglobinopathy, β-thalassemia, and this new field of research proved quite fruitful.

Following a number of isolated case reports describing the development of AS in patients with β-thalassemia, [61-63] a series of 100 patients, including 62 with thalassemia major and 38 with thalassemia intermedia, aged 14 to 62 years (mean 26 years), was investigated in 1989. [64] Angioid streaks were observed in 20 of 100 cases (20%), 9 with thalassemia major and 11 with thalassemia intermedia. All patients with AS were older than 20 years and AS were demonstrated to be positively correlated with age, as in SCD. Furthermore, the coexistence of PXE-like skin lesions with AS was noted in two patients with β-thalassemia. [65] This observation prompted the systematic investigation for PXE-like manifestations in the same 100-patient group that was previously investigated for AS. [66] In addition to the 20% occurrence of AS, 16% of patients had typical cutaneous lesions (Figure 1), confirmed by skin histopathology (Figure 2) and 26% had at least one of the two manifestations. All patients under the age of 19 years as well as 70 family members of cases with PXE-like findings had no skin or ocular lesions.

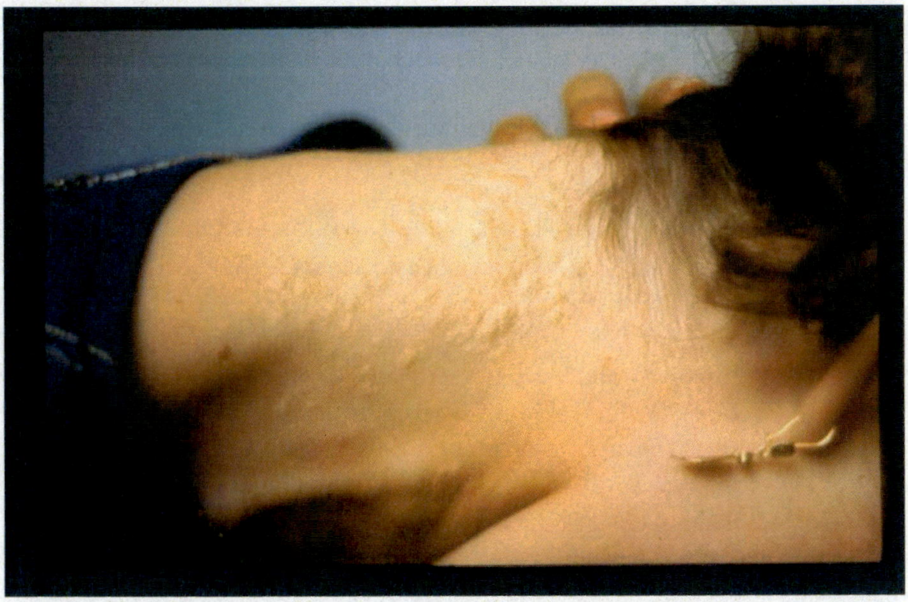

Figure 1. Typical Pseudoxanthoma Elasticum-like skin lesion on the dorsal aspect of the cervical area in a patient with thalassemia major.

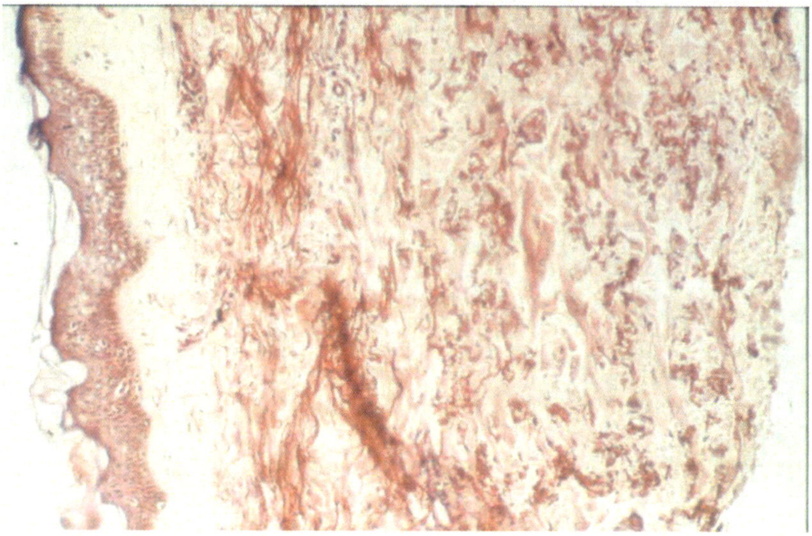

Figure 2. Histopathology of an affected skin area in a patient with thalassemia major: degeneration of elastic fibers with abnormal arrangement, swelling and fragmentation (orcein, x125).

A subsequent report of the same group of investigators focused on another typical manifestation of PXE, the arterial calcifications. Forty elderly thalassemic patients, aged over 30 years (mean 41 years), mostly with thalassemia intermedia, were studied. [11] Fifty five percent of patients - versus 15% of healthy controls - had calcification of the posterior tibial artery (Figure 3), 20% had typical skin lesions, 52% had AS while 85% had at least one of the three manifestations. Hence, the complete clinical spectrum of PXE, consisted of skin, ocular and vascular findings, has been encountered in β-thalassemia, while it is also clear that these manifestations become more frequent with advancing age.

In a latest study by Cianciulli et al., a group of 80 β-thalassemia patients, including 64 with thalassemia major and 16 with thalassemia intermedia, aged 11 to 59 years (mean 25 years) was investigated for disorders of elastic tissue. [67] Typical skin lesions, confirmed by histopathology, were present in 14 of 80 patients (17%), aged 17 to 43 years; skin changes appeared mostly during puberty and were located at the lateral neck in all patients as well as other flexular skin areas. Half of the skin-positive patients also had arterial calcifications and 14% of them AS. After a 12-year follow-up period, skin lesions had dramatically progressed in half of the patients and the same happened with AS in one of the affected cases.

The encountered occurrence of PXE-like manifestations in β-thalassemia was remarkable compared to the 1:70,000 to 1:160,000 prevalence of the syndrome in the general population, leading to the unquestionable establishment of the relationship between the two entities. As discussed earlier, such a relationship remained doubtful in the sickling syndromes until sickle thalassemia patients was systematically studied. Angioid streaks had initially been sporadically encountered in two cases. The first was observed by Goldberg et al. in a 42-year-old patient and the second by Napgal et al. in a 47-year-old American negro. [41, 44] These finding and the already established association of β-thalassemia with a PXE-like syndrome prompted the systematic investigation of a series of 58 with sickle-thalassemia patients, ranging in age from 19 to 58 years (mean 32.6 years). [68] In this study, AS were identified in 10% of cases (Figure 4), while half of the cases with AS also had typical cutaneous lesions, that were both clinically and histopathologically identical to PXE. Thus, sickle thalassemia was also related to a diffuse elastic tissue defect.

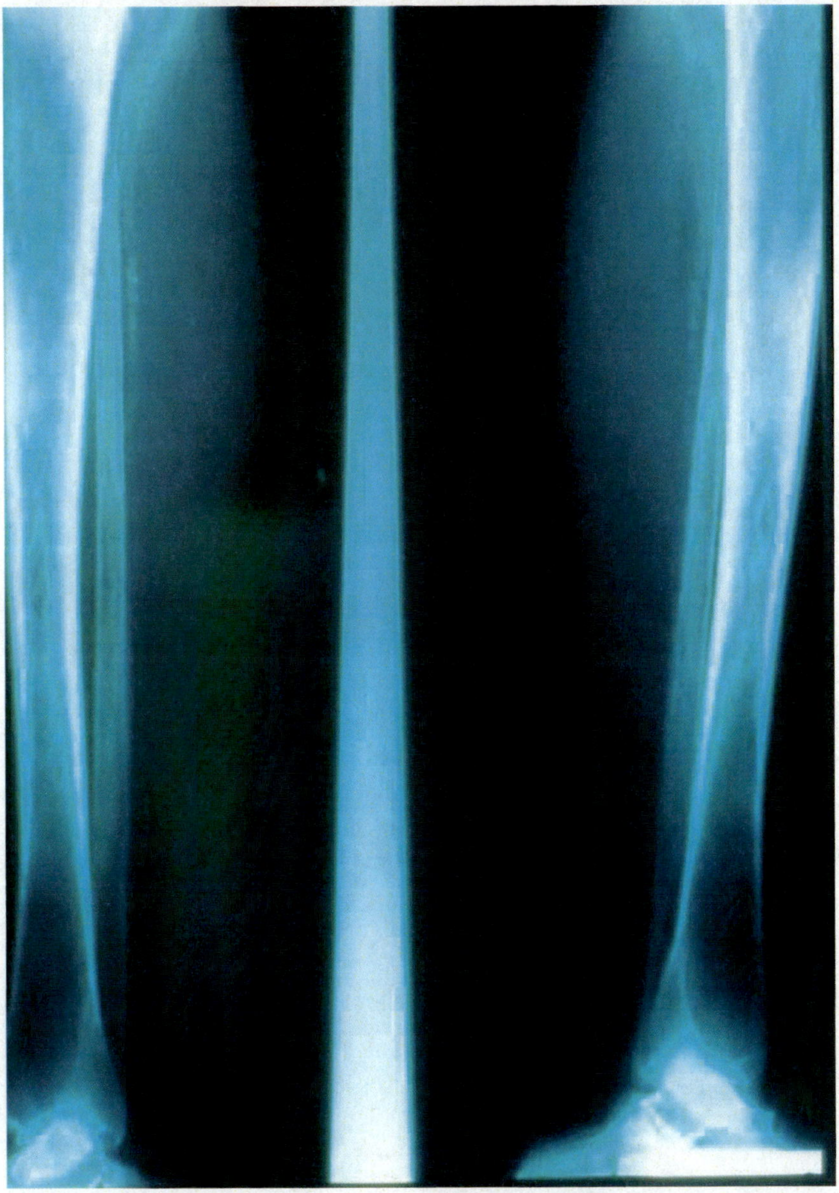

Figure 3. Tibial artery calcification in a 48-year-old patient with thalassemia intermedia.

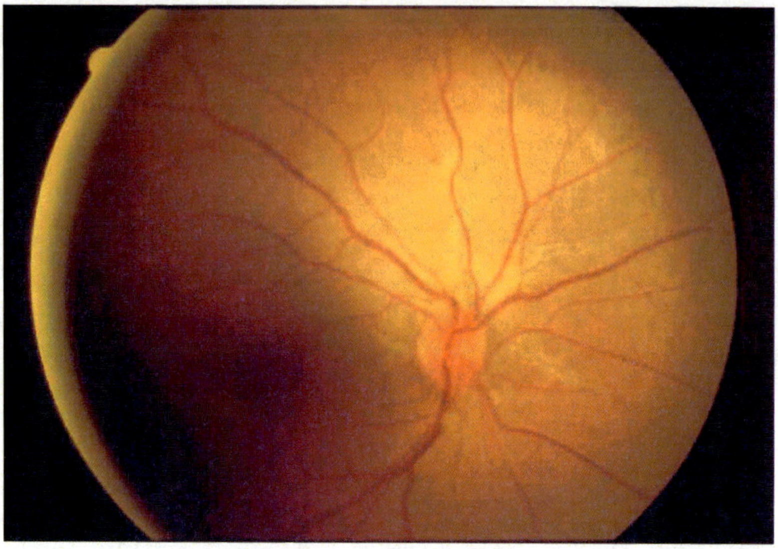

Figure 4. Angioid streaks in a 35-year-old patient with sickle thalassemia.

Besides sickle cell anemia, β-thalassemia and sickle thalassemia, it is interesting to note that AS and other PXE-like disorders have also been sporadically observed in a wide spectrum of hemoglobin and red blood cell disorders, even in the trait-carrier state of inherited hemoglobinopathies. Such findings may imply the potential presence of a diffuse elastic tissue defect in all these conditions as well. Thus, in 1965 Collomb et al. noticed the coexistence of AS along with a generalized disorder of elastic tissue in a case of sickle cell trait, introducing the term "systemic elastorrhexis" in SCD. [44] Later on, AS were also reported in another isolated case of sickle cell trait. [69] Angioid streaks have furthermore been recorded in a Greek Cypriot with hemoglobin H disease (α-thalassemia), in a case of hemoglobin C trait and another 2 cases with β-thalassemia minor. [70-73] PXE-like lesions have finally been observed in a patient with β-δ thalassemia. [74] Other conditions in which AS have been reported include hereditary spherocytosis, acanthocytosis secondary to abetalipoproteinemia and hypobetalipoproteinemia. [75]

In the recent years, an accumulation of significant data regarding elastic tissue pathology in SCD and β-thalassemia has been noted. In 1999, the morphological status of the umbilical cord in healthy, sickle cell trait and sickle cell anemia pregnancies was investigated using scanning and transmission electron microscopy. [76] Numerous alterations were seen in umbilical veins of the sickle cell anemia group, which besides endothelial and smooth muscle cell disorders also included abnormalities of the inner elastic lamina of the vessel wall. Similar vascular changes were encountered by another group of investigators who examined 17 spleens resected form SCD patients because of sequestration crises or infarction, along with 41 control samples. [77] Anomalies of arteries and veins were present in all SCD spleens but were almost absent in the control spleens. The findings included intimal proliferation of the large arteries and veins, reduplication of the internal elastic lamina of large arteries and subendothelial infiltration of the large veins by activated T cells. No correlation with age, sex, type of sickle hemoglobin or frequency of sequestration episodes could be established.

The extent of this phenomenon was impressively stressed by two very recent histopathological reports describing the presence of subclinical elastorrhexis in the vast majority of young cases with inherited hemolytic anemias. In the first of these studies, surgical splenic and liver biopsies taken from 45 patients with thalassaemia major, aged 6-25 years, were found to have typical stromal and arterial elastorrhexis in the striking occurrence of 96%. [78] Histopathological findings included fragmentation and multiple defects of the internal elastic lamina of the arteries or of the stromal elastic fibers, followed by deposits of iron and calcium salts. Motivated by these findings and bearing in mind the occurrence clinical tissue defects in other hemoglobinopathies besides β-thalassemia, the same investigators expanded their pathology study of stromal and arterial elastic tissue to include sickle thalassemia, thalassemia intermedia and hereditary spherocytosis. [79] Thus, surgical biopsy material including spleens, parasplenic lymph nodes, liver biopsies and gallbladders with regional lymph nodes, taken from 14 patients with sickle thalassaemia, 10 patients with thalassaemia intermedia and 18 with hereditary spherocytosis, were examined. Arterial elastorrhexis, similar to that revealed by the previous study in thalassaemia major, was found in up to 90% of extrasplenic and intrasplenic arteries in the entire study population. Stromal elastorrhexis was also found in the elastic tissue of spleens and parasplenic lymph nodes, in the absence of tissue iron overload. Based on their histopathology findings, the authors concluded that arterial elastorrhexis is the earliest and most frequent manifestation of a diffuse elastic tissue disorder, similar to PXE, which affects patients with inherited hemolytic anemias; this disorder appears in the first decade of life and is unrelated to various haematological parameters.

As discussed thoroughly, the clinical manifestations of the elastic tissue defect observed in sickling and thalassemic syndromes, including skin lesions, AS and vascular calcifications, are identical to those of inherited PXE. This phenotypical similarity also exists at the level of tissue pathology and cytochemistry, as showed by later data published in 2001. [80] In this study, dermal lesions were compared between β-thalassemia and inherited PXE by light and electron microscopy and by immunocytochemistry. The observed polymorphism, fragmentation and mineralization of elastic fiber as well as the abnormalities of collagen fibrils and filament aggregates were identical in both disorders. In addition, elastic fiber mineralization was associated with vitronectin, bone sialoprotein and alkaline phosphatase in both conditions. This structural identity was recently stressed by another study in patients with thalassemia major. [67] Examination of the affected skin areas with light and electron microscopy showed that the observed dermal alterations and mineralization of elastic fibres were identical to those of inherited PXE.

According to the hitherto accumulated evidence, it seems that the aforementioned skin, ocular and vascular findings in patients with hemoglobinopathies represent the evolving changes of an underlying elastic tissue disorder that develops early in life in these hereditary hemolytic disorders. In a series of 45 young patients with thalassemia major, aged 6 to 25 years, described earlier in this Chapter, although arterial elastorrhexis was present in 96% of cases, only 4 patients had clinically evident skin lesions and none had AS at the time of study. [78]

It is obvious that a systemic elastic tissue injury is present with a broad distribution in different types of inherited hemoglobinopathies. At the same time, the clinical manifestations of this disorder are characterized by a considerable variation in the different hemoglobinopathies and they can be found even in healthy heterozygotes (carrier state). Angioid streaks have extensively been studied primarily in SCD, probably because of the more prominent world-wide distribution of SCD and the frequent referral of these patients for other ocular abnormalities related to the main disease. In contrast, the occurrence of skin lesions and other PXE-like manifestations is much more striking in β-thalassemia.

PATHOGENESIS

The pathogenesis of the hemoglobinopathy-associated elastic tissue defect has not yet been clarified. The close clinical, structural and cytochemical resemblance between this entity and the inherited PXE may lead to the conclusion that the disorder is also hereditary. However, although the potential genetic link between the sickling and thalassemic syndromes and PXE has not yet been investigated, there are some indications against it. At first, the relatives of hemoglobinopathy patients and the PXE-like syndrome have not so far been found to bear any of the PXE stigmata. A study of AS in 58 patients with sickle thalassemia also included an extensive investigation of the family members of AS-positive cases; none of the 25 relatives that were examined had any PXE-like lesions. [68] Similarly, in another study of 100 patients with β-thalassemia, none of the 70 family members of cases with PXE findings had any skin or ocular lesions. [66] Cianciulli et al. also studied 13 parents and brothers of 14 patients with thalassemia major and PXE-like skin lesions; none of the relatives showed any clinical or structural findings of PXE. [67] In addition, the comparison of β-thalassemia genotypes between 30 Greek patients with PXE-like lesions and the general β-thalassemia population in Greece did not reveal any differences; this finding may imply that the PXE-like manifestations develop independently of the β-thalassemia genotype. [81] On the other hand, the MRP6 gene, some mutated forms of which are currently thought to cause PXE, is located on a different chromosome than the β-globin gene cluster, the defects of which are responsible for both the sickling and the thalassemic syndromes. [39, 82-86] MRP6 gene has been mapped to chromosome 16, while the β-globin gene cluster is located on chromosome 11. Previous PXE-candidate genes are also located on different chromosomes; elastin gene is located on chromosome 7, collagen type I gene on chromosome 17 and the same applies genes encoding for fibrillins 1 and 2, elastin-related glycoproteins and lysyl-oxidase. [39, 82-86] It is interesting to note, however, that the recently defined locus for PXE is located close to the α globin gene cluster, which is mapped to 16p13.3. [87]

In view of the above data, most of the investigators currently believe that the elastic tissue abnormalities observed in sickle cell anemia, β-thalassemia, sickle thalassemia and other hemoglobinopathies are most likely acquired, despite their resemblance to inherited PXE and the terms "PXE-like lesions" and "PXE-like syndrome" have been used to describe such abnormalities. [11, 66, 78, 81]

The term "acquired PXE" was not initially introduced in hemoglobinopathies. Indications of an acquired form of PXE can be found in the literature, but they are rather rare and obscure and therefore questionable. Trauma and renal failure have been both related to a potentially acquired PXE syndrome. Indeed, post-traumatic, localized, cutaneous lesions, lacking the generalized retinal and vascular manifestations of the inherited PXE, have been reported in a number of cases. [88-90] Similar findings encountered in patients with chronic renal failure were believed to be acquired, but this hypothesis was subsequently questioned by other investigators. [6, 91, 92]

To support the idea of an acquired elastic tissue defect that develops in association with inherited haemoglobin disorders, a number of acquired pathogenetic mechanisms have been suggested. A reasonable approach to this issue is to consider that some of the common features of these hemolytic conditions play an important pathogenetic role. A further support to this concept that AS have been reported in other hemolytic states, including inherited spherocytosis and congenital dyserythropoietic anemia type III. [93, 94] However, no statistical correlation between elastic tissue defects and variable hematological parameters has hitherto been found. The hemoglobin or serum ferritin levels, the number of blood units received or the chelation history have not been demonstrated to have a significant prognostic value for the development of elastic tissue disorders. [11, 63, 66, 78, 81, 95]

According to modern pathogenetic theories, oxidative stress is a common denominator in hemoglobinopathies and other hemolytic conditions. The destructive effect of free radicals is currently implicated in various abnormalities observed in hemoglobinopathies, such as the erythrocyte membrane defects or the tissue injury following iron overload. [96] Accordingly, it has been postulated that the elastic tissue disorders in these patients may also be the result of an oxidative process, induced by the combined and interactive effect of different factors. [11] Plasma membrane microparticles, derived from the oxidative damage of red cell membranes by the effect of denaturated hemoglobin products and free iron, [96-100] are considered to elicit inflammatory and oxidative reactions. [101] Moreover, the unbound fractions of hemoglobin and haem, which exceed the binding capacity of haptoglobin and hemopexin in the context of chronic hemolysis, also have powerful oxidative properties. [102] Particularly in sickling syndromes, an excessive free radical production follows the post-occlusive tissue reperfusion. [103] Moreover, iron overload has a central role in multiple organ injury in these hemoglobinopathies. Unbound iron catalyzes the formation of the most toxic hydroxyl radical through the Fenton and Haber-Weiss reactions, causing, in turn, peroxidation of membrane lipids and proteins. [104] The accumulated and prolonged effect of the above mechanisms may result in disturbance of elastin metabolism and structural deterioration of elastic fibers. [105] Accordingly, oxidative stress constitutes a potential acquired mechanism affecting the same trans-membrane proteins, which are genetically defective in inherited PXE. Indirect evidence of increased and prolonged tissue injury in thalassemic and sickle patients includes activation of polymorphonuclear neutrophils and monocytes and the increased levels of neutrophil elastase and circulating cytokines. [81, 101, 106-109]

COMPLICATIONS: THE CLINICAL IMPLICATIONS IN SICKLE CELL DISEASE AND OTHER HEMOGLOBINOPATHIES

The description of the relationship between inherited hemoglobinopathies and a PXE-like syndrome was followed by reports of PXE complications in patients with SCD and β-thalassemia. The association however is a recently established one and reports on elastic tissue complications have hitherto been mainly sporadic in patients with hemoglobinopathies. Since the hemoglobinopathy-associated elastic tissue defect is believed to be acquired, it is not known whether the severity of the resulting complications is similar to that of inherited PXE.

Complications in SCD result mainly from vascular occlusion, which is classically believed to be caused by sickling. It is known, on the other hand, that vascular involvement in inherited PXE is followed not only by hemorrhagic but by ischemic complications as well. Consequently, vascular elastic tissue abnormalities in patients with SCD may contribute to the development of vaso-occlusion in these patients.

Vascular Complications

The vascular system is characterized by the highest relative concentration of elastin in the body and therefore has an increased risk of complications in the context of an elastic tissue defect. [110]

Neurological complications occur generally in 18% to 29% of patients with SCD and thrombotic strokes represent a significant part of these complications. [111, 112] As stated above, the contribution of the defects of elastic laminae of cerebral arteries to the development of ischemic strokes remains an open question. Besides ischemic events, cerebral bleeding has also been encountered in these patients. In fact, subarachnoid hemorrhages, although relatively rare, is a well recognized cause of neurological manifestations and mortality in SCD, accounting for 1% to 2% of neurological complications. [111-119] In a series of 325 patients with SCD followed for 15 years, 11 cases of subarachnoid hemorrhages occurred; intracranial aneurysms were found in 10 of these patients, 3 of whom had multiple aneurysms. [120] In another cohort of 310 children with homozygous sickle cell anemia who were followed from birth, 17 developed a stroke by the age of 14 years, representing an incidence of 7.8%. [121] Two of the 17 strokes were subarachnoid hemorrhages; the first of these patients underwent aneurysm surgery and recovered completely, while the second died of a presumed recurrence of hemorrhage. In addition to a number of other sporadic cases found in the literature, Oyesiku et al. reported a series of 15 patients with SCD who suffered a subarachnoid hemorrhage due to ruptured intracranial aneurysms. [113] Two of 15 patients died of the subarachnoid hemorrhage. The rest 13 patients underwent craniotomy and clip ligation; 8 of them had a good recovery, 3 were left with moderate disability, one died of surgical complications and one died of complications related to SCD. The authors also described the clinical and pathological features of these aneurysms. Interestingly, in contrast to inherited cerebrovascular aneurysms, the majority of patients (60%) had multiple aneurysms, some of which were also found in unusual locations. Actually, there are strong statistical associations for aneurysm multiplicity and sites of occurrence among reported patients with SCD and a number of case reports stressed the multiple presentation of intracranial aneurysms in patients with SCD. [112, 117, 118, 121, 123] Impressively, one of the reported patients underwent three craniotomies for ablation of six different intracranial aneurysms. [111] Interestingly, a pathology examination of resected aneurysms in patients with SCD revealed fragmentation of the internal elastic lamina of the arterial wall, although the investigators did not suggest a correlation with an underlying elastic tissue defect. [113] These findings were identical to the ones reported in the vast majority of liver biopsies, spleens, lymph nodes and gall bladders resected from young patients with β-thalassemia, sickle thalassemia and hereditary spherocytosis. [78, 79]

Regarding the etiology and pathogenesis of cerebral aneurysms in patients with SCD, it is known that cerebral aneurysms are generally related to connective tissue disorders. [124] Both the frequent multiple and atypical presentation of aneurysms and the encountered elastic tissue defects in the wall of these aneurysms are highly suggestive of an underlying elastic tissue defect. The potential relationship between intracranial hemorrhages and elastic tissue disorders has recently been postulated in β-thalassemia. In a study of cerebrovascular events that occurred in 10 patients with thalassemia major or thalassemia intermedia, 4 cases of fatal intracranial hemorrhages were included; 2 of these 4 patients were known to have AS. [125] Besides intracranial, peripheral artery aneurysms have also been sporadically encountered. Multiple gastric artery aneurysms were found to cause recurrent episodes of gastrointestinal bleeding in a β-thalassemia patient with PXE-like skin lesions. [67]

Besides the risk of rupture with the resultant intracranial hemorrhage, cerebral aneurysms may also be associated with complications due to compression. In a patient with SCD suffering from acute monocular visual loss, no vitreal or retinal abnormalities were found; in contrast, a large aneurysm of the anterior communicating cerebral artery causing direct compression of the optic nerve was revealed. [123] On the other hand, subarachnoid hemorrhage is usually but not always associated with rupture of intranial aneurysms. [112, 120, 126] The occurrence of subarachnoid hemorrhage in the absence of a detectable cerebral aneurysm has also been reported and seems to be a feature of children with SCD. [126] Rupture of leptomeningeal collateral vessels has been postulated as a possible cause of subarachnoid hemorrhage in one of these cases. [112]

Arterial hypertension has been sporadically observed both in SCD and β-thalassemia and has been attributed to renal abnormalities. Whether elastic tissue defects play a role in this complication needs to be addressed. As already discussed, patients with PXE were found to have arterial hypertension due to renal artery stenosis. Pulmonary hypertension, on the other hand, is a well-known complication in patients with sickle cell anemia and has also recently been demonstrated to be a common finding in thalassemia intermedia. [127] Taking under consideration that lung pathology in patients with PXE revealed degeneration of elastic elements in the wall of pulmonary alveoli, [5] the pathogenesis of pulmonary hypertension in hemoglobinopathies should be reconsidered to include the potential contribution of elastic fiber disorders.

The high prevalence of mitral valve prolapse observed in SCD, [52] although it has been questioned, [60] may potentially render this group of patients more susceptible to a number of complications associated with this valvular abnormality, such as cerebral ischemic events, bacterial endocarditis, rupture chordae tendineae, progressive mitral insufficiency, ventricular arrhythmias and sudden death. Valvular and endocardial abnormalities have furthermore been encountered with a considerably high frequency in a large series of 110 patients with thalassemia intermedia, aged 32.5±11.4 years. [127] In this group, valvular leaflet thickening was present in 48% of cases, mitral regurgitation in 47%, aortic regurgitation in 15% and endocardial calcification in 21%. The potential correlation of these findings to a diffuse elastic tissue disorder was suggested by the authors. According to a very recently published case report, a 56-year-old male patient with thalassemia intermedia developed unstable angina. [128] The coronary arteries in coronary angiography were completely patent but heavily calcified. The patient also had AS and calcifications of the posterior tibial arteries and the authors postulated that coronary arterial calcification that leaded to unstable angina in a setting of severe anemia should be related to the coexistent PXE-like syndrome. It should be stated that, besides vascular and valvular abnormalities, histopathology has demonstrated that PXE may also be related to endocardial elastosis in the atrial wall and coronary arterial wall defects, including fragmentation of the elastica, deposition of collagen material and muscle loss. [3]

To investigate the long-term effects of elastic tissue disorders in β-thalassaemia, Cianciulli et al. followed 14 Italian patients with typical skin lesions for 12 years. [67] During the follow-up period, 6 of 14 patients developed significant morbidity due to serious vascular complications and 3 of them died from these complications. More specifically, one patient suffered from recurrent gastrointestinal bleeding episodes due to multiple gastric artery aneurysms and was treated with partial gastrectomy, as discussed earlier. A second patient had an intestinal infarct, for which he underwent colon resection and colonostomy. A third one died from acute myocardial infarction due to coronary calcification, as showed by autopsy. A fourth died from iron-induced heart failure that was complicated by arterial hypertension in association with renal artery calcification. Another two patients suffered cerebrovascular events, a transitory ischemic attack and a lethal intracranial haemorrhage, respectively.

Finally, a question that may arise is whether vascular involvement in the context of systemic elastic tissue alterations plays a role in the development of leg ulcerations, tibial cramps and easy bruising, features that are often in patients with SCD and thalassemia.

It is obvious that a broader spectrum of clinical complications have hitherto been observed in β-thalassemia compared with SCD, probably due to the fact that research efforts on elastic tissue disorders have focused mainly on this hemoglobinopathy over the last years. Furthermore, the coexistence of iron overload may be an additional factor of elastic tissue injury in thalassemia patients.

Ocular Abnormalities and Visual Acuity Impairment

The main complication of AS, as stated above, is the development of subretinal neovascularization and hemorrhage with macular involvement, that may lead to visual acuity deterioration, even blindness. As shown by the follow-up study of Cianciulli et al., AS may progress in the course of the disease. [67] Visual loss has been encountered both in SCD and β-thalassemia patients with AS. [61, 64, 123, 129, 130] More specifically, in β-thalassemia, visual acuity impairment due to subretinal neovascularization and hemorrhage has been described in three patients, two with thalassemia major and one with thalassemia intermedia. [61, 64, 130]

SURVEILLANCE AND MANAGEMENT

The presence of a diffuse elastic tissue defect and the associated risk of severe and life-threatening complications render the surveillance for the early detection of related manifestations indispensable. Dermatological and ophthalmological examination should also be regularly performed in these patients. A careful skin inspection, focusing mainly on the neck, axillae, antecubital and popliteal fossae and abdomen should be regularly performed and the suspected skin lesions should be evaluated histopathologically following acquisition of skin biopsies. A fundoscopic examination by an ophthalmologist on an annual basis beyond the second decade of life and an X-ray examination of the lower limbs to detect arterial calcifications beyond the third decade are also recommended. In cases with AS, a close follow-up with fundoscopy and fluorescein angiography is required. Moreover, patients with neurological symptoms should undergo magnetic resonance angiography or four-vessel angiography to detect potentially harmful, but neurosurgically treatable, pathological conditions.

The attending physicians should keep in mind that the recognition of elastic tissue disorders may be difficult in patients with hemoglobinopathies. Given the broad clinical spectrum of the hemoglobinopathies on one hand and the systemic nature of the elastic tissue degeneration with involvement of multiple organs on the other, these manifestations may be overlooked. It seems that cases with skin lesions, especially thalassemia ones, have probably a more severe elastic tissue defect that is expressed by significant vascular complications, as shown by the results published by Cianciulli et al. [67] In addition, the clinical manifestations of elastic tissue degeneration are often quite subtle and the related complications are recognized only when they become quite severe. As shown by different patient groups, vascular and ocular involvement may exist and lead to severe complications even in the absence of visible skin lesions. [44, 62, 68, 78, 128] Indeed, fatal intracranial hemorrhages, visual loss due to subretinal hemorrhage and coronary artery disease have been described in thalassemic patients without typical skin lesions. [61, 64, 125, 128]

Regarding the preventive and therapeutic interventions, it is known that no special treatment exists for PXE and related disorders. A primary concern in cases with elastic tissue disorders is the prevention of bleeding. Medication, such as platelet inhibitors that are often indicated both in SCD and in β-thalassemia, should be prescribed cautiously. [127] In the presence of arterial calcifications, hemoglobin concentration should be kept high to reduce the risk of myocardial and peripheral ischemia. The need of maintaining high hemoglobin levels has also been stressed regarding pregnancy in women with hemoglobinopathies and has an additional importance in view of the potential obstetrical complications of PXE. [27-32, 131] The reduction of dietary calcium intake has been proposed in cases with PXE as a means to reduce organ calcium deposition, but such a recommendation might be inappropriate given the frequent coexistence of osteoporosis in SCD and β-thalassemia. [132-134] In cases with AS, laser photocoagulation should be considered in the presence of choroidal neovascularization in order to lower the risk of subretinal hemorrhage and of the result impairment of visual acuity. [129, 135, 136] Finally, in the case that intracranial, aortic or other aneurysms are revealed, the patient should be referred for proper surgical management.

Patients should be actively involved in the process of prevention and early recognition of complications due to elastic tissue degeneration. They should be advised to refrain from activities that predispose to hemorrhage, including heavy straining, head trauma, football, wrestling and weight lifting. Keeping in mind the possibility of cardiovascular complications, patients should also be encouraged to quit smoking and adopt a way of living that would modify other cardiovascular risk factors.

Conclusion

The development of a diffuse degenerative disorder of elastic tissue resembling PXE is a well-established entity in patients with inherited hemoglobinopathies and has recently been associated with severe and sometimes lethal complications. Current therapy for hemoglobinopathies has significantly improved patients' survival but it does not seem to have an equally beneficial effect on elastic tissue disorders. Therefore, a greater frequency of such manifestations is likely to be seen in the near future. The awareness of this phenomenon by all implicated physicians is expected to result in the early recognition of the related complications and hopefully in their effective therapeutic management.

References

[1] Aessopos A, Farmakis D, Loukopoulos D. Elastic tissue abnormalities resembling pseudoxanthoma elasticum in beta thalassemia and the sickling syndromes. *Blood* 2002;99:30-35.

[2] Goodman G, von Sallmann L, Holland MG. Ocular manifestations of sickle-cell disease. *Arch Ophthalmol* 1957;58:655.

[3] McKusick VA. *Hereditable Disorders of Connective* Tissue. 4th ed. St Louis, CV: Mosby; 1972:475-520.

[4] Geeraets WJ, Guerry D. Angioid streaks and sickle-cell disease. *Am J Ophthalmol* 1960;49:450-470.

[5] Geeraets WJ, Guerry D. Elastic tissue degeneration in sickle-cell disease. *Am J Ophthalmol* 1960;50:213-227.

[6] Neldner KH. Pseudoxanthoma Elasticum. *Clin Dermatol* 1988;6:1-159.

[7] Rigal D. Observation pour servir à l'histoire de la chéloïde diffuse xantholasmique. *Ann Dermatol Syphiligr* 1881;2:491-495.

[8] Darier J. Pseudoxanthoma elasticum. *Mschr Prakt Derm* 1896;23:609.

[9] Sherer DW, Sapadin AN, Lebwohl MG. Pseudoxanthoma elasticum: an update. *Dermatology* 1999;199:3-7.

[10] Bolognia J, Braverman IM. Skin manifestations of internal disease. In: Isselbacher KJ, Brauwald E, Wilson JD, Martin JB, Fauci AS, Kasper DL, eds. *Harrison's Principles of Internal Medicine*. 13th ed. McGraw-Hill; 1994:302-303.

[11] Aessopos A, Samarkos M, Voskaridou E, et al. Arterial calcifications in beta-thalassemia. *Angiology* 1998;49:137-143.

[12] Gurwood AS, Mastrangelo DL. Understanding angioid streaks. *J Am Optom Assoc* 1997;68:309-324.

[13] Janotka H, Hess J, Wlodarczyk J. [Angioid streaks. Pathogenesis and the clinical picture]. *Klin Oczna* 1995;97:299-302.

[14] Doyne RW. Choroidal and retinal changes: The results of blows on the eyes. *Tr Ophthalmol Soc U Kingdom* 1889;9:128.

[15] Knapp H. On the formation of dark angioid streaks as an unusual metamorphosis of retinal hemorrhage. *Arch Ophthalmol* 1892;21:289.

[16] Gronblad E. Angioid streaks-Pseudoxanthoma elasticum: Vorlantige Mitteilung. *Acta Ophthalmol* 1929;7:329.

[17] Stranberg J. Pseudoxanthoma elasticum. *Z Haut Geschlechtskr* 1929;31:689.

[18] Böck J. Zur klinik und anatomie der gefässähnlichen Streifen im Augenhintergrund. *Ztschr f Augenh* 1938;95:1.

[19] Hagedoorn A. Angioid streaks. *Arch Ophthalmol* 1939;21:746.

[20] Paton D. *The relation of angioid streaks to systemic disease*. Charles C Thomas, Springfield; 1972.

[21] Green WR, Friedman-Kien A, Banfield WG. Angioid streaks in Ehlers-Danlos syndrome. *Arch Ophthalmol* 1966;76:197-204.

[22] Donaldson EJ. Angioid streaks. *Aust J Ophthalmol* 1983;11:55-58.

[23] Lonn LI, Smith TR. Ora serrata pearls. Clinical and histological correlation. *Arch Ophthalmol* 1967;77:809-813.

[24] Lebwohl M, Halperin J, Phelps RG. Occult pseudoxanthoma elasticum in patients with premature cardiovascular disease. *N Engl J Med* 1993;329:1237-1239.

[25] Morgan AA. Recurrent gastrointestinal hemorrhage: an unusual cause. *Am J Gastroenterol* 1982;77:925-928.

[26] Challenor VF, Conway N, Monro JL. The surgical treatment of restrictive cardiomyopathy in pseudoxanthoma elasticum. *Br Heart J* 1988;59:266-269.

[27] Yoles A, Phelps R, Lebwohl M. Pseudoxanthoma elasticum and pregnancy. *Cutis* 1996;58:161-164.

[28] Mansat-Krzyzanowska E, Sagot P, Le Neel N, Stalder JF. [Pseudoxanthoma elasticum and pregnancy]. *Ann Dermatol Venereol* 1993;120:391-394.

[29] Baratte I, Schaal JP, Laurent R. [Pseudoxanthoma elasticum in pregnancy]. *Rev Fr Gynecol Obstet* 1991;86:243-245.

[30] Elejalde BR, de Elejalde MM, Samter T, Burgess J, Lombardi J, Gilbert EF. Manifestations of pseudoxanthoma elasticum during pregnancy: a case report and review of the literature. *Am J Med Genet* 1984;18:755-762.

[31] Broekhuizen FF, Hamilton PR. Pseudoxanthoma elasticum and intrauterine growth retardation. *Am J Obstet Gynecol* 1984;148:112-114.

[32] Berde C, Willis DC, Sandberg EC. Pregnancy in women with pseudoxanthoma elasticum. *Obstet Gynecol Surv* 1983;38:339-344.

[33] Pope FM. Autosomal dominant pseudoxanthoma elasticum. *J Med Genet* 1974;11:152-157.

[34] Pope FM. Two types of autosomal recessive pseudoxanthoma elasticum. *Arch Dermatol* 1974;110:209-212.

[35] Struk B, Neldner KH, Rao VS, St Jean P, Lindpainter K. Mapping of both autosomal recessive and dominant variants of pseudoxanthoma elasticum to chromosome 16p13.1. *Hum Mol Genet* 1997;6:1823-1828.
[36] Le Saux O, Urban Z, Goring HH, et al. Pseudoxanthoma elasticum maps to an 820-kb region of the p13.1 region of chromosome 16. *Genomics* 1999;62:1-10.
[37] van Soest S, Swart J, Tijmes N, Sandkuijl LA, Rommers J, Bergen AAB. A locus for autosomal recessive pseudoxanthoma elasticum, with penetrance of vascular symptoms in carriers, maps to chromosome 16p13.1. *Genome Res* 1997;7:830-834.
[38] Cai L, Struk B, Adams MD, et al. A 500-kb region on chromosome 16p13.1 contains the pseudoxanthoma elasticum locus: high-resolution mapping and genomic structure. *J Mol Med* 2000;78:36-46.
[39] Ringpfeil F, Lebwohl MG, Christiano AM, Uitto J. Pseudoxanthoma elasticum: mutations in the MRP6 gene encoding a transmembrane ATP-binding cassette (ABC) transporter. *Proc Natl Acad Sci USA* 2000;97:6001-6006.
[40] Le Saux O, Urban Z, Tschuch C, et al. Mutations in a gene encoding an ABC transporter cause pseudoxanthoma elasticum. *Nat Genet* 2000;25:223-227.
[41] Napgal KC, Asdourian G, Goldbaum M, Apple D, Goldberg MF. Angioid streaks and sickle haemoglobinopathies. *Br J Ophthalmol* 1976;60:31-34.
[42] Condon PI, Serjeant GR. Ocular findings of elderly cases of homozygous sickle-cell disease in Jamaica. *Br J Ophthalmol* 1976;60:361-364.
[43] Hamilton AM, Pope FM, Condon PI, et al. Angioid streaks in Jamaican patients with homozygous sickle cell disease. *Br J Ophthalmol* 1981;65:341-347.
[44] Goldberg MF, Charache S, Acacio I. Ophthalmologic manifestations of sickle cell thalassemia. *Arch Intern Med* 1971;128:33-39.
[45] Bertrand JJ, Hart ML, Voisin J. [Angioid streaks and sickle cell anemia]. *Bull Soc Ophtalmol Fr* 1970;70:1184-1190.
[46] Kent D, Arya R, Aclimandos WA, Bellingham AJ, Bird AC. Screening for ophthalmic manifestations of sickle cell disease in the United Kingdom. *Eye* 1994;8:618-622.
[47] Elebesunu-Amadasu M, Okafor LA. Ocular manifestations of sickle cell disease in Nigerians; experience in Benin City, Nigeria. *Trop Geogr Med* 1985;37:261-263.
[48] Majekodunmi SA, Akinyanju OO. Ocular findings in homozygous sickle cell disease in Nigeria. *Can J Ophthalmol* 1978;13:160-162.
[49] Paton D. Angioid streaks and sickle cell anemia. *Arch Ophthalmol* 1959;62:852-858.
[50] Condon PI, Serjeant GR, Ikeda H. Unusual chorioretinal degeneration in sickle cell disease. Possible sequelae of posterior ciliary vessel occlusion. *Br J Ophthalmol* 1973;57:81-88.
[51] Jampol LM, Acheson R, Eagle RC, Jr., Serjeant G, O'Grady R. Calcification of Bruch's membrane in angioid streaks with homozygous sickle cell disease. *Arch Ophthalmol* 1987;105:93-98.
[52] Lippman SM, Ginzton LE, Thigpen T, Tanaka KR, Laks MM. Mitral valve prolapse in sickle cell disease. Presumptive evidence for a linked connective tissue disorder. *Arch Intern Med* 1985;145:435-438.
[53] Perloff JK. Evolving concepts of mitral-valve prolapse. *N Engl J Med* 1982;307:369-370.

[54] Lebwohl MG, Distefano D, Prioleau PG, Uram M, Yannuzzi LA, Fleischmajer R. Pseudoxanthoma elasticum and mitral-valve prolapse. *N Engl J Med* 1982;307:228-231.

[55] Pyeritz RE, Wappel MA. Mitral valve dysfunction in the Marfan syndrome. Clinical and echocardiographic study of prevalence and natural history. *Am J Med* 1983;74:797-807.

[56] Leier CV, Call TD, Fulkerson PK, Wooley CF. The spectrum of cardiac defects in the Ehlers-Danlos syndrome, types I and III. *Ann Intern Med* 1980;92:171-178.

[57] King BD, Clark MA, Baba N, Kilman JW, Wooley CF. "Myxomatous" mitral valves: collagen dissolution as the primary defect. *Circulation* 1982;66:288-296.

[58] Frable WJ. Mucinous degeneration of the cardiac valves: the "floppy valve" syndrome. *J Thorac Cardiovasc Surg* 1969;58:62-70.

[59] Lippman SM, Abergel RP, Ginzton LE, et al. Mitral valve prolapse in sickle cell disease: manifestation of a generalized connective tissue disorder. *Am J Hematol* 1985;19:1-12.

[60] Simmons BE, Santhanam V, Castaner A, Rao KR, Sachdev N, Cooper R. Sickle cell heart disease. Two-dimensional echo and Doppler ultrasonographic findings in the hearts of adult patients with sickle cell anemia. *Arch Intern Med* 1988;148:1526-1528.

[61] Gibson JM, Chaudhuri PR, Rosenthal AR. Angioid streaks in a case of beta thalassaemia major. *Br J Ophthalmol* 1983;67:29-31.

[62] Singerman LJ. Angioid streaks in thalassaemia major [Letter]. *Br J Ophthalmol* 1983;67:558.

[63] Gartaganis S, Ismiridis K, Papageorgiou O, Beratis NG, Papanastasiou D. Ocular abnormalities in patients with beta thalassemia. Am J Ophthalmol 1989;108:699-703.

[64] Aessopos A, Stamatelos G, Savvides P, et al. Angioid Streaks in Homozygous β Thalassemia. *Am J Ophthalmol* 1989;108:356-359.

[65] Aessopos A, Stamatelos G, Savvides P, Rombos I, Tassiopoulos T, Kaklamanis P. Pseudoxanthoma elasticum and angioid streaks in two cases of beta-thalassaemia. *Clin Rheumatol* 1989;8:522-527.

[66] Aessopos A, Savvides P, Stamatelos G, et al. Pseudoxanthoma elasticum-like skin lesions and angioid streaks in beta-thalassemia. *Am J Hematol* 1992;41:159-164.

[67] Cianciulli P, Sorrentino F, Maffei L, et al. Cardiovascular involvement in thalassaemic patients with pseudoxanthoma elasticum-like skin lesions: a long-term follow-up study. *Eur J Clin Invest* 2002;32:700-706.

[68] Aessopos A, Voskaridou E, Kavouklis E, et al. Angioid streaks in sickle-thalassemia. *Am J Ophthalmol* 1994;117:589-592.

[69] Gerde LS. Angioid streaks in sickle cell trait hemoglobinopathy. *Am J Ophthalmol* 1974;77:462-464.

[70] Daneshmend TK. Ocular findings in a case of haemoglobin H disease. *Br J Ophthalmol* 1979;63:842-844.

[71] McBrayer GM, Semes L, Stephens GG. Angioid streaks and AC hemoglobinopathy--a newly discovered association. *J Am Optom Assoc* 1993;64:250-253.

[72] Kinsella FP, Mooney DJ. Angioid streaks in beta thalassaemia minor. *Br J Ophthalmol* 1988;72:303-304.

[73] O'Donnel BF, Powell FC, O'Loughlin S, Acheson RW. Angioid streaks in beta thalassaemia minor. *Br J Ophthalmol* 1991;75:639.

[74] Rodriguez-Cano L, Luelmo-Aguilar J, Mieras-Barcelo C, Salvador-Rodriguez F, Castells-Rodellas A. Pseudoxanthoma elasticum and β-δ thalassaemia. *J Eur Acad Dermatol Venereol* 1994;3:363-368.

[75] Dieckert JP, White M, Christmann L, Lambert HM. Angioid streaks associated with abetalipoproteinemia. *Ann Ophthalmol* 1989;21:173-175, 179.

[76] Decastel M, Leborgne-Samuel Y, Alexandre L, Merault G, Berchel C. Morphological features of the human umbilical vein in normal, sickle cell trait, and sickle cell disease pregnancies. *Hum Pathol* 1999;30:13-20.

[77] de Chadarevian JP, Balarezo FS, Heggere M, Dampier C. Splenic arteries and veins in pediatric sickle cell disease. *Pediatr Dev Pathol* 2001;4:538-544.

[78] Tsomi K, Karagiorga-Lagana M, Fragodimitri C, Karabatsos F, Katsiki V. Arterial elastorrhexis: manifestation of a generalized connective tissue disorder in beta-thalassaemia major. *Eur J Haematol* 1999;63:287-294.

[79] Tsomi K, Karagiorga-Lagana M, Karabatsos F, et al. Arterial elastorrhexis in beta-thalassaemia intermedia, sickle cell thalassaemia and hereditary spherocytosis. *Eur J Haematol* 2001;67:135-141.

[80] Baccarani-Contri M, Bacchelli B, Boraldi F, et al. Characterization of pseudoxanthoma elasticum-like lesions in the skin of patients with beta-thalassemia. *J Am Acad Dermatol* 2001;44:33-39.

[81] Samarkos M, Aessopos A, Fragodimitri C, et al. Neutrophil elastase in patients with homozygous beta-thalassemia and pseudoxanthoma elasticum-like syndrome. *Am J Hematol* 2000;63:63-67.

[82] Sandberg LB, Davidson JM. Elastin and its gene. In: Hern BTW, ed. *Peptide and Protein Review*. New York: Marcel Dekker; 1984:169-226.

[83] Huerre C, Junien C, Weil D, et al. Human type I procollagen genes are located on different chromosomes. *Proc Natl Acad Sci USA* 1982;79:6627-6630.

[84] Christiano AM, Lebwohl MG, Boyd CD, Uitto J. Workshop on pseudoxanthoma elasticum: molecular biology and pathology of the elastic fibers. Jefferson Medical College, Philadelphia, Pennsylvania, June 10, 1992. *J Invest Dermatol.* 1992;99:660-663.

[85] Christiano AM, Uitto J. Polymorphism of the human genome: markers for genetic linkage analyses in heritable diseases of the skin. *J Invest Dermatol* 1992;99:519-523.

[86] Deisseroth A, Nienhuis A, Lawrence J, Giles R, Turner P, Ruddle FH. Chromosomal localization of human beta globin gene on human chromosome 11 in somatic cell hybrids. *Proc Natl Acad Sci USA* 1978;75:1456-1460.

[87] Scriver C, Beaudet A, Sly A, Valle D, eds. *Metabolic and molecular basis of inherited disease.* 7th edition. Boston: Blackwell Scientific Publications; 1995:196.

[88] Karp DL, O'Neill MS, Haberman AL, Taylor RM. A yellow plaque with keratotic papules on the abdomen. Perforating calcific elastosis (periumbilical perforating pseudoxanthoma elasticum [PXE], localized acquired cutaneous PXE). *Arch Dermatol* 1996;132:224-225, 227-228.

[89] Neldner KH, Martinez-Hernandez A. Localized acquired cutaneous pseudoxanthoma elasticum. *J Am Acad Dermatol* 1979;1:523-530.

[90] Hicks J, Carpenter CL Jr, Reed RJ. Periumbilical perforating pseudoxanthoma elasticum. *Arch Dermatol* 1979;115:300-303.

[91] Nickoloff BJ, Noodleman FR, Abel EA. Perforating pseudoxanthoma elasticum associated with chronic renal failure and hemodialysis. *Arch Dermatol* 1985;121:1321-1322.

[92] Sapadin AN, Lebwohl MG, Teich SA, Phelps RG, DiCostanzo D, Cohen SR. Periumbilical pseudoxanthoma elasticum associated with chronic renal failure and angioid streaks--apparent regression with hemodialysis. *J Am Acad Dermatol* 1998;39:338-344.

[93] McLane NJ, Grizzard WS, Kousseff BG, Hartmann RC, Sever RJ. Angioid streaks associated with hereditary spherocytosis. *Am J Ophthalmol* 1984;97:444-449.

[94] Sandstrom H, Wahlin A, Eriksson M, Holmgren G, Lind L, Sandgren O. Angioid streaks are part of a familial syndrome of dyserythropoietic anaemia (CDA III). *Br J Haematol* 1997;98:845-849.

[95] Rinaldi M, Della Corte M, Ruocco V, DOnofrio C, Zanotta G, Romano A. Ocular involvement correlated with age in patients affected by major and intermedia beta-thalassemia treated or not with desferrioxamine. *Metab Pediatr Syst Ophthalmol* 1993;16:1-2, 23-25.

[96] Olivieri NF. The β-Thalassemias. *N Engl J Med* 1999;341:99-109.

[97] Hebbel RP. Auto-oxidation and a membrane-associated 'Fenton reagent': a possible explanation for development of membrane lesions in sickle erythrocytes. *Clin Haematol* 1985;14:129-140.

[98] de Franceschi L, Shalev O, Piga A, et al. Deferiprone therapy in homozygous human beta-thalassemia removes erythrocyte membrane free iron and reduces KCl cotransport activity. *J Lab Clin Med* 1999;133:64-69.

[99] Sugihara T, Repka T, Hebbel RP. Detection, characterization, and bioavailability of membrane-associated iron in the intact sickle red cell. *J Clin Invest* 1992;90:2327-2332.

[100] Browne P, Shalev O, Hebbel RP. The molecular pathobiology of cell membrane iron: the sickle red cell as a model. *Free Radic Biol Med* 1998;24:1040-1048.

[101] Belcher JD, Marker PH, Weber JP, Hebbel RP, Vercellotti GM. Activated monocytes in sickle cell disease: potential role in the activation of vascular endothelium and vaso-occlusion. *Blood* 2000;96:2451-2459.

[102] Gutteridge JM, Smith A. Antioxidant protection by haemopexin of haem-stimulated lipid peroxidation. *Biochem J* 1988;256:861-865.

[103] Osarogiagbon UR, Choong S, Belcher JD, Vercellotti GM, Paller MS, Hebbel RP. Reperfusion injury pathophysiology in sickle transgenic mice. *Blood* 2000;96:314-320.

[104] Hershko C, Link G, Cabantchik I. Pathophysiology of Iron Overload. *Ann N Y Acad Sci* 1998;850:191-201.

[105] Hanley ME, Repine JE. Elastase and oxygen radicals: Synergistic interactions. *Agents Actions* 1993;42(Suppl):39-47.

[106] Uguccioni M, Meliconi R, Nesci S, et al. Elevated interleukin-8 serum concentrations in beta-thalassemia and graft-versus-host disease. *Blood* 1993;81:2252-2256.

[107] Dore F, Bonfigli S, Pardini S, Longinotti M. Serum interleukin-8 levels in thalassemia intermedia. *Haematologica* 1995;80:431-433.

[108] Salsaa B, Zoumbos NC. A distinct pattern of cytokines production from blood mononuclear cells in multitransfused patients with β-thalassaemia. *Clin Exp Immunol* 1997;107:589-592.

[109] Makis AC, Hatzimichael EC, Bourantas KL. The role of cytokines in sickle cell disease. *Ann Hematol* 2000;79:407-413.

[110] Uitto J, Ryhanen L, Abraham PA, Perejda AJ. Elastin in diseases. *J Invest Dermatol* 1982;79(Suppl 1):160s-168s.

[111] Overby MC, Rothman AS. Multiple intracranial aneurysms in sickle cell anemia. Report of two cases. *J Neurosurg* 1985;62:430-434.

[112] Carey J, Numaguchi Y, Nadell J. Subarachnoid hemorrhage in sickle cell disease. *Childs Nerv Syst* 1990;6:47-50.

[113] Oyesiku NM, Barrow DL, Eckman JR, Tindall SC, Colohan ART. Intracranial aneurysms in sickle cell anemia: clinical features and pathogenesis. *J Neurosurg* 1991;75:356-363.

[114] Firth GP, Peterfreund AR. Management of multiple intracranial aneurysms: neuroanesthetic considerations of sickle cell disease. *J Neurosurg Anesthesiol* 2000;12:366-371.

[115] McConachie NS, Jaspan T. Complications of sickle cell disease: intracranial aneurysms and their treatment. *Clin Radiol* 1998;53:388-389.

[116] Preul MC, Cendes F, Just N, Mohr G. Intracranial aneurysms and sickle cell anemia: multiplicity and propensity for the vertebrobasilar territory. *Neurosurgery* 1998;42:971-7; discussion 977-978.

[117] Diggs LW, Brookoff D. Multiple cerebral aneurysms in patients with sickle cell disease. *South Med J* 1993;86:377-379.

[118] Chalif DJ, Decker RE. Intracranial aneurysms in sickle-cell anemia. *J Neurosurg* 1992;76:1051-1052.

[119] Batjer HH, Adamson TE, Bowman GW. Sickle cell disease and aneurysmal subarachnoid hemorrhage. *Surg Neurol* 1991;36:145-149.

[120] Anson JA, Koshy M, Ferguson L, Crowell RM. Subarachnoid hemorrhage in sickle-cell disease. *J Neurosurg* 1991;75:552-558.

[121] Balkaran B, Char G, Morris JS, Thomas PW, Serjeant BE, Serjeant GR. Stroke in a cohort of patients with homozygous sickle cell disease. *J Pediatr* 1992;120:360-366.

[122] Begue P, Faure C, Rousseau MC, Bonnet-Gadjos M, Lasfargues G. [Cerebrovascular accidents in children with homozygous sickle cell anemia: report on three cases (author's transl)]. *Ann Med Interne* (Paris) 1981;132:190-194.

[123] Caprioli J, Fagadau W, Lesser R. Acute monocular visual loss secondary to anterior communicating artery aneurysm in a patient with sickle cell disease. *Ann Ophthalmol* 1983;15:873-876.

[124] Carrizo AG. Epidemiological features and diagnostic evaluation of intracranial aneurysms. *Critical Reviews in Neurosurgery* 1999;9:79-86.

[125] Aessopos A, Farmakis D, Karagiorga M, Rombos I, Loucopoulos D. Pseudoxanthoma elasticum lesions and cardiac complications as contributing factors for strokes in beta-thalassemia patients. *Stroke* 1997;28:2421-2424.

[126] Van Hoff J, Ritchey AK, Shaywitz BA. Intracranial hemorrhage in children with sickle cell disease. *Am J Dis Child* 1985;139:1120-1123.

[127] Aessopos A, Farmakis D, Karagiorga M, et al. Cardiac Involvement in Thalassemia Intermedia: A Multicenter Study. *Blood* 2001;97:3411-3416.

[128] Farmakis D, Moyssakis I, Perakis A, et al. Unstable angina associated with coronary arterial calcification in a thalassemia intermedia patient with a pseudoxanthoma elasticum-like syndrome. *Eur J Haematol* 2003;70:64-66.

[129] Moriarty BJ, Webb DK, Serjeant GR. Treatment of subretinal neovascularization associated with angioid streaks in sickle cell retinopathy. Case report. *Arch Ophthalmol* 1987;105:1327-1328.

[130] Theodossiadis G, Ladas I, Koutsandrea C, Damanakis A, Petroutsos G. [Thalassemia and macular subretinal neovascularization]. *J Fr Ophtalmol* 1984;7:115-118.

[131] Aessopos A, Karabatsos F, Farmakis D, et al. Pregnancy in patients with well-treated beta-thalassemia: outcome for mothers and newborn infants. *Am J Obstet Gynecol* 1999;180:360-365.

[132] Reeve EB, Neldner KH, Subryan V, Gordon SG. Development and calcification of skin lesions in thirty-nine patients with pseudoxanthoma elasticum. *Clin Exp Dermatol* 1979;4:291-301.

[133] Renie WA, Pyeritz RE, Combs J, Fine SL. Pseudoxanthoma elasticum: high calcium intake in early life correlates with severity. *Am J Med Genet* 1984;19:235-244.

[134] Hacker SM, Ramos-Caro FA, Beers BB, Flowers FP. Juvenile pseudoxanthoma elasticum: recognition and management. *Pediatr Dermatol* 1993;10:19-25.

[135] Lim JI, Bressler NM, Marsh MJ, Bressler SB. Laser treatment of choroidal neovascularization in patients with angioid streaks. *Am J Ophthalmol* 1993;116:414-423.

[136] Gelisken O, Hendrikse F, Deutman AF. A long-term follow-up study of laser coagulation of neovascular membranes in angioid streaks. *Am J Ophthalmol* 1988;105:299-303.

In: Focus on Sickle Cell Research
Editor: Ralph L. Plasmar, pp. 193-213
ISBN 1-59033-920-7

Chapter XIII

IK CHANNELS – A MOLECULAR TARGET FOR INHIBITION OF ERYTHROCYTE DEHYDRATION IN SICKLE CELL ANAEMIA

Bo Skaaning Jensen* and Nanna Koschmieder Jorgensen
Department of Molecular Anatomy and Physiology, NeuroSearch
Denmark

ABSTRACT

The so-called Gardós channel from human erythrocytes is the first described Ca^{2+}-activated K^+ channel – and it is a Ca^{2+}-activated K^+ channel of intermediate conductance (IK channel). This review discusses the IK channels, and their classical biophysical characteristics, physiological function, as well as their role as pharmacological targets for novel drugs in sickle cell anaemia. The IK channels, with an intermediate conductance that distinguishes them from the related Ca^{2+}-activated K^+ channels of small (SK) or large (BK) conductance, have been described from a wide variety of tissues. The cloning of the human IK channel gene has, furthermore, enabled a detailed mapping of the expression in various tissues. Although recent data suggest the presence of IK channels in sensory neurons, IK channel expression is found predominately in cells of the blood, in epithelia and endothelia. Physiologically, IK channels set the membrane potential at fairly negative values and thereby build up large electrical gradients across the cell membrane. These IK channel generated gradients are important for the passive transport of ions such as Ca^{2+} influx controlling T-lymphocyte proliferation, and Cl^- efflux driving water and Na^+ secretion from epithelia.
The IK channels share several important biophysical and molecular characteristics with the SK channels: they are voltage-independent, inwardly rectifying and gated solely by Ca^{2+}. The molecular cloning of IK (and SK) channels has allowed for the surprising

* Address correspondance to: Bo Skaaning Jensen, Department of Molecular Anatomy and Physiology, NeuroSearch A/S, 93 Pederstrupvej, DK-2750 Ballerup, Denmark, Tel: +45 44 60 83 05, Fax: +45 44 60 80 80, E-mail: BSJ@neurosearch.dk

discovery that these channels gain their Ca^{2+}-sensitivity from tightly bound calmodulin (CaM). The IK channel has a unique pharmacology and is potently blocked by the scorpion toxins charybdotoxin (ChTx) and maurotoxin (MaTx) as well as by the antimycotic clotrimazole (CLT). ChTx and MaTx are not selective towards IK channels, and therefore systemic administration of these toxins is not possible. In contrast, CLT has been tested for the treatment of sickle cell disease and diarrhoea in clinical trials. Further, CLT relieves the symptoms of rheumatoid arthritis. However, inhibition of cytochrome P450 enzymes by CLT limits its therapeutic value. Currently, new drug candidates derived from CLT are entering the stage – most notably ICA-17043. It is discussed whether these novel inhibitors of IK channels may be beneficial in sickle cell anaemia.

INTRODUCTION

Essentially all mammalian cells express Ca^{2+}-activated K^+ channels. These channels link Ca^{2+}-based second messenger systems and the electrical activity of cells. Activation of the channels leads to a hyperpolarisation of the cell when the intracellular Ca^{2+} concentration increases, and this may constitute either a negative or a positive feed-back on the Ca^{2+} signal, depending on the route of the Ca^{2+} entry.

The Ca^{2+}-activated K^+ channels are divided into three groups based on their pharmacology, single-channel conductance, gating properties as well as their primary structure (see Table 1): big-conductance, Ca^{2+}-activated K^+ channels, intermediate-conductance Ca^{2+}-activated K^+ channels and small-conductance, Ca^{2+}-activated K^+ channels [see Vergara et al., for a review]. The big-conductance, Ca^{2+}-activated K^+ channel, or BK channel, is voltage-dependent and has a large (big) single-channel conductance (200-250 pS in symmetric K^+ solutions). Ca^{2+} shifts the voltage-dependent activation curve of BK channels towards more negative potentials, but at the prevailing physiological membrane potentials BK channels are relatively Ca^{2+}-insensitive ($K_{0.5} \approx$ 30 μM at – 30 mV) [Barrett et al., 1982; Latorre et al., 1983]. Only one gene for the human BK channel has been cloned (*KCNMA1*). The channel consists of the pore forming α-subunit as well as a regulatory β-subunit [Knaus et al. 1994]. The gene encoding the alpha subunit gives rise to multiple splice variants [Tseng-Clark et al., 1994]. The calcium sensitivity of the channel is conferred by the direct binding of Ca^{2+} to a Ca^{2+} bowl motif in the C-terminal of the α-subunit [Schreiber et al., 1997]. Several toxins isolated from scorpion venom inhibit BK channels with high affinity, but selective inhibition is only obtained with the peptide blocker iberiotoxin. The small-conductance, Ca^{2+}-activated K^+ channels - SK channels - are small conductance, inward rectifying channels (5-10 pS at 0 mV) with no voltage-dependency. SK channels are activated by even small increments in the Ca^{2+} concentration, without the need for simultaneous depolarizations, and the activity of the SK channels therefore closely reflects the intracellular Ca^{2+} concentration. The high sensitivity to Ca^{2+} is conferred the SK channels by constitutively bound calmodulin (CaM) [Xia et al., 1998]. CaM is located at the proximal C-terminal and confers allosteric Ca^{2+} sensitivity to these channels [Xia et al., 1998]. Three subtypes of SK channels have been cloned (SK1-3 encoded by *KCNN1-3*), which apparently only differ in their sensitivity towards the peptide blocker apamin [Ishii et al., 1997; Strøbæk et al., 2000; Shah et al., 2000].

The third group of Ca^{2+}-activated K^+ channels consists of the intermediate-conductance, Ca^{2+}-activated K^+ channels or IK channels. These channels have an intermediate conductance (20-40 pS at 0 mV), are weakly inward rectifying, and exhibit gating properties resembling SK channels (including the obligatory Ca^{2+} dependency conferred by CaM). In contrast to the SK channels, only one IK channel gene, *KCNN4,* has been identified [Ishii et al., 1997; Joiner et al., 1997; Logsdon et al., 1997; Jensen et al., 1998]. This channel has been denominated SK4 (due to the molecular relationship to the SK channels), SKCa4 (due to the molecular relationship to the SK channels and the calcium sensitivity) IK or IK1 (due to the single channel conductance), and IKCa1 (due to the single channel conductance and the calcium sensitivity). Although the notation assigned by GenBank is KCNN4 (Ghanshani et al., 1998), we will use the IK notation mainly due to the fact that most literature on this channel uses either this or related nomenclature. No selective IK blocking peptides are available: However, maurotoxin has recently been described as a fairly selective IK channel blocker, although with some effect on Kv1.2 channels. Furthermore, the imidazole antimycotic drug clotrimazole (CLT) is a potent and relatively selective blocker of IK channels [Alvarez et al., 1992; Brugnara et al., 1993].

Each of the three groups of Ca^{2+}-activated K^+ channels has a distinct physiological role. BK and SK channels are found in excitable as well as non-excitable cells, whereas IK channels are almost exclusively expressed in non-excitable cells, although some recent reports suggest expression of IK channels also in sensory neurons [Boettger et al., 2002]. The activity of Ca^{2+}-activated K^+ channels is typically linked to the firing of action potentials in neurons, [for a review, see Sah, 1996]. BK channels may be activated/deactivated during the course of single action potentials and give rise to the ultra-fast (msec) afterhyperpolarization (AHP) due to their combined Ca^{2+}- and voltage-dependency. The physiological function of BK channels has been suggested to be to counteract action potential broadening and slowing of the repolarising phase [Shao et al., 1999] as is the case for other voltage-activated K^+ channels. In contrast, the rise in intracellular Ca^{2+} that occurs during trains of action potentials progressively activates the SK channels. SK channels give rise to AHP's of intermediate duration (100 msec) resulting in spike-frequency adaptation. Repetitive action potential firing generates substantial Ca^{2+} influx and thus SK channel activation, eventually shutting off repetitive firing. Although recent studies indicate that IK channels can be found in sensory neurons [Boettger et al., 2002], IK channels are primarily expressed in epithelia and in blood cells [Logsdon et al., 1997; Joiner et al. 1997; Jensen et al., 1998]. In a secretory epithelia such as the colon, activation of a basolateral Ca^{2+}-dependent K^+-conductance is essential for sustained secretion of salt and water [Devor et al., 1996]. In both T- and B-lymphocytes, IK channels play an important role in the signalling process that results in activation of these cells. During these physiological important processes, it is a common feature of IK channels to provide large driving forces for Cl^- in the salt-secretion and for Ca^{2+} in clonal expansion of lymphocytes, respectively. In erythrocytes from patients suffering from sickle cell anaemia, the IK channel (the Gardós channel) is active and therefore contributes to the pathological dehydration of erythrocytes that underlies the sickling of the red blood cells. Table 1 summarizes the characteristics of the Ca^{2+}-activated K^+ channels.

Table 1. Characteristics of the Ca^{2+}-activated K^+ channels

The three main groups of Ca^{2+}-activated K^+ channels are compared with respect to gating mechanisms, biophysical properties and pharmacology.

	SK	IK	BK
Conductance	5-10 pS	20-40 pS	200-250 pS
Ca^{2+} sensitivity	$K_{0.5}$ = 300 nM	$K_{0.5}$ = 300 nM	$K_{0.5}$ ~30 μM (-40 mV)
Voltage-dependent gating	no	no	yes
Function	afterhyperpol. spike.freq.adapt. volume regulation	sets $V_{m, rest}$ fluid secretion	repol. actionpot. repol. hyperact. cells
Distribution	Neurons skeletal muscle dorsal root ganglia bladder smooth muscle Immature smooth muscle cells dorsal root ganglia	endothelial cells erythrocytes epithelial cells monocytes T- and B-lymphocytes	Neurons epithelial cells skeletal muscle smooth muscle
Toxin blockers (peptides)	apamin scyllatoxin	charybdotoxin maurotoxin	charybdotoxin iberiotoxin
Small molecule modulators			
Inhibitors	dequalinium UCL 1684 ICA-17043	clotrimazole TRAM-34	paxilline
Openers	1-EBIO Riluzole CZ ZOX Theophylline Caffeine IBMX	1-EBIO DCEBIO CZ	NS1619 DHS I BMS-204352

ENDOGENOUS IK CHANNELS

The Gardós Channel

In the middle of the last century, it was observed that metabolic inhibition induced an increase in the potassium efflux from human red cells, an effect that was dependent on extracellular Ca^{2+} [Wilbrandt, 1940, Gardós, 1958]. This, the first description of Ca^{2+}-activated K^+ permeability, was due to activation of the human red cell IK channel [Gardós,

1958]. Since then activation of the erythrocyte Ca^{2+}-activated K^+ permeability in suspensions of erythrocytes are traditionally called a Gardós experiment. Although the ion channel aspects of this observation remained obscure for many years, the erythrocyte Ca^{2+}-activated K^+ channel has accordingly been termed the Gardós channel.

After Dr. Gardós' observation, it was subsequently shown that the phenomenon was not a consequence of erythrocyte poisoning, but represented a genuine membrane property of the red blood cell. The Ca^{2+}-dependent loss of potassium was observed both in red blood cell ghosts and in preparations of membrane vesicles [Knauf et al., 1975, Yingst & Hoffman, 1984, Lew et al., 1982]. Furthermore, it was shown that the activation of the K^+ efflux could be induced by substitution of Ca^{2+} by Pb^{2+} [Riordan & Passow, 1971]. Later, detailed studies showed that the localization of the Ca^{2+} binding was at the intracellular side of the membrane [Blum & Hoffman, 1972]. The study of the Ca^{2+}-activated K^+ conductance in intact red blood cells was greatly facilitated by the synthesis of the electrically silent Ca^{2+} ionophore, A23187 [Reed & Lardy, 1972, Reed, 1976]. A23187 allowed a more reproducible Ca^{2+} loading of ATP-depleted as well as metabolically undisturbed red cells and thus constituted a major technological advantage. Whether an electric charge-separation occurred during the Gardós effect was investigated by attempting to measure the membrane potential directly using microelectrodes. The human red blood cell is, however, not suited for such studies, due to the small size of the human erythrocyte. Therefore, such studies were performed using the giant erythrocytes from the South American salamander *Amphiuma means*. Due to the size of these erythrocytes and their higher electrical capacitance, more time was available for the measurements. In an elegant series of experiments Dr. Lassen demonstrated Ca^{2+}-mediated hyperpolarisations in these giant red blood cells [Lassen et al., 1974, Lassen et al., 1976].

Despite several studies that indicated that the Gardós effect was due to the activation of a transport pathway with electrogenic properties, a number of studies pointed at a carrier-mediated transport rather than ion channel activity. One of these was the influence of extracellular potassium on the net transport rate. For a transporter, the extracellular concentration of the transported ion (K^+ in this case) contributes to the driving force on the transported ion. The driving force on K^+ decreases with the increasing extracellular K^+, and thus, low extracellular K^+ stimulates the K^+ loss. In the extreme of essentially no extracellular K^+, the Gardós effects disappeared irreversibly [Heinz & Passow, 1980]. The existence of an extracellular K^+ bindingsite for activation of the Gardós permeability was also supported by studies showing that certain blockers competed with extracellular K^+ [Reichstein & Rothstein, 1981]. At the time such complicated trans-kinetics was taken as evidence for carrier-mediated transport.

Evidence that the Gardós pathway unequivocally belongs in the K^+ channel family came from Vestergaard-Bogind & Bennekou, who were able to record simultaneously the net- and single-fluxes (by $^{42}K^+$ tracing) as well as membrane potentials from human erythrocytes [Macey et al., 1978,Vestergaard-Bogind et al., 1985]. Using this approach the important question on free diffusion (follows the classical Ussing flux-ratio equation [Ussing, 1948]) through the Gardós pathway could be addressed [Vestergaard-Bogind et al., 1985]. Deviations from the Ussing flux-ratio give important clues to the mechanisms of permeation. The experiments clearly demonstrated that the Gardós pathway does not offer an unrestricted diffusion pathway for potassium. On the contrary, permeation via the Gardós pathway follows a modified version of Ussings equation raised to a power of 2.7 clear-cut evidence that the Gardós pathway was a K^+ channel. Previously, a classical study had shown this exact behaviour for the squid axon delayed rectifier channel [Hodgkin & Keynes, 1955]. Three years before Gardós described the loss of K^+ from red blood cells, Hodgkin and Keynes [Hodgkin & Keynes, 1955] presented the visionary interpretation of this K^+ efflux as a "long pore" effect. This was described as an open channel pathway containing several potassium ions (at least 3 if the exponent is 2.7), which are restricted to concerted moves in "single-file" [Hodgkin & Keynes, 1955]. MacKinnon and coworkers finally confirmed the nature of the "long pore" when the crystallization of the pore section of the bacterial KscA channel was presented [Doyle et al. 1998]. Fifty years after Hodgkin and Keynes the crystal structure visualized that indeed three K^+ ions are trapped in the conductance pathway. It is now universally accepted that the multi-ion character is a likely common functional/structural signature for the superfamily of highly selective potassium channels. The multi-ion character of the Gardós channel was confirmed by the demonstration of high-power block by intracellular Na^+ [Stampe & Vestergaard-Bogind, 1989].

Single Channel Studies

Final evidence for the Gardós pathway as an ion channel became available only after a series of successful patch clamp studies on human red cells [Hamill, 1981; Grygorczyk & Schwarz, 1983; Grygorczyk et al., 1984; Grygorczyk & Schwarz, 1985; Grygorczyk, 1987; Christophersen, 1991]. These studies showed genuine Ca^{2+}-dependent, single-channel events recorded in the inside out configuration. The Gardós channel exhibited weak, inward rectification and a single channel conductance of approximately 20 pS in high potassium solutions symmetrical across the membrane. A single-channel conductance in that range reflects a high turnover number for K^+-transport that cannot be mediated by any classical transporter [for a review, see Latorre et al., 1983]. Further, significant protein rearrangements during transport are typically temperature-dependent. This is in contrast to the modest temperature dependency of the single channel conductance (Q_{10} = 1.3) for the Gardos channel [Grygorczyk, 1987]. The inside out configuration studies allowed variations in the Ca^{2+} concentration in the solutions on the intracellular side of the patch. The Ca^{2+}-dependency of the channel was shown to be obligatory and half-maximal activation could be obtained at a concentration of $\approx$ 1 μM, which is consistent with most estimates of EC_{50} values based on flux experiments [Simons, 1982]. Also in accordance with previous studies, Pb^{2+} could substitute for Ca^{2+} as intracellular gating ligand in the patch clamp studies [Fehlau et al., 1989]. The open state probability of the channel is independent of the membrane potential at a given intracellular Ca^{2+}-concentration.

The first patch clamp studies estimated a K^+/Na^+ permeability ratio of only 15, an observation, which was inconsistent with previous findings concerning the Gardós pathway. The Gardós pathway was highly selective for K^+ over Na^+ with a ratio of about 1000 as estimated from tracer flux experiments [Lew et al., 1982]. Furthermore, $^{86}Rb^+$ could substitute for K^+ as tracer in Gardós experiments. The low K^+/Na^+ permeability ratio found in the early patch clamp studies could, however, not be reproduced in later studies [Christophersen, 1991]. Na^+-currents were not detectable at the single-channel level, and this observation was supported by the measurement of permeability ratios towards a series of monovalent cations. The permeation sequence corresponds to the general selectivity fingerprint for K^+ channels: Eisenmans series IV or V for binding to a site of intermediate field strength [Latorre & Miller, 1983]. These studies unexpectedly showed a clear gating-dependency on the nature of the permeating ion species: Rb^+ stabilized the channel in the open conformation relative to K^+, whereas NH_4^+ had the opposite effect. In bi-ionic experiments, the stabilization/destabilization followed the direction of the current, indicating that gating is influenced by the specific channel occupancy [Christophersen & Bennekou, 1990]. Similar gating effects of the permeating ions have been described for BK channels [Demo & Yellen, 1992].

The molecular cloning of the human IK channel finally led to the experimental evidence that the Gardós channel is encoded by *KCNN4* – the gene for hIK (Hoffman et al., 2003). In an elegant study, Joe Hoffman and coworkers showed that IK channels are expressed in red blood cells by means of RT-PCR (using mRNA from erythroid progenitor cells), Western blotting (using ghosts from human red blood cells) and detailed biophysical characterization of the cloned IK channel, including demonstration of irreversible inhibition of the cloned channel in the absence of extracellular K^+ (Hoffman et al., 2003). This study undoubtedly place the molecular identity of the Gardós channel as the IK channel encoded by *KCNN4.*

Despite almost 50 years of research on the Gardós channel, the physiological role of the channel in erythrocytes remains a mystery. Red blood cells have very low cation permeability and the Ca^{2+} concentration is kept very low with no internal stores. It has been speculated that the Gardós channel operates to maintain a constant cell volume to avoid complement-mediated osmotic lysis. Another putative role of the Gardós channel might be involvement in the erythroid proliferation and differentiation.

NON-ERYTHROID IK CHANNELS

Native, Ca^{2+}-activated channels with IK channel characteristics have also been identified in non-erythroid cells and tissues. IK channels have been described in T- and B-lymphocytes, where the channels are selectively up-regulated in response to antigens and mitogens and may play an important role in the immune response by maintaining the electrical driving force for Ca^{2+} entry [Grissmer et al., 1993, Parseti et al., 1992, Verheugen et al., 1995, Jensen et al., 1999, see Jensen et al., 2002]. Another role for IK channels in growth has been proposed in fibroblast, where the endogenous IK channels (FIK) are suggested to be involved both in growth and in the cellular response to mitogenic stimuli [Pena & Rane, 1999, Pena et al., 2000; Rane, 2000].

In blood vessel endothelial cells, the presence of IK channels has also been described [Sauvé et al., 1988, Olesen & Bundgaard, 1993]. The Ca^{2+}-activated IK channels have been proposed to mediate endothelial hyperpolarisation in response to humeral stimulation [Vaca et al., 1996], providing the driving force for Ca^{2+} entry and thereby leading to synthesis of vasodilating factors [Lückhoff & Busse, 1990] and gene expression [Lampugnani et al., 1990]. A role for IK channels in the action of EDHF (endothelium-derived hyperpolarizing factor) has also been suggested from studies on rat hepatic arteries [Andersson et al., 2000], and changes in IK channel expression have been shown to occur in endothelial cells from human mesenteric arteries in patients with colonic adenocarcinoma compared with non-cancer patients [Köhler et al., 2000].

IK channels are present in enteric neurons, where they are proposed to regulate the afterhyperpolarization [Furness et al., 1998, Vogalis et al., 1998, 2002]. In a recent study, the presence of IK channels in enteric neurons of the human colon and in myenteric plexus in inflamed colons from patients with Crohn's disease has been demonstrated. These findings might provide a possible explanation for the diarrhoea and abdominal pain in inflammatory bowel disease and by IK blockers such as pyridine drugs prescribed for neuromuscular disorders [Arnold et al., 2003]. In the urinary bladder, IK channels have been identified at the RNA level [Ishii et al., 1997, Joiner et al., 1997] as well as functionally in the urinary bladder smooth muscle using patch clamp electrophysiology [Ohya et al., 2000], suggesting that IK channels may contribute to the control of the membrane potential and muscle tone in this tissue.

In secretory epithelia, IK channels are important for maintaining the electrochemical gradient required for transepithelial secretion [Devor et al., 1996]. A high expression of IK channels in salivary glands has been indicated by RNA dot blot analysis [Jensen et al., 1998]. The presence of IK channels in mouse parotid acinar cells has recently been confirmed using Northern blot, in situ analysis and patch clamp electrophysiology [Nehrke et al., 2003]. However, no effect of the IK channel inhibitor CLT on acetylcholine-induced secretion was found in a study using perfused rabbit submandibular glands [Stummann et al., 2003], arguing against a primary role for IK channels in secretion in the rabbit gland.

Human dorsal root ganglion (DRG) neurons possess both SK1 and IK channels. The expression level and distribution of the channels change in injured neurons as estimated from immunohistochemistry. The expression of SK1 thus decreased in injured human DRG neurons, while IK-immunoreactivity decreased distal to the injury site suggesting that both SK and IK channels may play a role in pain following nerve injury [Boettger et al., 2002].

In a study using rabbit osteoclasts, IK channels have been identified using whole cell and single channel patch clamp recordings, and the channel was suggested to be involved in osteoclast spreading and bone resorption [Espinosa et al., 2002].

IK channels have also been described to be present in cell lines, such as human osteoblast-like cells [Weskamp et al., 2000], Erhlich ascites tumour cells [Valdeolmillos et al., 1982; Christensen & Hoffmann, 1992] and HeLa cells [Sauve et al., 1986].

PHARMACOLOGY OF IK CHANNELS

Inhibitors of IK Channels

The pharmacology of the Gardos channel was investigated in some of the early studies. These revealed a relatively weak inhibition of the Gardos channel by oligomycin [Wood, 1984], quinine [Reichstein & Rothstein, 1981], and cetiedil [Berkowski & Orringer, 1982]. Even though cetiedil (see Fig. 1 for chemical structure) was a low potency inhibitor of the Gardós channel ($IC_{50} \approx 50$ μM), it was tested for the treatment of sickle cell anaemia. Thus, cetiedil is important, since it introduced the concept of prevention of sickle erythrocyte dehydration by blocking the Gardós channel as an anti-sickling therapy [Benjamin et al., 1986] (see also Fig. 2). Analogues of cetiedil have been synthesed and tested on the Ca^{2+}-induced K^+ permeability in erythrocytes. The compound UCL1608 was the most potent of these analogues, with an IC_{50} of 1.5 μM [Benton et al., 1999, Roxburgh et al., 2001] (see Fig. 1 for chemical structure).

An early clue to the molecular diversity in the family of Ca^{2+}-activated K^+ channels was the observation that apamin, a constituent of honeybee venom, which was effective in blocking Ca^{2+}-activated K^+ transport in hepatocytes, had no effect on the Gardós channel [Burgess et al., 1981. Another venom, from the scorpion *Leirus quinquestritus,* was shown to block the Ca^{2+} activated BK channels from muscle cell T-tubules. The toxin, ChTx [Smith et al., 1986], responsible for the BK channel inhibition was initially thought to be a selective agent for these channels. However, ChTx also potently inhibited the Gardós channel [Castle & Strong, 1986; Wolff et al., 1988] as well as Ca^{2+}-activated K^+-transport in other cells not supposed to express BK channels, such as airway epithelia [McCann et al., 1990] and Ehrlich ascites tumor cells [Young et al., 1993]. The Gardós channel has a distinct pharmacological profile as evaluated by studies employing ChTx and related K^+ channel toxins blockers. In flux-assays, the high-affinity blockers were ChTx (IC_{50} = 5.4 nM), stichodactylatoxin (IC_{50} = 24.5 nM), and margatoxin, while neither iberiotoxin, which blocks BK channels, nor apamin, which as mentioned above blocks SK channels, has any effect. The cloned IK channel has an IC_{50} for block by ChTx in the range 2-28 nM. Chandy and coworkers have developed a ChTx mutant that is selective for IK channels over K_v channels [see Rauer et al., 2000 for details]. The cloned IK channel has furthermore been confirmed to be insensitive to apamin in concentrations that prominently block SK channels (100-1000 nM) and to concentrations of iberiotoxin that would cause a prominent block of BK channels (50-1000 nM) [Brugnara et al., 1995; Ishii et al., 1997; Joiner et al., 1997; Logsdon et al., 1997; Jensen et al., 1998; Khanna et al., 1999]. IK channels expressed in CHO cells have recently been shown to be blocked by a 34 amino acid toxin from *Scorpio maurus*, maurotoxin, with an IC_{50} of 1 nM [Castle et al., 2003]. This toxin has no inhibitory effect on SK or BK channels in concentrations up to 300 nM, but maurotoxin has previously been shown to inhibit K_v1 channels expressed in Xenopus oocytes [Fajloun et al., 2000]. Studies on the cloned IK channels has confirmed the block by the peptide toxins stichodactylatoxin (IC_{50} = 290 nM), and margatoxin (IC_{50} = 460 nM), while a third toxin, kaliotoxin, which blocks $K_v1.3$, has been shown not to inhibit the cloned IK channels in the range 50-1000 nM [Logsdon et al., 1997; Jensen et al., 1998]. Table 2, below, summarizes the effect of the toxins on IK channels.

Some dihydropyridines (marketed anti-hypertensive drugs), blocked the Gardós channel [Kaji, 1990, Ellory et al., 1992] with nitrendipine being the most potent compound (for chemical structure, see Fig. (1)) suggesting that potent non-peptide inhibitors of this channel could be developed from this class of compounds. It was concluded that selective and potent Gardós channel blocking dihydropyridines might be developed for the treatment of sickle cell anemia since the effect of the dihydropyridines on the Gardós channel did not parallel the potency at the L-type voltage-gated Ca^{2+} channel [Ellory et al., 1994]. Somewhat surprisingly, a completely different chemical and therapeutic class of compounds provided the proof of concept for Gardós channel blockers as anti-sickling compounds (see below).

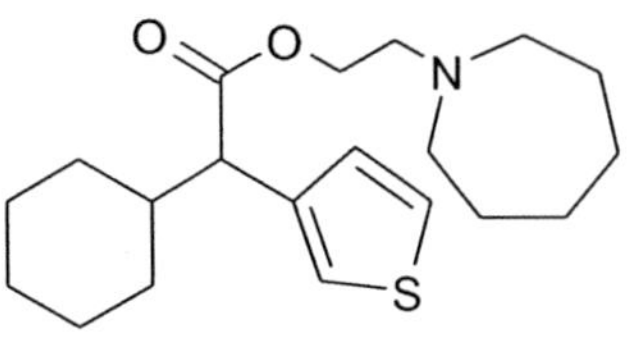

Cetiedil

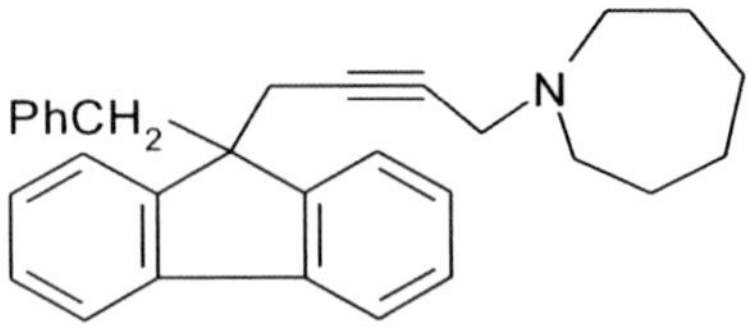

UCL1608

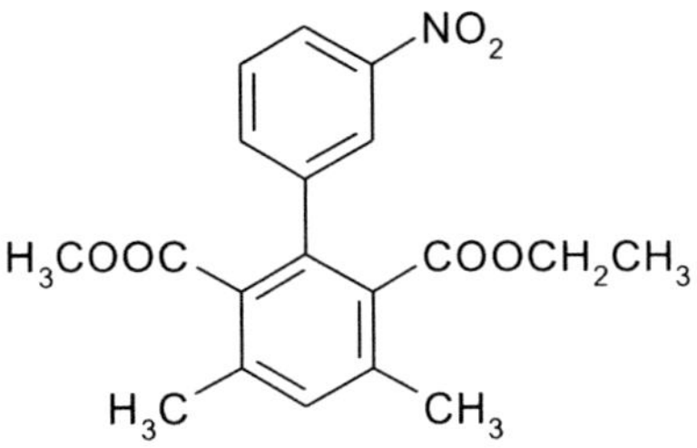

Nitrendipine

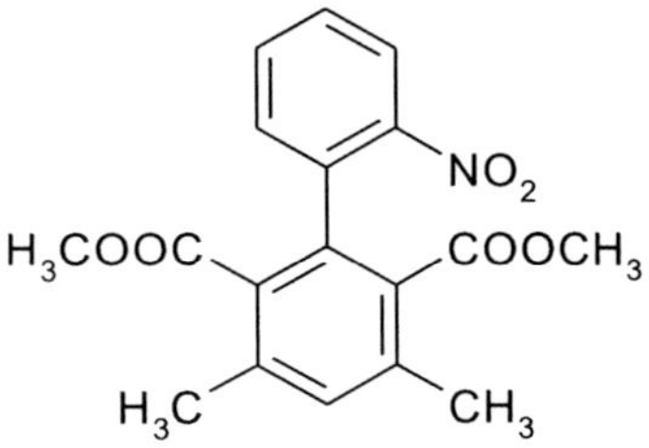

Nifedipine

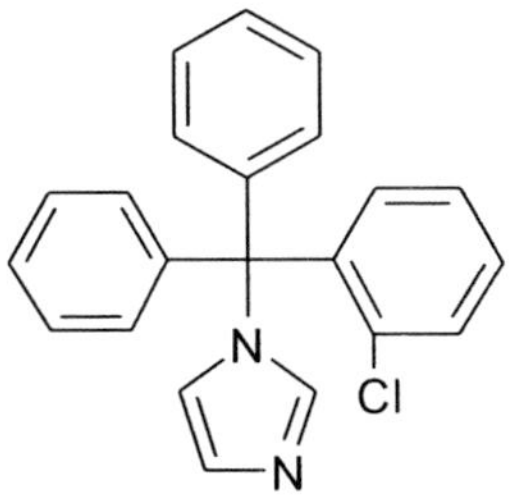

Clotrimazole

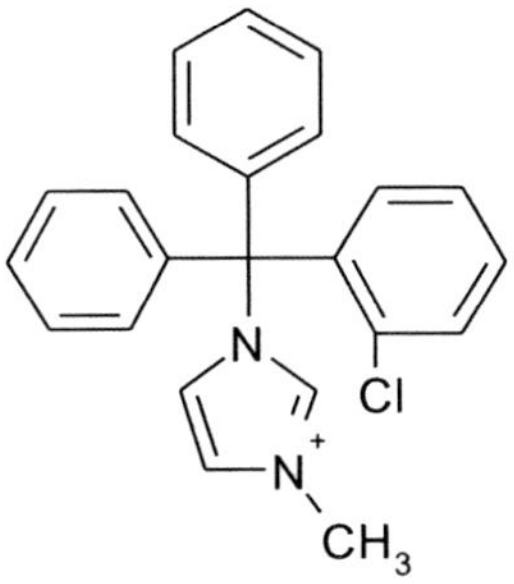

UCL1559

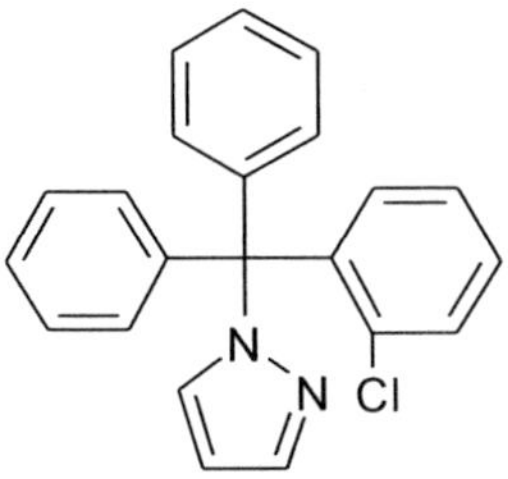

TRAM-34

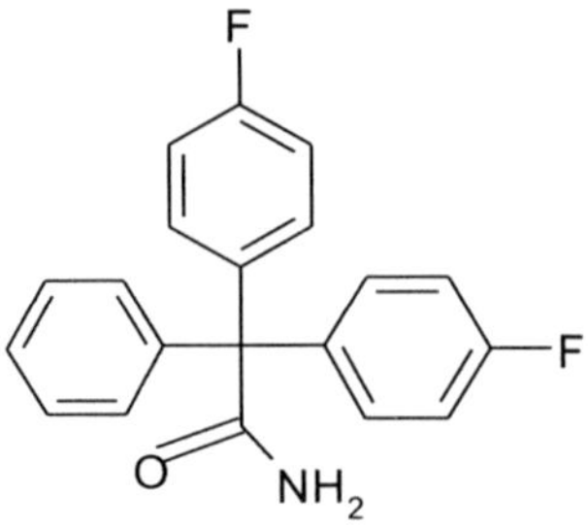

ICA-17043

Figure 1. Chemical Structures of some IK channel blockers.

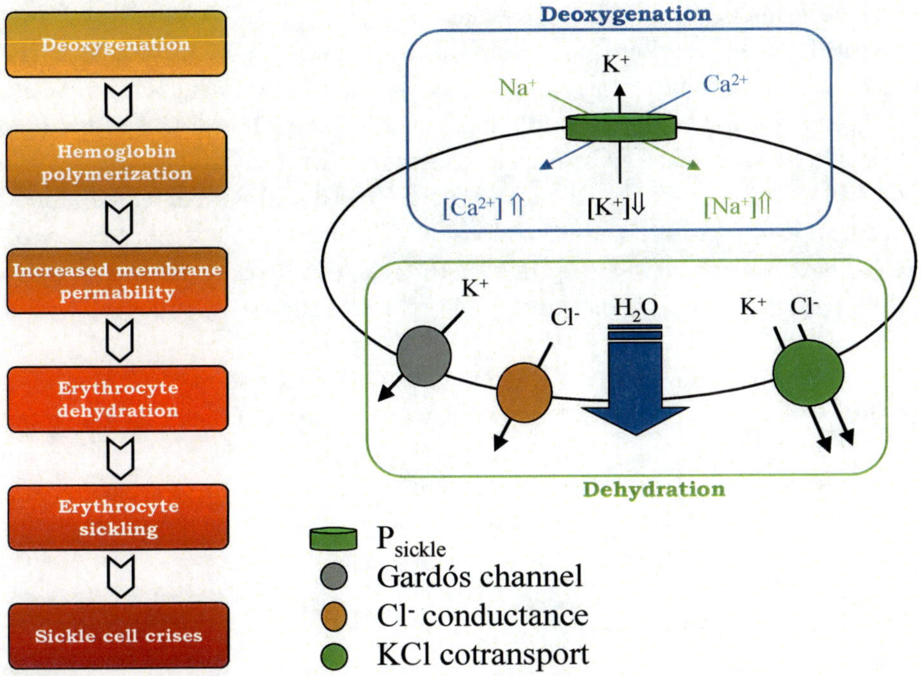

Figure 2. Schematic presentation of the cellular events that lead to erythrocyte sickling. Red blood cell dehydration plays a key role in the pathophysiology of sickle cell disease. Dehydration occurs as potassium and chloride pathways are activated and water follows driven by the osmotic gradient. This results in a cell volume decrease that consequently cause an increase in the cellular hemoglobin concentration. This increase in HbS concentration leads to an increased rate of HbS polymerisation during deoxygenation resulting in erythrocyte morphological changes, the so-called sickling. The mechanisms shown in the blue box represent the primary membrane changes in response to repeated cycles of oxygenation/deoxygenation and sickling/unsickling and are found only in sickled red blood cells that have undergone deoxygenation. The mechanisms in the green box represent the pathways underlying the loss of salt and water: dehydration of mature erythrocytes is due to the loss of K^+ and Cl^- that occurs via the Gardós channel operating in parallel with a Cl^- conductance and via the electroneutral KCl cotransporter. As the deoxygenation-induced polymerisation of hemoglobin S (HbS) is inversely porportional to the HbS concentration, even a minor reduction in HbS concentration will be beneficial for reducing the HbS polymerisation, i.e. prevention of the water loss from RBC will counteract the HbS polymerisation.

The effect of a series of imidazole antimycotic compounds was tested on the Gardós channel and CLT was identified as a very potent blocker [Alvarez et al., 1992] (for chemical structure, see Fig. (1)). The whole cell current experiments revealed an IC_{50} of 50 nM, and at the level of single channels, CLT significantly reduced P_{open} without affecting the single channel conductance [Dunn, 1998]. CLT has been shown to bind to an intracellular site on the IK channel in studies using a membrane impermant, quaternary ammonium analougue of CLT (UCL 1559 – see Fig. 1), which blocked IK channels in inside-out patches from erythocytes [Dunn, 1998]. The therapeutic use of CLT has, however, been limited by the compounds inhibitory effect on the cytochrome P450 enzyme CYP3A4. Analogues of CLT without effects on CYP3A4, but retaining the inhibitory effect on the IK channel, have been synthesized, and one of these, TRAM-34 (1-[(2-chlorophenyl)-diphenylmethyl]-1*H*-pyrazole) has a K_d value for inhibition of cloned IK channels expressed in COS-7 cells of 20 nM (see Fig. 1). TRAM-34 has 200-1500 fold selectivity for IK channels over other K^+ channels or Na^+ and Ca^{2+} channels [Wulff et al., 2000]. Another interesting compound of this class is ICA-17043 (see Fig. 1), which is currently being evaluated in clinical trials for the potential of treating sickle cell anaemia (see below). The effect of ICA-17043 on IK channels has been tested on red blood cells only. The calcium-induced Rb efflux from human red blood cells is inhibited with an IC50 of 11 nM and from mouse RBC with an IC50 of 50 nM [Stocker et al., 2003]. ICA-17043 appears fairly specific for IK channels as only limited effects on the binding to more than 30 different receptors could be demonstrated (IC50 > 10 μM; Stocker et al., 2003].

In addition to CLT, other imidazole antimycotics have been found to inhibit the Gardós channel [Alvarez et al., 1992]. The cloned IK channels are thus inhibited by miconazole with an IC_{50} of 0.79 μM [Jensen et al., 1998], econazole with an IC_{50} of 2.4-12 μM [Jensen et al., 1998, Ghanshani et al., 2000] and ketoconazole with IC_{50} of 30 μM [Ghanshani et al., 2000]. Table 2, below, gives an overview of IK channel pharmacology.

Activators of IK Channels

Openers of IK channels include 1-EBIO, which was first identified by its effects on epithelial transport in studies using monolayers of T-84 cells as well as in intact colon epithelia. It was shown that 1-EBIO stimulated Cl^--secretion through activation of a Ca^{2+}-activated K^+ conductance and that the stimulatory effect of the compound could be counteracted by application of ChTx at the basolateral side of the epithelia [Devor et al., 1996]. The activation of IK channels by 1-EBIO has been confirmed in studies on the cloned channel. 1-EBIO activates the cloned IK channel with an EC_{50} value of 74 μM [Jensen et al., 1998], and the effect of 1-EBIO depends on intracellular Ca^{2+} [Pedersen et al., 1999]. More recently the compounds chlorzoxazone and zoxazoloamine have been shown to activate IK channels from various epithelia and as well as cloned channels [Syme et al., 2000, Singh et al., 2000], although the potency is lower than that reported for 1-EBIO [Singh et al., 2000]. It should be noted, however, that neither 1-EBIO nor chlorzoxazone are selective for IK channels, they also act as openers of SK channels. Chlorzoxazone is a mucle relaxant and the effect in muscle cells may thus be through activation of SK channels, not specifically through activation of IK channels.

The well-known β-adrenergic antagonist, propanolol, may also act as an IK channel activator, as single-channel studies have shown that the drug increases the Ca^{2+}-sensitivity of IK channels [Schwarz et al., 1989].

Table 2. Pharmocolgy of cloned and native IK channels.

	hIK [a] in CHO	hIK [b] in Oocytes	hIK1 [c] in HEK-293	hIK [d] in HEK-293	hIK [e] in CHO	hIK [f] in COS-7	hIK [g] in CHO	hIK [i] in T cells	hIK [h] in RBC
Block by peptide toxins IC_{50}; K_d or K_i in nM									
Maurotoxin							1		
Charybdotoxin	2	2.5	10	28	1.7			6	5.4
Stichdactyla toxin				291					24.5
Margatoxin			>100	459				>10	
Kaliotoxin			>1000	>50					
Iberiotoxin		>50	>1000	>300	>200			>200	>1000
Apamin	>100	>100	>1000	>100	>100			>100	>100
Scyllatoxin			>1000						
Block by antimycotics IC_{50}; K_d or K_i in μM									
Clotrimazole		0.025	0.39	0.15	0.056	0.070		0.040	0.050
Miconazole				0.79					
Econazole				2.4		12			
Ketoconazole		>10		>5		30		>1	
Block by Ca^{2+} channel antagonists IC_{50}; K_d or K_i in μM									
Nitrendipine				0.027		0.9		<1	0.100
Nimodipine						1.0			
Nifedipine				1.5		4			
Verapamil				72					
Diltiazem				154					

Table 2. Pharmocolgy of cloned and native IK channels.

	hIK [a] in CHO	hIK [b] in Oocytes	hIK1 [c] in HEK-293	hIK [d] in HEK-293	hIK [e] in CHO	hIK [f] in COS-7	hIK [g] in CHO	hIK [i] in T cells	hIK [h] in RBC
Block by miscellaneous compounds IC_{50}; K_d or K_i in μM									
ICA-17043								0.025	0.01
TRAM-34						0.02			
Cetiedil				79					25
UCL1608									1.5
Dequalinium Chl.				>1					>10
UCL1407									0.9
D-tubocurarine								>250	
Ba^{2+}	340								
Cs^{+}	>1000								
TEA	>5 mM		30,000						

(a) [Joiner et al., 1997]. Experiments performed with 130 mM K^+ in the pipette and 3 mM K^+ in the bath solution. $[Ca^{2+}]_{free}$ = 907 nM. Dose-response at +80 mV from whole-cell experiments. IK was named hSK4 in this study.

(b) [Ishii et al., 1997]. Experiments performed in symmetrical 120 mM K^+. Dose-response at –100 mV at outside-out patches. hIK was named hIK1 in this study.

(c) [Logsdon et al., 1997]. Experiments performed in symmetrical 160 mM K^+ with $[Ca^{2+}]_{free}$ buffered at 1 μM. Dose-response at –95 mV from whole-cell experiments. IK was named $hK_{CA}4$ in this study.

(d) [Jensen et al., 1998]. Experiments performed in symmetrical 144 mM K^+ with $[Ca^{2+}]_{free}$ buffered at 300 nM. The IC_{50} values were calculated from single concentration non-equalibrium whole-cell experiments at +80 mV. IK was named hIK1 in this study.

(e) [Khanna et al., 1999]. Experiments performed with 130 mM K^+ in the pipette and 5 mM K^+ in the bath solution. $[Ca^{2+}]_{free}$ = 1.1 μM. Dose-response from whole-cell experiments. IK was named hSK4 in this study.

(f) [Ghanshani et al., 2000]. Experiments performed with 145 mM K^+ in the pipette and 4.5 mM K^+ in the bath solution. $[Ca^{2+}]_{free}$ = 1 μM. Reduction of slope conductance at –80 mV from whole-cell experiments. hIK was named IKCA1 in this study.

(g) [Castle et al., 2003] Experiments performed with 130 mM K^+ in the pipette and 5.4 mM K^+ in the bath solution. $[Ca^{2+}]_{free}$ = 1 μM. Reduction of slope conductance at 0 mV from whole-cell experiments. IK was named hIK1 in this study.

(h) Data compiled from [Brugnara et al., 1995; Roxburgh et al., 2001; Ellory et al., 1992; Dunn, 1998]. Most data obtained using 86-Rb flux studies. hIK was named IK in most of these studies.

(i) Data compiled from [Khanna et al., 1999; Ghanshani et al., 2000; Jensen et al., 1999]. 1: Experiments performed with 145 mM K^+ in the pipette and 4.5 mM K^+ in the bath solution. $[Ca^{2+}]_{free}$ = 1 μM. Reduction of slope conductance at –80 mV from whole-cell experiments. IK was named IKCA1 [Ghanshani et al., 2000] in this study. 2: The bath K^+ concentrations were 5 mM for lymphoblasts, with 140 mM K^+ in the pipette and a calculated $[Ca^{2+}]_{free}$ = 1.1μM. IK was named hSK4 in this study [Khanna et al., 1999]. 3: Experiments performed with 150 mM K^+ in the pipette and 5 mM K^+ in the bath solution. $[Ca^{2+}]_{free}$ = 1 μM. [Jensen et al., 1999].

ON THE ROLE OF IK CHANNELS IN SICKLE CELL ANAEMIA

Sickle cell anaemia is a genetic disease characterized by a mutation in hemoglobin (Hb) resulting in hemoglobin polymerization and resultant cell deformation (sickling) under low oxygen conditions. The mutation is in the haemoglobin ß-chain and gives rise to haemoglobin S (HbS). The sickling process is accelerated as the concentration of HbS increases. In the majority of patients suffering from sickle cell anaemia, dehydrated erythrocytes are found in varying quantities. These cells are thought to be critically involved in the pathophysiology of the vaso-occlusion as it occurs in sickle cell anaemia. The current therapy of sickle cell anaemia is very limited with respect to both efficacy and duration.

Optimal delivery of oxygen to respiring tissues requires very high concentrations of haemoglobin in red blood cells (up to 32-34 g/dl). HbS has, however, an increased tendency to form hydrophobic interactions with other HbS molecules, resulting in the formation of large polymer aggregates. Most acute and chronic manifestations of sickle cell anaemia are not due to anaemia, but rather to an impaired blood flow due to vaso-occlusion and a blockade of capillaries and venules by sickle red blood cells.

A new approach to treat sickle cell anaemia is based on the observation that the HbS polymerisation rate is concentration-dependent and dilution of the haemoglobin by increased hydration (or decreased dehydration) of the erythrocytes will delay the onset of the sickling process. Prevention of erythrocyte dehydration represents an efficient experimental strategy due to a very steep concentration-dependency of HbS polymerisation. The dense dehydrated erythrocytes are important contributors to the vaso-occlusive manifestations of sickle cell anaemia, and prevention or inhibition of the dehydration process may thus result in a reduced number of sickle crises. Such an approach is based on the use of inhibitors of the ion transport pathways that mediate the dehydration of the erythrocytes. Haemoglobin SS erythrocytes have increased amounts of calcium stored in intracellular vesicles, but maintain normal steady-state concentrations of Ca^{2+} in the cytosol [Lew et al., 1985]. The HbS polymerisation and subsequent cell sickling might result in localized transient increases in cytosolic calcium, which results in a large K^+ loss concomitant with a loss of Cl^- and water [Rhoda et al., 1990; Murphy et al., 1987]. It is now well established that the Gardós channel is activated in sickle cells and is a major cause of salt loss and dehydration. Consequently, IK channel blockers have potential in the symptomatic treatment of sickle cell anaemia. This channel can be activated *in vitro* in sickle erythrocytes by deoxygenation, which results in mobilization of calcium from the external medium [Ohnishi et al., 1989; Brugnara et al., 1993]. The role of the Gardós channel in the dehydration process *in vivo* has been addressed using a mouse model of sickle cell anaemia (the SAD mouse). Under both nomoxic and hypoxic conditions, the Gardós channel facilitates cell dehydration, a process that can be prevented by pharmacological inhibition of the channel [De Franceschi et al., 1994; 1999].

IK Channel Blockers as a Strategy for Treatment of Sickle Cell Anaemia

Carlo Brugnara and co-workers have in a series of papers showed that: 1) CLT blocks dehydration of sickle erythrocytes in vitro [Brugnara et al., 1993), 2) CLT blocks the Gardós channel and reverses red cell dehydration after per oral administration to SAD mice [De

Franceschi et al., 1994; 1999), 3) CLT blocks the Gardós channel upon dosing in healthy human volunteers [Brugnara et al., 1996], and finally that 4) CLT improves the erythrocyte state of hydration in patients with sickle cell disease [Brugnara et al., 1996].

This work has formed the basis for the development of novel chemical entities, and currently one compound, ICA-17043 is in clinical development for sickle cell anaemia.

Clotrimazole

CLT inhibits the dehydration of sickle cells in vitro [Brugnara et al., 1993]. Further, CLT blocks the Gardós channel in vivo in SAD mice after oral administration. The systemic administration of CLT to SAD mice results in an increased K^+ content in erythrocytes, an increase in the hematocrit, a reduction in erythrocyte density and in mean corpuscular haemoglobin concentration [De Franceschi et al., 1994; 1996]. This study provided the proof-of concept in animals for the treatment of sickle cell anaemia by prevention of erythrocyte dehydration by Gardós channel blockade, and as such validated the mechanism of action.

Unfortunately, besides the fungal P450 enzymes, CLT also inhibits mammalian P450 enzymes. In humans, CLT is absorbed via the gastrointestinal tract after oral administration. Side effects of CLT administration include gastrointestinal symptoms such as nausea, vomiting and diarrhoea; transient increases in liver enzymes alanine aminotransferase (ALT) and aspartate aminotransferase (AST), chemical cystitis, contact dermatitis, and rarely neurological effects such as anxiety, vertigo and hallucinations (seen only at the highest doses) [Weuta, 1974; Sawyer et al., 1975, Seo et al. 1977; Tettenborn, 1974]. Also in humans, oral administration of CLT results in an inhibition of the Gardós channel. The inhibition is due to metabolites of CLT rather CLT itself [Brugnara et al., 1995; Rifai et al., 1995]. In patients suffering from sickle cell anaemia, oral administration of CLT results in Gardós channel inhibition, an increased K^+ content in erythrocytes, and a reduction in erythrocyte density and in mean corpuscular haemoglobin concentration [Brugnara et al., 1996]. CLT only had an effect on mature erythrocytes, whereas sickled reticulocytes were unaltered. Side effects at 20 mg/kg per day were mild, whereas at 30 mg/kg/day significant nausea and vomiting as well as increases in plasma ALT and AST levels that returned to normal levels when CLT was withdrawn. Effects on the liver had previously only been observed at much higher doses of CLT (above 100 mg/kg/day), and the increased sensitivity of sickle cell patients may be explained by an altered liver function of these patients. Despite these adverse affects, this study indicated that inhibition of the Gardós channel might have beneficial effects on erythrocyte function in patients with sickle cell anaemia [Brugnara et al., 1996].

Development of CLT as an orally administered drug in humans for the treatment of sickle anaemia is troublesome since CLT is poorly absorbed, has a short biological half-life after oral administration, and, furthermore, the effects on liver enzymes are a major limiting factor in achieving complete and sustained long-term effects.

ICA-17043

Despite the pharmacokinetic and toxicological problems associated with CLT, this compound has inspired new medicinal chemistry aimed at synthesizing a non-toxic, high-affinity blocker of the IK channel. One such compound is ICA-17043 (See Fig. 1). The main difference between CLT and ICA-17043 is that the imidiazole connected to the triphenylmethane group in CLT has been replaced by a primary amide in ICA-17043. Further, ICA-17043 possesses fluorogroups in the *para* position in two of the aryl rings rather than the *ortho*chloro substitutions found in CLT. In human red blood cells, ICA-17043 inhibited the Ca^{2+}-induced $^{86}RB^{+}$ efflux with an IC_{50} of 11 ±2 nM. In comparison, the IC_{50} of CLT in the same assay was estimated at 100 (±12) nM [Stocker et al., 2003]. In vitro, ICA-17043 dose-dependently inhibited the increase in cellular haemoglobin as induced by activation of the Gardós channel with a Ca^{2+} ionophore in human red blood cells. This effect indicates a potential for the treatment of sickle cell anaemia, which has been confirmed in studies using SAD mice using a dosing regime of 10mg/kg twice daily [Stocker et al., 2003]. ICA-17043 significantly inhibited the Gardós channel activity measured at day 11 and day 21 of a three-week dosing regiment of ICA-17043. The inhibition of the Gardós channel was accompanied by an increase in cellular K^{+} content, an increase in hematocrit and a decrease in erythrocyte density, altogether indicating a reduction in red cell dehydration [Stocker et al., 2003]. Clinical studies are currently in progress to assess the efficacy and safety of ICA-17043 in patients with sickle cell anaemia. The study is designed as a multi-center, twelve-week, randomised, double-blind, dose-range finding study in combination with or without hydroxyurea in patients with SCD aimed at estimating safety and efficacy of ICA-17043. The total enrolment is expected at 90 patients. The clinical outcome will be awaited with much interest as this will document whether the concept of inhibiting IK channels for symptomatic treatment of sickle cell anaemia will prove valid.

SUMMARY

The Gardós channel is a Ca^{2+}- activated, intermediate-conductance K^{+} channel encoded by KCNN4. Pharmacological inhibition of the Gardós channel is a promising therapeutic option in the treatment of sickle cell disease. Currently, ICA-17043, a specific inhibitor of the Gardóschannel, is under clinical evaluation in patients suffering from sickle cell disease. Data from this study is eagerly awaited.

REFERENCES

[1] Alvarez, J.; Montero, M.; Garcia-Sancho, J. (1992) *J. Biol. Chem.,* **267**, 11789-11793.

[2] Andersson, D.A., Zygmunt, P.M., Movahed, P., Andersson, T.L.G. and Högestätt, E.D. (2000) *British J. Pharmacol.*, **129**, 1490-1496.

[3] Arnold, S.J., Facer, P., Yiangou, Y., Chen, M.X., Plumpton, C., Tate, S.N., Bountra, C., Chan, C.L.H., Williams, N.S. and Anand, P. (2003) *Neuroreport*, **14**, 191-195.

[4] Barrett, J.N.; Magleby, K.L. and Pallota, B.S. (1982) *J. Physiol. (Lond),* **331**, 211-230.

[5] Benjamin, L.J, Berkowitz, L.R.; Orringer, E.; Mankad, V.N.; Prasad, A.S.; Lewkow, L.M.; Chillar, R.K.; and Peterson, C.M. (1986) *Blood,* **67**, 1442-1447.

[6] Benton, D.C.; Roxburgh, C.J.; Ganelli, C.R.; Shiner, M.A. and Jenkinson, D.H. (1999) *Br. J. Pharmacol.*, **126**, 169-178

[7] Berkowitz, L.R. and Orringer, E.P. (1982) *Blood Cells,* **8**, 283-288.

[8] Blum, R.M. and Hoffman, J.F. (1972) *Biochim Biophys. Res. Comm.,* **46**, 1146-1152.

[9] Boettger, M.K., Till, S., Chen, M.X., Anand, U., Otto, W.R:, Plumpton, C., Trezise, D.J., Tate, S.N., Bountra, C., Coward, K., Birch, R. and Anand, P. (2002) *Brain*, **125**, 252-263

[10] Brugnara C, De Franceschi L, Alper SL. (1993) *J Biol Chem.*, **268**, 8760-8768.

[11] Brugnara, C.; De Franceschi, L.; Alper, S.L. (1993) *J. Clin. Invest.,* **92**, 520-526

[12] Brugnara C.; De Franceschi L.; Armsby CC.; Saadane N.; Trudel M.; Beuzard Y.; Rittenhouse A.; Rifai N.; Platt O.; Alper SL. (1995) *Ann N Y Acad Sci.,* **763**, 262-271.

[13] Brugnara, C.; Armsby, C.C.; De Franseschi, L.; Crest, M.; Euclaire, M.F.; and Alper, S.L. (1995) *J. Membr. Biol.,* **147**, 71-82.

[14] Brugnara C, Gee B, Armsby CC, Kurth S, Sakamoto M, Rifai N, Alper SL, Platt OS. (1996) *J Clin Invest.*, **97**, 1227-1234.

[15] Burgess G.M.; Claret, M. and Jenkinson, D.H. (1981) *J. Physiol. (Lond),* **317**, 67-90.

[16] Castle, N.A. and Strong, P.N. (1986) *Febs Lett.,* **209**, 117-121.

[17] Castle, N.A.; London DO, Creech C, Fajloun Z, Stocker JW, Sabatier JM. (2003) *Mol. Pharmacol.*, **63**, 409-418

[18] Christensen, O. and Hoffmann, E.K. (1992) *J. Membrane Biol.*, **129**, 13-36

[19] Christophersen, P. (1991) *J. Membr. Biol.,* **119**: 75-83.

[20] Christophersen, P. and Bennekou, P. (1990) *Biochim. Biophys. Acta,* **1030**, 183-187.

[21] De Franceschi L, Saadane N, Trudel M, Alper SL, Brugnara C, Beuzard Y. (1994) *J Clin Invest.*, **93**, 1670-1676.

[22] Demo, S.D. and Yellen, G. (1992) *Biophys. J.,* **61**, 639-648.

[23] Devor, D.C., Singh, A.K., Bridges, R.J. and Frizzell, R.A. (1996) *Am. J. Physiol.*, **271**, L785-L795.

[24] Devor, D.C.; Singh, A.K.; Frizzell, R.A. and Bridges, R.J. (1996) *Am. J. Physiol.,* **271**, L775-L784.

[25] Doyle, D.A.; Morais Cabral, J.; Pfuetzner, R.A.; Kuo, A.; Gulbis, J.M.; Cohen, S.L.; Chait, B.T. and MacKinnon, R. (1998) *Science*, **280**, 69-77.

[26] Dunn, P.M. (1998) *J. Membr. Biol.,* **165**, 133-143.

[27] Ellory, J.C.; Culliford, S.J.; Smith, P.A.; Wolowyk, M.W. and Knaus, E.E. (1994) *Br. J. Pharmacol.,* **111**, 903-905.

[28] Ellory, J.C.; Kirk, K.; Culliford, S.J.; Nash, G.B.; Stuart, J. (1992) *Febs Lett.,* **296**, 219-221.

[29] Espinosa, L.; Paret, L.; Ojeda, C.; Tourneur, Y.; Delmas, P.D. and Chenu, C. (2002) *J. Cell Sci.*, **115**, 3837-3848

[30] Fajloun, Z.; Ferrat G.; Carlieri, E.; Fathallah, M.; Lecomte, C.; Sandozi, G.; Luccio, E.; Mabruk, E.; Legros, C.; Darbon, H.; Rochat, H.; Sabatier, J.-M.; and Waardi, M.D. (2000) *J. Biol. Chem.*, **275**, 13605-13612

[31] Fehlau, R.; Grygorczyk, R.; Fuhrmann, G.F. and Schwarz, W. (1989) *Biochim. Biophys. Acta,* **978**, 37-42.

[32] Furness, J.B., Kunze, W.A:, Bertrand, P.P., Clerc, N. and Bornstein, J.C. (1998) *Prog. Neurobiol.*, **54**, 1-18.

[33] Gardós, G. (1958) *Biochim. Biophys. Acta,* **30**, 653-654.

[34] Ghanshani, S., Wulff, H., Miller, M.J., Rohm, H., Neben, A., Gutman, G.A., Cahalan, M.D. and Chandy, K.G. (2000) *J. Biol. Chem.*, **275**, 37137-37149

[35] Ghanshani, S.; Coleman, M.; Gustavsson, P.; Wu, A.C.; Gargus, J.J.; Gutman, G.A.; Dahl, N.; Mohrenweiser, H. and Chandy, K.G. (1998) *Genomics* **51** (1), 160-161

[36] Grissmer, S., Nguyen, A.N. and Cahalan, M.D. (1993) *J. Gen. Physiol.*, **102**, 601-630.

[37] Grygorczyk, R. (1987) *Biochim. Biophys. Acta,* **902**, 159-168.

[38] Grygorczyk, R. and Schwarz, W. (1983) *Cell Calcium,* **4**, 499-510.

[39] Grygorczyk, R. and Schwarz, W. (1985) *Eur. Biophys. J.,* **12**, 57-65.

[40] Grygorczyk, R.; Schwarz, W. and Passow, H. (1984) *Biophys. J.,* **45**, 693-698.

[41] Hamill O. P. (1981) *J. Physiol. (Lond),* **319**, 97-98p.

[42] Heinz, A. and Passow, H. (1980) *J. Membr. Biol.,* **57**, 119-131.

[43] Hodgkin, A.L. and Keynes, R.D. (1955) *J. Physiol. (Lond.),* **128**, 61 – 88.

[44] Hoffman J. K. and Blum, R.M. (1977) in *Erythrocytes, Trombocytes and Leucocytes* (Gerlach, E. Maser, K. Beutch, E. and Wilmans, W, eds.) Georg Thieme. Stuttgart. pp. 66 – 77.

[45] Hoffman, J.F.; Joiner, W.; Nehrke, K.; Potapova, O.; Foye, K. and Wickrema, A. (2003) *Proc Natl Acad Sci U S A.* **100** (12), 7366-7371

[46] Ishii, T.M.; Maylie J.; and Adelman J.P. (1997) *J. Biol. Chem.,* **272,** 23195-23200.

[47] Ishii, T.M.; Silvia, C.; Hirschberg, B.; Bond, C.T.; Adelman, J.P. and Maylie J. (1997) *Proc. Natl. Acad. Sci. USA.,* **94**, 11651-11656.

[48] Jensen, B.S., Hertz, M., Christophersen, P.C., Madsen, L.S. (2002) *Expert Opin. Ther. Targets,* **6**, 1-14.

[49] Jensen, B.S., Ødum, N., Jorgensen, N.K., Christophersen, P.C., Olesen, S.-P. (1999) *PNAS,* **96**, 10917-10921.

[50] Jensen, B.S.; Strøbæk, D.; Christophersen, P; Jørgensen, T.D; Hansen, C.; Silahtaroglu, A.; Olesen, S.P.; Ahring, P.K, (1998) *Am. J. Physiol.*, **275**, C848-C856.

[51] Joiner, W.J.; Wang, L.Y.; Tang, M.D. and Kaczmarek L.K. (1997) *Proc. Natl. Acad. Sci. USA.,* **94,** 11013-11018.

[52] Kaji, D.M. (1990) *Am. J. Physiol.,* **259**, C332-C339.

[53] Khanna, R.; Chang, M.C.; Joiner, W.J.; Kaczmarek, L.K. and Schlichter, L.C. (1999) *J. Biol. Chem.* **274** (21), 14838-14349

[54] Knauf, P.A.; Riordan, J.R.; Schuhman, B.; Wood-Guth, I. Passow, H. (1975) *J. Membr. Biol.,* **25**, 1-22.

[55] Knaus, H.G.; Folander, K.; Garcia-Calvo, M.; Garcia, M.L.; Kaczorowski, G.J.; Smith, M. and Swanson, R. (1994) *J. Biol. Chem.,* **269**, 17274-17278.

[56] Köhler, RF., Degenhardt, C., Kühn, M., Runkel, N., Paul, M. And Hoyer, J. (2000) *Circ. Res.*, **87**, 496-503.

[57] Lampugnani, M.G., Colotta, F., Polentarutti, N., Pedenovi, M., Mantovani, A. and Dejana, E. (1990) *Blood,* **76**, 1173-1180.

[58] Lassen, U.V.; Pape, L. and Vestergaard-Bogind, B. (1976) *J. Membr. Biol.,* **26**, 51-70.

[59] Lassen, U.V.; Pape, L.; Vestergaard-Bogind, B. and Bengtson, O. (1974) *J. Membr. Biol.,* **18**, 125-144.

[60] Latorre, R. and Miller, C. (1983) *J. Membr. Biol.,* **71**, 11-30.

[61] Latorre, R.; Vergara, C. and Moczydlowski, E. (1983) *Cell Calcium,* **4,** 343-357.

[62] Lew, V.L.; Muallem, S. and Seymour, C.A. (1982) *Nature,* **296**, 742-744.

[63] Logsdon, N.J.; Kang, J.; Togo, J.A.; Christian, E.P. and Aiyar, J. (1997) *J. Biol. Chem.*, **272**, 32723-32726.

[64] Lückhoff, A. and Busse, R. (1990) *Pflügers Arch.*, **416**, 305-311.

[65] Macey, R.I.; Adorante, J.S. and Orme, F.W. (1978) *Biochim. Biophys. Acta,* **512**, 284 – 295.

[66] McCann, J.D.; Matsuda, J. Garcia, M. Kaczorowski, G.; Welsh, M.J. (1990) *Am. J. Physiol.,* **258**, L334-L342.

[67] Nehrke, K., Quinn, C.C. and Begenisich, T. (2003) *Am. J. Physiol.*, **284**, C535-C546.

[68] Ohya, S., Kimura, S., Kitsukawa, M., Muraki, K., Watanabe, M. and Imaizumi, Y. (2000) *Jnp. J. Pharmacol.*, **84**, 97-100.

[69] Olesen, S.-P. and Bundgaard, M. (1993) *Circ. Res.*, **73**, 492-495.

[70] Parseti, M., Choquet, D., Diu, A. And Korn, H. (1992) *J. Immunol.*, **148**, 3361-3368.

[71] Pedersen, K.A., Schrøder, R.L., Skaaning-Jensen, B., Strøbæk, D., Olesen, S.-P. And Christophersen, P. (1999) *Biochem. Biophys. Acta*, **1420**, 231-240

[72] Pena, T.L. & Rane, S.G. (1999) *J. Membrane Biol.*, **172**, 249-257

[73] Pena, T.L., Chen, S.H., Konieczny, S.F. and Rane, S.G. (2000) *J. Biol. Chem.*, **275**, 13677-13682

[74] Rane, S.G. (2000) *Biochem. Biophys. Res. Commun.*, **269**, 457-463

[75] Rauer, H.; Lanigan, M.D.; Pennington, M.W:, Aiyar, J.; Ghanshani, S.; Cahalan, M.D; Norton, R.S. and Chandy, K.G. (2000). *J. Biol. Chem.*, **275**, 1201-1208

[76] Reed, P.W. (1976) *J. Biol. Chem.,* **251**: 3489-3494.

[77] Reed, P.W. and Lardy, H.A. (1972) *J. Biol. Chem.,* **247**, 6970-6977.

[78] Reichstein, E. and Rothstein, A. (1981) *J. Membr. Biol.,* **59**, 57-63.

[79] Riordan, J.R. and Passow, H. (1971) *Biochim Biophys. Acta,* **249**, 601-605.

[80] Rittenhouse A.; Rifai N.; Platt O.; Alper SL. (1995) *Ann N Y Acad Sci.,* **763**, 262-271.

[81] Roxburgh, C.J.; Ganelli, C.R.; Athmani, S.; Bisi, A.; Quaglia, W.; Benton, D.C.; Shiner, M.A.; Malik-Hall, M.; Haylett, D.G. and Jenkinson, D.H. (2001) *J. Med. Chem.*, **44**, 3244-3253

[82] Sah, P. (1996) *Trends Neurosci.,* **19**, 150-154.

[83] Sauvé, R., Parant, C., Simoneau, C. and Roy, G. (1988) *Pflügers Arch.*, **412**, 469-481.

[84] Sauve, R., Simoneau, C., Monette, R. and Roy, G. (1986) *J. Membrane Biol.*, **92**, 269-282.

[85] Schreiber, M. and Salkoff, L. (1997) *Biophys. J.,* **73**, 1355-1363.

[86] Schwarz, W., Keim, H., Fehlau, R. and Furhmann, G.F. (1989) *Biochem. Biophys. Acta*, **978**, 32-36

[87] Shah, M. and Haylett, D.G. (2000) *Br. J. Pharmacol.,* **129,** 627-630.

[88] Shao, L.R.; Halvorsrud, R.; Borg-Graham, L.; Storm, J.F. (1999) *J. Physiol.*, **521**, 135-146.

[89] Simons, T.J.B. (1982) *J. Membr. Biol.,* **66**, 235-247.

[90] Singh, A.K., Devor, D.C., Gerlach, A.C., Gondor, M., Pilewski, J.M. and Bridges, R.J. (2000) *J. Pharmacol. Exp. Ther.*, **292**, 778-787

[91] Smith, C.; Phillips, M. and Miller, C. (1986) *J. Biol. Chem.,* **261**, 14607-146.

[92] Stampe P. and Vestergaard-Bogind, B. (1989) *J. Membr. Biol.,* **112**, 9-14.

[93] Stocker, J.W.; De Franceschi, L.; McNaughton-Smith, G.A.; Corrocher, R.; Beuzard, Y. and Brugnara, C. (2003) *Blood*; **101** (6), 2412-2418

[94] Strøbæk, D. Jørgensen, T.D.; Christophersen, P.; Ahring, P.K. and Olesen, S.P. (2000) *B. J. Pharmacol.,* **129**, 991-999.

[95] Stummann, T.C:, Poulsen, J.H., hay-Schmidt, A., Grunnet, M., Klaerke, D.A:, Rasmussen, H.B., Olesen, S.-P. and Jorgensen, N.K. (2003) *Pflügers Arch.*, **446**, 78-87.

[96] Syme, C.A:, Gerlah, A.C., Singh, A.K. and Devor, D.C. (2000) *Am. J. Physiol.*, **278**, C570-C581

[97] Tseng-Crank, J.; Foster, C.D.; Krause, J.D.; Mertz, R.; Godinot, N.; DiChiara, T.J. and Reinhart, P.H. (1994) *Neuron,* **13**, 1315-1330.

[98] Ussing, H.H. (1948) *Acta Physiol. Scand.,* **19**, 43 – 56.

[99] Vaca, L., Licea, A. and Possani, L.D. (1996) *Am. J. Physiol.*, **270**, C819-C824.

[100] Valdeolmillos, M., Garcia-Sanchos, J. and Herreros, B. (1982) *Biochem. Biophys. Acta.*, **685**, 273-278

[101] Vergara, C.; Latorre, R.; Marrion, N.V. and Adelman, J.P. (1998) *Curr. Opin. Neurobiol.,* **8**, 321-329.

[102] Verheugen, J.A:, Vijverberg, H.P., Oortgiesen, M., Cahalan, M.D. (1995) *J. Gen. Physiol.*, **105**, 765-794.

[103] Vestergaard-Bogind, B.; Stampe, P. and Christophersen, P. (1985) *J. Membr. Biol.*, **88**, 67 – 75.

[104] Vestergaard-Bogind, B.; Stampe, P. and Christophersen, P. (1987) *J. Membr. Biol.,* **95**, 121-130.

[105] Vogalis, F., Harvey, J.R., Neylon, C.B. and Furness, J.B. (2002) *Clin. Exp. Pharmacol. Physiol.*, **29**, 935-943.

[106] Vogalis, F., Zhang, Y. and Goyal, R.K. (1998) *Biochem. Biophys. Acta.*, **1371**, 309-316.

[107] Weskamp, M., Seidl, W., and Grissmer, S. (2000) *J. Membrane Biol.*, **178**, 11-20

[108] Wilbrandt, W. (1940) *Pflügers Arch.* **243**, 519-536.

[109] Wolff, D.; Cecchi, X.; Spalvins, A.; and Canessa, M. (1988) *J. Membr. Biol.,* **106**, 243-252.

[110] Wood, P.G. (1984) *Biochim. Biophys. Acta,* **774**, 103-109.

[111] Wulff, H., Miller, M.J., Hansel, W., grissmer, S., Cahalan, M.D. and Chandy, K.G. (2000) *Proc. Natl. Acad. Sci. USA*, **97**, 8151-8156

[112] Xia, X.M.; Fakler, B.; Rivard, A.; Wayman, G.; Johnson-Pais, T.; Keen, J.E.; Ishii, T.; Hirschberg, B.; Bond, C.T.; Lutsenko, S.; Maylie, J. and Adelman J.P. (1998) *Nature*, **395,** 503-507.

[113] Yingst, D.R. and Hoffman, J.E. (1984) *J. Gen. Physiol.,* **83**, 19-45.

[114] Young R.J.; Smith, T.C.; and Levinson, C. (1993) *Biochim. Biophys Acta.,* **1146,** 81-86.

In: Focus on Sickle Cell Research
Editor: Ralph L. Plasmar, pp. 215-229

ISBN 1-59033-920-7

Chapter XIV

EFFECT OF G6PD DEFICIENCY UPON SICKLE CELL ANEMIA AS REFLECTED BY ERYTHROCYTE PYRIDINE NUCLEOTIDE REDOX POTENTIAL

S. Al-Ateeq and A. K. Al-Ali*

Department of Clinical Biochemistry, College of Medicine,
King Faisal University, Dammam, Saudi Arabia.

ABSTRACT

Sickle cell anemia (SCA) and glucose 6 phosphate dehydrogenase (G6PD) deficiency are common genetic abnormalities among the population of the Eastern Province of Saudi Arabia. The incidences of these abnormalities are particularly high in this area where malaria was hyperendemic. Erythrocytes with coexisting SCA and G6PD deficiency represent a haematological condition in which there is an association between an increased oxidant production with a condition associated with an impaired antioxidant defence mechanism. The ratio of reduced (NAD(P)H) to total pyridine nucleotide [NAD(P)(T) i.e. NAD(P)H plus $NAD(P)^+$] can be used as an indicator of the redox status of erythrocytes. Therefore, we studied the effect of the interaction of SCA and G6PD deficiency as reflected by erythrocytes pyridine nucleotide redox potential. Through the utilization of a spectrophotometric cycling assay, the NAD and NADP redox potentials were determined. Erythrocytes NAD redox potential in subjects with SCA, G6PD deficiency or SCA with G6PD deficiency were significantly lower when compared to normal. This was mainly due to a significant increase in oxidized NAD (NAD^+) and NAD_T in these groups. Similarly, the significant decrease in NADP redox potential in G6PD deficient erythrocytes with or without SCA was coupled with a significant increase in oxidized NADP ($NADP^+$) and $NADP_T$ when compared to normal or sickle RBCs. There was no difference in NAD redox potential of sickle erythrocytes when compared to those with both SCA and G6PD deficiency. On the other hand, although,

* Correspondence to: Dr. A K Al-Ali, Chairman, Department of Clinical Biochemistry, King Faisal University, P.O.Box 2114, Dammam 31451, Kingdom of Saudi Arabia, ameinali@hotmail.com

sickle erythrocytes had a significant increase in NADP redox potential compared to those with combined SCA and G6PD deficiency, it cannot be concluded that there is a disadvantage of the interaction on the redox state of the RBCs since other factors are involved. Interestingly, the values of erythrocytes NAD and NADP redox potentials of Saudi subjects with SCA or with the combination of SCA and G6PD deficiency are higher than those reported for African Americans with SCA. The higher levels of NAD redox potential in Saudi subjects may contribute toward the decrease in oxidative susceptibility of sickle RBCs. This finding is consistent with the milder clinical form of SCA reported in the local population. However, the high fetal hemoglobin in Saudis with SCA is considered to be the major ameliorating factor.

INTRODUCTION

Both glucose-6-phosphate dehydrogenase (G6PD) deficiency and sickle cell anemia (SCA) are commonly found in the Eastern Province of Saudi Arabia where malaria was hyperendemic [1-6]. Mediterranean G6PD which is prevalent in the area is a polymorphic, severely deficient variant, underlying not only favism but also neonatal jaundice and acute hemolytic anemia triggered by drugs or by infection [7-8]. The molecular basis of G6PD-Mediterranean is due to a single point mutation (C-T substitution) resulting in a serine to phenyl alanine replacement at amino acid position 188 [9-10]. The frequency of G6PD deficiency among the population of the Eastern Province of Saudi Arabia is considered to be one of the highest in the world [1]. Other variants such as G6PD A^- and G6PD Aures are also present among the population but in a lower frequency [8, 11]. This is believed to be due to gene flow from the surrounding countries [10]. G6PD is responsible for the generation of NADPH which is a cofactor involved in maintaining GSH in the reduced form. Due to a marked enzyme deficiency in G6PD deficient cells, these cells are unable to increase the rate of NADPH production to respond adequately to oxidative stress. This results in a decrease in reduced glutathione (GSH) concentrations which enhances the formation of Heinz bodies and contributes to increased membrane rigidity [12]. Under oxidant stress, the accumulation of oxidizing species with subsequent membrane oxidation precedes hemolysis of G6PD deficient cells and leads to decreased RBC life span.

Sickle cell anemia also occurs in high frequency in the Eastern Province of Saudi Arabia [2]. This genetic disease is extremely varied in its clinical manifestations. Perrine et al. has revealed a remarkably benign clinical course of Saudi sickle cell disease compared to that found in African Americans [3]. The complete nucleotide sequence of β-globin gene in this population has been determined and shows the expected A-T substitution which results in substitution of glutamic acid by valine in position 6 of the β-globin chain. The intracellular polymerization of sickle hemoglobin that occurs when sickle erythrocytes are partially deoxygenated in their hypoxic conditions of microcirculation is considered as the primary cause of clinical symptoms of SCA. The characteristic mild clinical picture exhibited by Saudi subjects with SCA has been ascribed in part to the unusually high levels of fetal haemoglobin and to the fact that the average age of the RBC could be increased with the elevation of fetal haemoglobin [3, 13]. It has been proven, by use of transgenic mice that progressive increase in HbF from less than 3% to 20% to 40% correlated with a progressive increase in hematocrit and progressive decrease in reticulocyte count [14]. However, the complex pathophysiology of the disease is influenced not only by multiple genetic factors but also by non genetic ones affecting phenotypic diversity. Oxidative pathobiology has been suggested to play an important role in modulating the disease expression [15].

The oxidant stress in SCA may play an important role in the sickling process, the development of vasoocclusion and the shortened lifetime of sickle red blood cells [15-19]. Unstable haemoglobin variants like sickle haemoglobin are more readily oxidized to methemoglobin than normal. The rate of oxidation of sickle haemoglobin is approximately three times as fast as that for normal on lipid (1.7-fold faster for HbS than for HbA in solution) [19]. In addition, it is well recognized that iron plays a central role in generating reactive oxygen species such as the potent oxidant hydroxyl radical [20]. Under normal conditions iron is transported and stored bound to transferrin, ferritin and heme proteins which minimize its reactions with reduced oxygen metabolites [21-22]. However iron released from haemoglobin or its derivatives, is able to induce oxidative reactions and membrane damage [23, 24]. Unstable haemoglobins, such as sickle haemoglobin undergo rapid autooxidation with consequent release of increased amount of free iron [24]. Therefore, the deposition of iron in various forms in sickled membranes creates another source of potential deleterious cell damage [25]. They catalyse the conversion of hydrogen peroxide into the reactive species namely hydroxyl radical. It has been reported that sickle RBCs generate twice the normal level of hydroxyl radicals [24]. This increased generation of a highly reactive species can initiate self amplifying redox reactions with subsequent acceleration of haemoglobin oxidation into methemoglobin. The methemoglobin formation is a proximate step in haemoglobin denaturation and the production of hemichrome [26]. Thus, the tendency of a haemoglobin molecule to oxidize and ultimately form hemichrome can be considered as being an important determinant of the severity of the anemia and its clinical manifestation [27].

It is a well known fact that the removal of old erythrocytes from blood is carried out by mononuclear phagocytes that can distinguish senescent from mature cells. The recognition of senescent cells depends on the appearance of a neo-antigen on the surface of these cells, to which autologous antibodies bind [28-30]. The latter ones attach to macrophages, initiating the elimination of old cells. It has been suggested that oxidative alterations of membrane proteins underlie senescent cell antigen formation [28,31]. Thus, the observation concerning the removal of two thirds of sickle RBCs by macrophages can be an indication of increased oxidation of sickle cell membrane proteins [32]. This supports the presence of a relationship between the haemolytic rate and the increased appearance of senescent cell antigens on sickle cell membrane [18].

A number of major cellular defense mechanisms exist in normal cells to neutralize and resist these damaging effects. In erythrocytes reduced pyridine nucleotides, namely nicotinamide adenine dinucleotide (NADH) and nicotinamide adenine dinucleotide phosphate (NADPH) are directly linked to key antioxidant defense mechanisms. They are required to convert methemoglobin back to its more stable, reduced form [33]. Decreased erythrocyte NAD redox potential and abnormal pyridine nucleotide content has been reported in sickle cell anemia [34]. It has also been suggested that an induced increase in pyridine nucleotide redox potential may result in a reduction in the occurrence of painful crises in patients with SCA [35].

Coexistence of G6PD deficiency with SCA was one of the factors reported to modify the severity of sickle cell disease in the Saudi population [36]. Contradictory studies have suggested that G6PD deficiency has beneficial, deleterious or no influence upon the course of SCA [37-40]. Erythrocytes with coexisting SCA and G6PD deficiency represent a haematological condition in which there is an association between an increased oxidant production with a condition associated with an impaired antioxidant defence mechanism. Little is known about the effect of the interaction of both genetic abnormalities on the redox status of RBCs. We were prompted to determine and compare pyridine nucleotide redox potentials of erythrocytes of Saudi sickle cell disease patients with or without G6PD deficiency and study the effect of their coexistence on pyridine nucleotides levels.

MATERIALS AND METHODS

Spectrophotometric grade ethanol was purchased from Aldrich Chemical Co. (UK). All other analytical grade chemicals were purchased from Sigma, Dorset, UK. After obtaining informed consent, blood samples were drawn by routine venipuncture in EDTA and heparin coated tubes (15 U heparin/ml whole blood) from healthy Saudi male and female volunteers and from individuals with SCA, G6PD deficiency or carriers of both abnormalities who were attending King Fahad Teaching Hospital. Blood lysates were prepared according to the method of Drabkin. Cellulose acetate haemoglobin electrophoresis was performed on the Helena electrophoresis system using Tris-EDTA Borate (pH 8.6). G6PD activity was determined spectrophotometrically according to the method reported by Battistuzzi [41]. 50 μl of hemolysate was mixed with 3ml of a solution containing triethanolamine buffer (50 mmol/l. pH 7.6), EDTA (5 mmol/l) and 0.01 ml of 10 mmol/l NADP. The mixture was incubated for 5 mins at 25^0C. The reaction was then started by addition of 50 μl of glucose 6 phosphate (31 mmol/l) and the absorbance was recorded at 0, 1, 2, 3 mins at 340 nm.

Whole blood was used for the determination of nucleotide concentration. Changes in the concentration of blood NAD levels reflect changes in the RBCs pyridine nucleotide content. The concentration of pyridine nucleotides was determined according to a dye-based spectrophotometric cycling assay developed by Zerez et al., with certain modifications [42-43]. Twenty microliters of heparinized whole blood was mixed with 1,980μl of an alkaline solution containing 10mM nicotinamide, 20mM $NaHCO_3$ and 100mM Na_2CO_3 at 0°C. The mixture was immediately frozen in a dry-ice acetone bath, thawed quickly in a room temperature water bath, and then promptly chilled to 0°C and kept in the dark. To destroy NAD^+ and $NADP^+$ (oxidized nucleotides), 700μl of this mixture was incubated at 60°C for 30 minutes. The mixture was then chilled to 0°C. A volume of 50 μl of heat treated (NADH) extract or the untreated (NAD_T) extract was added to 850 μl solution containing 100 μmol Tris-HCl (pH 8), 2 μmol PES. 0.5 μmol MTT and 0.2 mg alcohol dehydrogenase. The mixture was incubated for 5 minutes at 37^0C and 100 μl of 6M ethanol was added. The rate of increase of absorbance was measured over a 10 minute period at 570nm. Two blanks were prepared, one for the heated extract and one for the unheated extract. NADPH and $NADP_T$ were estimated in a similar assay condition using a cycling buffer consisiting of 100 μmol Tris-HCl (pH 8), 5 μmol Na_4EDTA, 2 μmol PES, 0.5 μmol MTT, and 1.3 IU/ml G6PD.One micromole of glucose 6 phosphate was added after 5 min incubation at 37ºC. The reaction was followed over a period of 100s.

Hemoglobin A_2 and reticulocyte count were determined to exclude ß-thalassemia and active hemolysis, respectively. The data were analysed using SPSS for Windows. Anova and Kruskal-Wallis tests were used to evaluate the difference in nucleotide concentrations between the groups.

RESULTS

Study Subjects and Blood Samples

Blood samples were obtained from normal male and female Saudi individuals and from subjects with SCA, G6PD deficiency or carriers of both abnormal genes. Only individuals who met the criteria of being free of active hemolysis or ß-thalassemia trait were included in the study.

NAD and NADP Redox Potentials

The mean erythrocyte concentrations of the nucleotides NAD^+, NAD_T, NADH and the NAD redox potentials in normal subjects and those with SCA, G6PD deficiency and SCA with G6PD deficiency are presented in table 1. The normal levels of these nucleotides presented here are comparable to those found in other populations [42]. RBCs with SCA ($p<0.0001$), G6PD deficiency ($p<0.00005$) or with coexisting SCA and G6PD deficiency ($p<0.0001$) have a significant increase in the NAD_T concentration when compared to normal (Figure 1). While this increase is mainly due to an increase in NAD^+, there was a slight increase in NADH concentration. The ratio of $NADH/NAD_T$, which is an indicator of the cellular redox potential, was significantly lower in RBC with SCA ($p=0.001$), G6PD deficiency ($p=0.038$) and in RBC with coexisting SCA and G6PD deficiency ($p=0.04$) when compared to normal (Figure 2).

There was no significant difference in the concentrations of all NAD nucleotides concerned or in NAD redox potential in erythrocytes with coexisting genetic abnormalities when compared to either sickle or G6PD deficient RBCs (Figures 1, 2).

The mean erythrocyte concentrations of the nucleotides NADPH, $NADP_T$ and the NADP redox potential of normal, SCA, G6PD deficient and G6PD deficiency with SCA subjects are presented in table 2. Erythrocytes with G6PD deficiency with or without SCA had a significantly lower NADPH concentration when compared to normal ($p=0.028$ and $p=0.001$ respectively) or sickle erythrocytes ($p<0.0001$) (Figure 3). However, the concentrations of $NADP_T$ in G6PD deficient cells with or without SCA are significantly increased when compared with normal or SCA erythrocytes ($p<0.0001$) (Figure 4). This increase is mainly due to an increase in $NADP^+$ concentration. Consequently, the ratio of $NADPH/NADP_T$ in these erythrocytes was significantly lower when compared to normal or SCA ($p<0.0001$) (Figure 5). There was no significant difference in the $NADPH/NADP_T$ values between normal and sickle RBCs. These results are in agreement with previous data reported for

African Americans with SCA [34]. Our data indicate that the increase in the $NADP_T$ in non-deficient cells is mainly due to an increase in NADPH, while in G6PD deficient cells the increase was in the oxidized form.

Table 1 NAD concentrations and NADH/ NAD_T ratio in RBCs from normal, sickle, G6PD deficient and from individuals with coexistence of both abnormalities

Subjects		Pyridine nucleotide, nmol/ml of RBC			
		NAD_T	**NADH**	**NAD+**	**NADH/NAD_T**
Normal (n=27)	Mean±SD	88.04±14.24	41.1±8.05	46.89±13.06	0.46±0.087
	Min-Max	70.06-124.7	29.32-56.99	21.97-67.71	0.34-0.66
SCA (N=27)	Mean±SD	121.68±17.7	46.65±8.35	75.03±19.07	0.38±0.074
	Min-Max	88.89-150.6	31.37-63.35	45.39-108.93	0.24-0.53
G6PD deficient (n=21)	Mean±SD	109.68±10.14	42.25±11.74	67.43±11.65	0.38±0.095
	Min-Max	95.7-122.79	26.64-59.98	46.58-95.8	0.22-0.52
SCA & G6PD deficient (n=20)	Mean±SD	125.19±24.04	47.62±14.36	77.56±24.61	0.39±0.12
	Min-Max	100.28-172.16	26.92-66.31	39.14-118.11	0.24-0.621

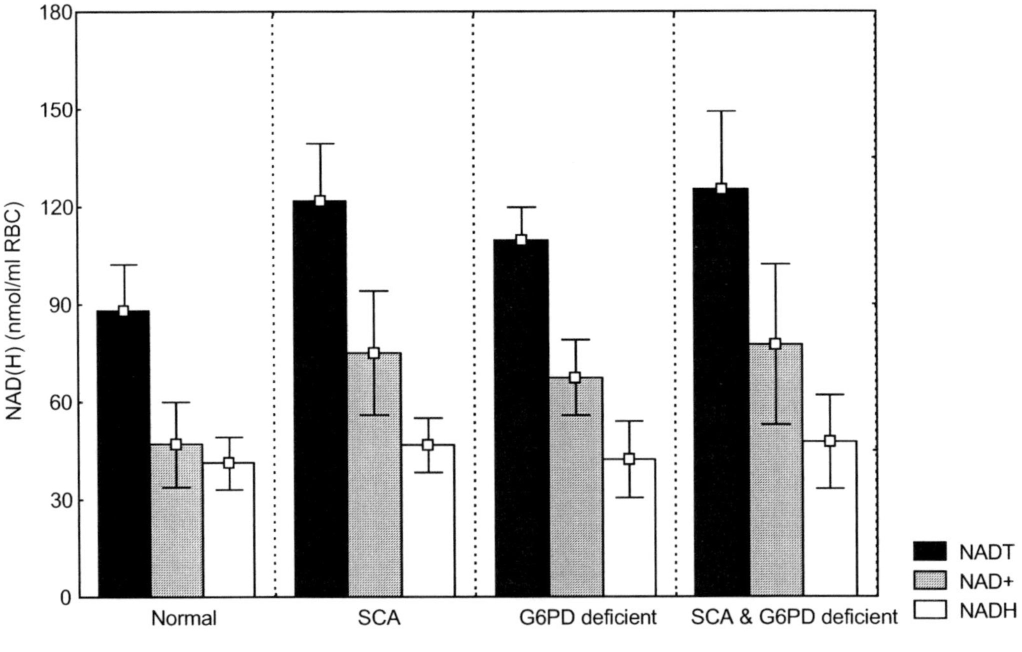

Figure 1. NAD_T, NADH and oxidized NAD in RBCs from normal, sickle, G6PD deficient and from individuals with coexistence of both abnormalities.

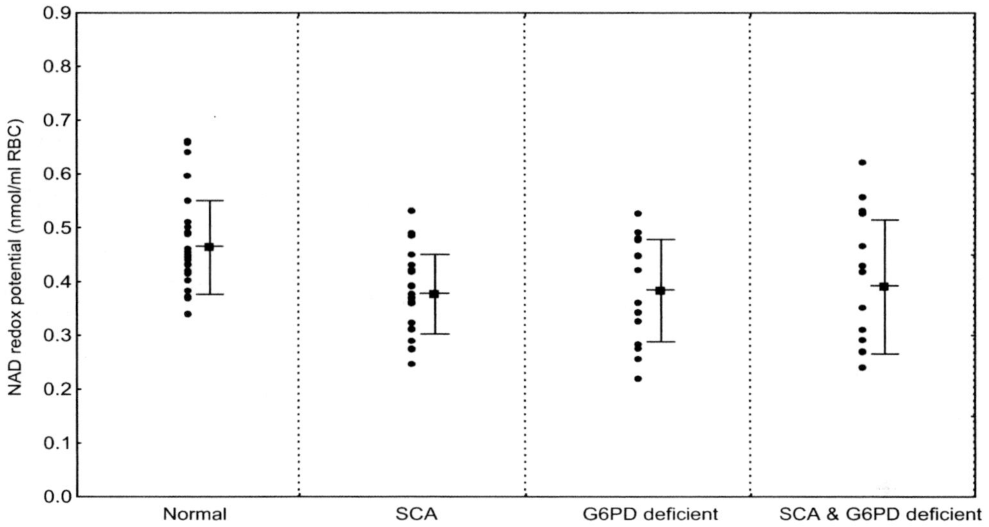

Figure 2. NAD redox potential in RBCs from normal, sickle, G6PD deficient and from individuals with coexistence of both abnormalities.

Table 2 NADP concentrations and NADPH/ $NADP_T$ ratio in RBCs from normal, sickle, G6PD deficient and from individuals with coexistence of both abnormalities

		Pyridine nucleotide, nmol/ml of RBC		
		$NADP_T$	NADPH	$NADPH/NADP_T$
Normal (n=27)	Mean±SD	39.61±7.33	42.52±8.77	1.07±0.096
	Min-Max	29.21-55.7	30.78-66.10	0.91-1.3
SCA (n=27)	Mean±SD	57.72±8.82	60.7±10.93	1.05±0.083
	Min-Max	41.86-77.03	42.98-84.8	0.93-1.25
G6PD deficient (n=21)	Mean±SD	77.04±10.26	30.65±9.98	0.4±0.12
	Min-Max	55.6-92.89	14.08-44.57	0.18-0.55
SCA & G6PD deficient (n=20)	Mean±SD	88.17± 9.63	33.36±9.15	0.38±0.1
	Min-Max	75.55-104.79	16.87-45.41	0.2-0.55

Although, sickle RBCs had a significant increase in NADP redox potential compared to those with coexisting SCA and G6PD deficiency ($p<0.0001$), no significant differences were found between erythrocytes with G6PD deficiency and those with combined genetic abnormalities.

There is a statistically significant correlation between NAD_T and $NADP_T$ ($r=0.533$, $p<0.0001$), which confirms that NAD and NADP synthesis are interdependent (Figure 6).

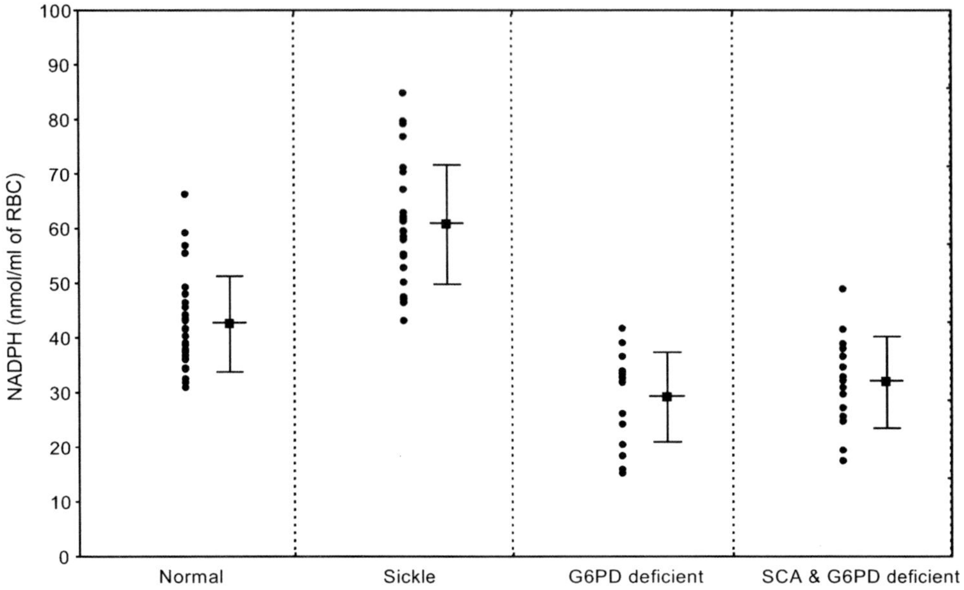

Figure 3. NADPH in RBCs from normal, sickle, G6PD deficient and from individuals with coexistence of both abnormalities.

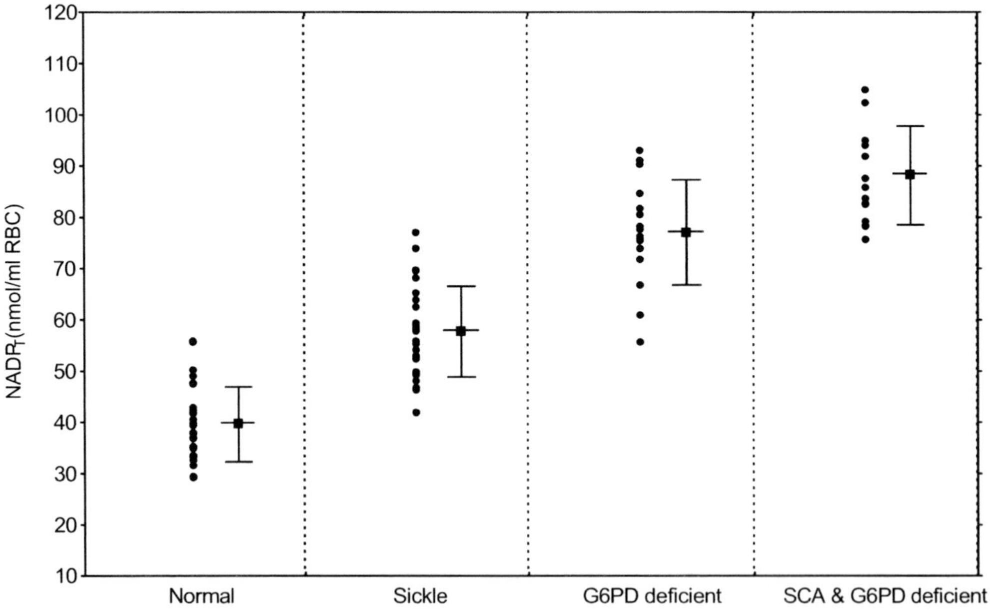

Figure 4. $NADP_T$ in RBCs from normal, sickle, G6PD deficient and from individuals with coexistence of both abnormalities.

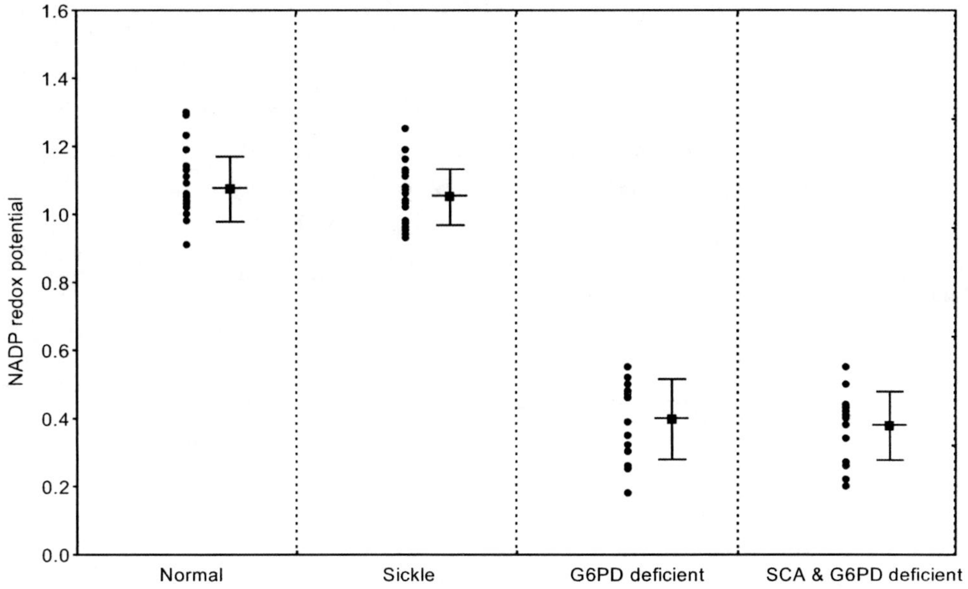

Figure 5. NADP redox potential in RBCs from normal, sickle, G6PD deficient and from individuals with coexistence of both abnormalities.

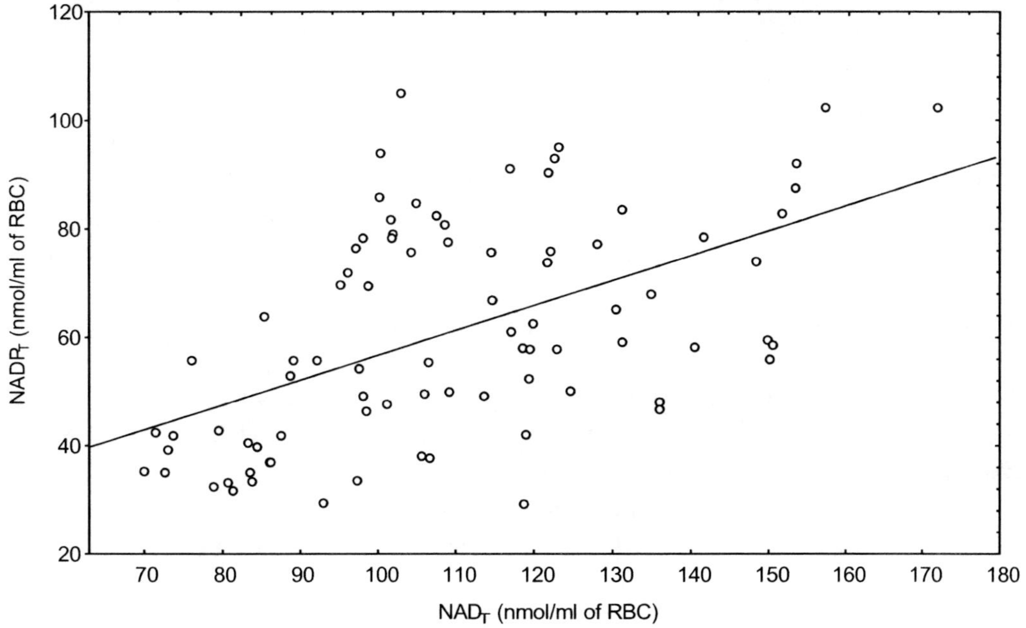

Figure 6. Scatter plot and best fitted line for NAD_T and $NADP_T$.

DISCUSSION

Sickle cell anemia and G6PD deficiency occur at a high frequency in the Eastern Province of Saudi Arabia where malaria was hyperendemic. Consequently, the co-existence of SCA with G6PD deficiency occurs at a high frequency in the Eastern Province [36, 44]. It has been reported that the high prevalence of G6PD deficiency in individuals with SCA was not caused by a selective advantage as previously suggested, but the result of heterogeneous genetic composition [11, 45]. Piomelli et al. suggested that a high prevalence of G6PD deficiency in patients with SCA reflects a clinically beneficial effect of this interaction, while Beutler et al. found a similar frequency of G6PD deficiency in SCA patients as their normal and heterozygous siblings [37-38]. In addition Steinberg et al. found that the prevalence of G6PD deficiency was not significantly different in patients stratified by age groups [46]. In a previous report, Al-Ali et al. showed that, based on levels of glycated haemoglobin, there was little survival advantage or disadvantage for erythrocytes with combined SCA and G6PD deficiency [40].

The tendency of HbS to oxidize more quickly than HbA is well documented in literature [19, 47-49]. Spectroelectrochemical experiments have demonstrated that HbS revealed an altered redox potential relative to HbA_0 that favored methemoglobin formation [49]. This may underlie the increased rate of autooxidation of HbS under aerobic conditions. In addition, sickle erythrocyte membranes were shown to manifest increased iron dependent, peroxide driven formation of hydroxyl radicals compared with normal RBC membranes [50]. NADH-cytochrome b5 is the main defense mechanisms that convert methemoglobin back to its reduced form. NADPH plays an important role as a cofactor in a chain of reactions that defend the RBCs against oxidative damage. Hence, in the absence of the intrinsic reducing systems (NADH, NADPH) of the red blood cell, the reduced heme-iron can be oxidized to form increased levels of methemoglobin that can give rise to free radicals and oxidative cellular damage. Erythrocyte pyridine nucleotide redox potential therefore, can be used as an indicator of cellular metabolism and oxidant susceptibility. Consequently, they are important parameters in assessing the effect of the coexistence of a disease characterized by an increased oxidant production (SCA) with a disorder characterized by an impaired intrinsic reductive system (G6PD deficiency).

Our data indicate that the NADH concentration in erythrocytes of SCA with or without G6PD deficiency are comparable, but these values are slightly higher than that found for normal erythrocytes. The NAD_T concentration was found to be significantly increased in these cells compared to normal. The increase in NAD_T is mainly due to an increase in oxidized NAD. Therefore, in spite of the slight increase in the NADH concentration, the ratio of $NADH/NAD_T$, which is an indicator of cellular redox potential, was lower than that determined for normal. Sickle RBCs show a comparable level of NAD redox potential to those with coexisting G6PD deficiency. It is worth mentioning that the redox potential for Saudi SCA subjects with or without G6PD deficiency is higher than that reported for African Americans with SCA [34]. Our results are not necessarily in conflict with those reported elsewhere. This is due to the fact that the redox potential was significantly decreased in both Saudis and their African American counterparts with SCA when compared to normal [34, 51]. Interestingly, NAD redox potential in G6PD deficient erythrocytes is also significantly reduced when compared to normal. This finding agrees with the postulation that the decrease in NAD redox potential is a result of a lack of increase in NAD reduction, probably indicating a metabolic control, rather than a decrease in NADH caused by increased utilization due to HbS instability [52]. It has also previously been shown that the level of 2,3 diphosphoglycerate (2,3 DPG), a potent inhibitor of glycolysis, is significantly elevated in both Saudis and African Americans with SCA [53-54]. However, the value of 2,3 DPG in Saudis is not as highly elevated as in the case of African Americans with SCA [55]. Therefore one might argue that glycolysis should be relatively less inhibited in the erythrocytes of Saudis with SCA than in their African American counterparts. Alayash has reported that the activity of lactate dehydrogenase, a glycolytic enzyme, in Saudis with SCA is comparable to normal subjects, which supports the above hypothesis [56]. The $NADP_T$ concentration was significantly increased in erythrocytes with SCA when compared to normal. This increase was accompanied by an increase in NADPH. However, the NADP redox potential of these cells was comparable to normal. On the other hand, NADPH concentration in G6PD deficient erythrocytes with or without SCA is significantly reduced when compared to normal or sickle erythrocytes. The increase in $NADP_T$ is coupled with a significant increase in oxidized NADP. This resulted in a decreased redox potential in these cells when compared to sickle erythrocytes. NADPH was reported to bind with high affinity to β–chain anion–binding site of deoxy hemoglobin [57]. At high concentrations, NADPH, NADH and oxidized NADP can appreciably change the oxygen-binding properties of hemoglobin [58]. Our data indicate that erythrocytes with SCA had a significant increase in NADPH compared to those with coexisting SCA and G6PD deficiency. However, this level is considered relatively low for a significant physiological effect. The implications on oxygen-binding properties of hemoglobin and on cofactor-dependent metabolic processes remain to be elucidated.

The altered pyridine nucleotide content and the decreased NAD and NADP redox potentials indicate that the presence of G6PD deficiency may impose an additional burden on the metabolic process in sickle RBCs, which is exhibited by their increased oxidant sensitivity. However, it cannot be inferred that the presence of G6PD deficiency has a detrimental effect on sickle cell anemia based only on these findings since other metabolic changes have been reported which may offer an advantageous factor to the coexistence of both disorders. It has been reported that the ability of the sickle membrane to generate the potentially oxidizing hydroxyl radical and other oxidative radicals is strictly dependent on the availability of some cytoplasmic reducing agents. This has been demonstrated by a study in which the addition of a physiological concentration of either ascorbate or glutathione to sickle cell ghost restored hydroxyl radical generation [50]. In addition, it has been shown that GSH-depleted RBCs have a reduced rate of iron-mediated hemoglobin oxidation, which can be reversed by the addition of GSH [59]. Atamma and Ginsburg demonstrated that the co-incubation of GSH and heme lead to the emergence of free iron and the generation of oxidative radicals [60]. GSH levels are lower in sickle RBCs with G6PD deficiency when compared to sickle RBCs with normal G6PD activity which may offer an advantage in reducing the oxidant generation under normal conditions [61]. In conclusion, we believe that the coexistence of G6PD deficiency with SCA does not affect the clinical course of SCA as there is no concrete evidence that this coexistence enhances erythrocyte's survival.

REFERENCES

[1] Gelpi AP. Glucose-6-phosphate dehydrogenase deficiency in Saudi Arabia: a survey. *Blood* 1965; 25: 486-93.

[2] Lehman H. Maranjian G, Mourant AE. Distribution of Sickle cell haemoglobin in Saudi Arabia. *Nature* 1963; 198: 492-3.

[3] Perrine RP, Brown MH, Weatherall DJ, Clegg JB, May A. Benign sickle-cell anaemia. *Lancet* 1972; 2: 1163-7.

[4] Perrine RP, Pembrey ME, John P, Perrine S, Shoup F. Natural history of sickle cell anemia in Saudi Arabs. *Ann Intern Med* 1978; 88: 1-6.

[5] Nagel RL, Roth EF. Jr. Malaria and red cell genetic defects. Blood 1989; 74: 1213-21.

[6] Daggy RH, Malaria in Oasis of Eastern Saudi Arabia. *Am J Trop Med Hyg* 1959; 8: 223-291.

[7] Beutler E. Glucose-6-phosphate dehydrogenase deficiency. In: Stanbury Wyngaarden JB, Fredrickson DS, Goldstein JL, Brown MS (eds). *The metabolic basis of inherited disease*, 5th ed. NY. McGraw-Hill, 1983: 1629-53.

[8] Al-Ali AK, Al-Mustafa ZH, Al-Madan M, Qaw F, Al-Ateeq S. Molecular characterization of Glucose-6-phosphate dehydrogenase deficiency in the Eastern Province of Saudi Arabia. *Clin Chem Lab Med* 2002; 40: 814-6.

[9] Vulliamy TJ, Beutler E, Luzzatto L. Variants of glucose 6 phosphate dehydrogenase are due to missense mutations spread throughout the coding region of the gene. *Human Mutation* 1993; 2: 159-67.

[10] Kurdi-Haidar B, Mason PJ, Berrebi A, Ankra-Badu G, Al-Ali A, Oppenheim A, Luzzatto L. Origin and spread of the glucose 6 phosphate dehydrogenase variant (G6PD Mediterranean) in the Middle East. *Ann J Hum Genet* 1990; 47: 1013-9.

[11] Beutler E. Glucose 6 phosphate dehydrogenase deficiency. *Blood* 1994; 84: 3613-36.

[12] Hasegawa S, Rodgers GP, Shio H, Schechter AN, Uyesaka N.Impaired deformability of Heinz body-forming red cells. *Biorheology*. 1993; 30:275-86.

[13] Franco RS, Lohmann J, Silberstein EB, Mayfield-Pratt G, Palascak M, Nemeth TA, Joiner CH, Weiner M, Rucknagel DL. Time-dependent changes in the density and hemoglobin F content of biotin-labeled sickle cells. *J Clin Invest*. 1998; 101:2730-40

[14] Fabry ME, Suzuka SM, Weinberg RS, Lawrence C, Factor Sm, Gilman J, Costantini F, Nagel RL. Second generation knockout sickle mice: the effect of HbF. *Blood* 2001; 97: 410-8.

[15] Hebbel RP. Beyond hemoglobin polymerization: the red cell membrane and sickle disease pathophysiology. *Blood* 1991;77: 214-37.

[16] Browne PV, Hebbel RP. CD36-positive stress reticulocytosis in sickle cell anemia. *J Lab Clin Med* 1996; 127: 340-7.

[17] Kannan R, Labotkai R, Low PS. Isolation and characterization of the hemichrome-stabilized membrane protein aggregates from sickle erythrocytes: major site of autologous antibody binding. *J Biol Chem* 1988; 263: 13766-73.

[18] Hebbel RP, Miller WJ, Phagocytosis of Sickle erythrocytes: Immunological and oxidative determinants of haemolytic anemia. *Blood* 1984; 64: 733-41.

[19] Marva E, Hebbel RP. Denaturing interaction between sickle hemoglobin and phosphatidylserine liposomes. *Blood* 1994; 83:242-9.

[20] Halliwell B, Gutteridge JMC. Oxygen toxicity, oxygen radicals, transition metals and disease. *Biochem. J* 1984; 219: 1–14.

[21] Crichon RR, Charloteaux-Wauters M. Iron transport and storage. *Eur J Biochem* 1987; 164: 485-506.

[22] Richardson DR, Ponka P. The molecular mechanisms of the metabolism and transport of iron in normal and neoplastic cells. *Biochem Biophys Acta* 1997; 1331: 1-40.

[23] Monteiro HP, Winterbourn CC. Release of iron from ferritin by divicine, isouramil, acid-hydrolyzed vicine and dialuric acid and initiation of lipid peroxidation. *Arch Biochem Biophys* 1989; 271: 536-45.

[24] Hebbel RP. Auto-oxidation and a membrane-associated 'Fenton reagent': a possible explanation for development of membrane lesions in sickle erythrocytes. *Clin Haematol* 1985; 14: 129-40.

[25] Browne P, Shalev O, Hebbel RP. The molecular pathobiology of cell membrane iron: the sickle red cell as a model. *Free Rad. Biol. Med.* 1998; 24:1040–1048.

[26] Babior BM. Oxidizing radicals and red cell destruction; in Wallach DFA (ed): *The function of red cells: Erythrocyte Pathobiology*. New York, Liss, 1981, P 173.

[27] Shinar E, Rachmilewitz EA. Hemoglobinopathies and the red cell membrane function. *Baillieres Clin Haematol.* 1993; 6: 357-69.

[28] Kay MMB, Goodman SR, Sorensen K, Whitfield CF, Wong P, Zaki L, Rudloff V. Senescent cell antigen is immunologically related to band 3. *Proc Natl Acad Sci USA* 1983; 80: 1631-5.

[29] Kay MMB. Localization of senescent cell antigen on band 3. *Proc Natl Acad Sci USA* 1984; 81: 5753-7.

[30] Low PS, Waugh SM, Zinke K, Drenckhahn D. The role of hemoglobin denaturation and band 3 clustering in red blood cell aging. *Science* 1985; 227: 531-3.

[31] Comporti M, Signorini C, Buonocore G, Ciccoli L. Iron release, oxidative stress and erythrocyte aging. *Free Rad Biol Med* 2002; 32: 568-576.

[32] Bensinger TA, Gillette PN. Hemolysis in sickle cell disease. *Arch Intern Med.* 1974; 133: 624-31.

[33] Jaffe ER. The formation and reduction of methemoglobin in human erythrocytes; in Yoshikawa H, Rapoport SM (eds): *Cellular and molecular biology of erythrocytes.* Baltimore University Park, 1971.

[34] Zerez CR, Lachant NA, Lee SJ, Tanaka KR. Decreased erythrocyte nicotinamide adenine dinucleotide redox potential and abnormal pyridine nucleotide content in sickle cell disease. *Blood* 1988; 71: 512-5.

[35] Niihara Y, Zerez CR, Akiyama DS, Tanaka KR, Oral L-glutamine therapy for sickle cell anemia: I. Subjective clinical improvement and favourable changes in red cell NAD redox potential. *Am J Hematol* 1998; 58: 117-21.

[36] Warsy AS. Frequency of Glucose-6-phosphate dehydrogenase deficiency in sickle cell disease. *Hum Hered* 1985; 35: 143-7.

[37] Piomelli S, Reindorf CA, Arzanian MT. Corash LM. Clinical and biochemical interactions of glucose-6-phosphate dehydrogenase deficiency and sickle cell anemia. *New Eng J Med* 1972; 287: 213-7.

[38] Beutler E, Johnson C, Powards D, West C. Prevalence of glucose-6-phosphate dehydrogenase deficiency in sickle cell disease. *New Engl J Med* 1974; 290: 826-8.

[39] Steinberg MH, Dreiling BJ. Glucose-6-phosphate dehydrogenase deficiency in sickle cell anemia. *Ann Intern Med* 1974; 80: 217-21.

[40] Al-Ali AK, Ahmed MAM, Al-Idrissi H, Al-Sibai MH, Al-Mutairy AR, Al-Awamy M. Effects of glucose-6-phosphate dehydrogenase deficiency upon sickle cell anemia. *Ann Clin Biochem* 1989; 26: 477-80.

[41] Battistuzzi G, Esan GJF, Fasuan FA, Mediano G, Luzzatto. Comparison of GdA and GdB activities in Nigerians. A Study of the variation of the G6PD activity. *Am J Hum Genet* 1977; 29: 31-6.

[42] Zerez CR, Lee SJ, Tanaka KR. Spectrophotometric determination of oxidized and reduced pyridine nucleotides in erythrocytes using a single extraction procedure. *Anal Biochem* 1987; 164: 367-73.

[43] Wagner TC, Scott MD. Single extraction method for the spectrophotometric quantification of oxidized and reduced pyridine nucleotides in erythrocytes. *Anal Biochem* 1994; 222: 417-26.

[44] Awamy BH. Effect of G6PD deficiency on sickle cell disease in Saudi Arabia. *Ind J Pediat* 1992; 59: 331-4.

[45] Lewis RA, Kay RW, Hathorn M. sickle cell disease and glucose 6 phosphate dehydrogenase deficiency. *Acta Haematol* 1966; 36: 399-411.

[46] Steinberg MH, West MS, Gallagher D, Mentzer W. Effect of glucose-6-phosphate dehydrogenase deficiency upon sickle cell anemia. *Blood* 1988; 71: 784-52.

[47] Hebbel RP, Morgan WT, Eaton JW, Hedlund BE. Accelerated autoxidation and heme loss due to instability of sickle hemoglobin. *Proc Natl Acad Sci* 1988; 85: 237-41.

[48] Sheng K, Shariff M, Hebbel RP. Comparative oxidation of hemoglobins A and S. *Blood* 1998; 9: 3467-70.

[49] Bonaventura C, Taboy CH, Low PS, Stevens RD, Lafon C, and Crumbliss AL: Heme redox properties of S-nitrosated hemoglobin A and hemoglobin S: Implications for interactions of nitric oxide with normal and sickle cells. *J Biol Chem* 2002; 277: 14557-63.

[50] Repka T, Hebbel. Hydroxyl formation by sickle erythrocytes role of pathologic iron deposits and cytoplasmic reducing agents. *Blood* 1991; 78: 2753-8.

[51] Al-Ali AK. Pyridine nucleotide redox potential in erythrocytes of Saudi subjects with sickle cell disease. *Acta Haematol* 2002; 108: 19-22.

[52] Zerez CR, Lanchant NA, Tanaka KR. Impaired erythrocyte methemoglobin reduction in sickle cell disease: dependence of methemoglobin reduction on reduced nicotinamide adenine dinucleotide conten. *Blood* 1990; 76: 1008-14.

[53] Poillon WN, Kim BC, Welty EV, Walder JA: The effect of 2,3 DPG on the solubility of deoxyhemoglobin. *Arch Biochem Biophys* 1986; 249: 301-5.

[54] Alayash AI, Dafallah A, Al-Husayni H, Al-Ali AK, Al-Quorain A, Omer AHS, Wilson MT. Glycosylated hemoglobin levels in a benign form of sickle cell anemia in Saudi Arabia. *Acta Haemat* 1986; 75: 160-4.

[55] Charche S, Grisolia S, Fiedler AJ, Hellegers AE. Effect of 2,3 DPG on oxygen affinity of blood in sickle cell anemia. *J Clin Invest* 1970; 49: 806-12.

[56] Alayash AL. Zinc and some zinc dependent enzymes in sickle cell anemia. *Int J Vitam Nutr Res* 1989; 59: 388-9.

[57] Ogo S, Focesi A, Cashon R, Bonaventura J, Bonaventura C. Interactions of Nicotinamide adenine dinucleotides with varied states and forms of hemoglobin. *J Biol Chem* 1989; 264: 11302-06.

[58] Cashon R, Bonaventura C, Bonaventura J, Focesi A J. The nicotinamide adenine dinucleotides as allosteric effectors of human hemoglobin. *J Biol Chem* 1986; 261: 12700-12705.

[59] Scott MD, Eaton JW. Thalassemic erythrocytes: cellular suicide arising from iron and glutathione-dependent oxidation reactions. *Br J Haematol* 1995; 91: 811-9.

[60] Atamma H, Ginsburg H. Heme degradation in the presence of glutathione. A proposed mechanism to account for the high levels of non-heme iron found in the membranes of hemoglobinopathic red blood cells. *J Biol Chem* 1995; 270: 24876-83.

[61] Al-Ali AK. Erythrocyte reduced glutathione level in sickle cell anaemia and glucose-6-phosphate dehydrogenase deficient Saudi subjects. *Ann Clin Biochem* 1994; 31: 296-7.

In: Focus on Sickle Cell Research
Editor: Ralph L. Plasmar, pp. 231-244
ISBN 1-59033-920-7

Chapter XV

ORAL HEALTH STATUS AND ANTHROPOMETRIC FINDINGS IN SICKLE CELL DISEASE

F. A. Oredugba*
Department of Child Dental Health,
K. O. Savage
Department of Preventive Dentistry,
College of Medicine, University of Lagos, Nigeria.

ABSTRACT

Sickle Cell Disease (SCD) is an inherited hemoglobin disorder which primarily affects the Black race and their descendants. It has a prevalence of 2% in Nigeria with an even distribution in all the geographical zones of the country. There is no gender difference and it cuts across social classes. It arises as a result of the inheritance of a defective hemoglobin S caused by the substitution of amino acid valine for glutamic acid on one of the ß-polypeptide chains of the hemoglobin at position 6. When it is inherited from both parents, the homozygous state (HbSS) results, which manifests as SCD. Other variants of the abnormal hemoglobin are the HbC and Hb- ß-thalasemia. The combination of the HbS with these other variants produce HbSC or HbS-ß-thal. The symptoms of the SCD are less severe in these other variants than in the homozygous SS state.

Affected individuals have been reported to present with increased susceptibility to infections including oral infections, various dental abnormalities such as hypoplasia and hypomineralization, various anthropometric deficits including low weight, low height-for-age, gnathopathy, frontal bossing and reduced skin fold thickness. Conflicting reports have been presented in the literature concerning these parameters.

A hospital-based cross-sectional study was carried out in Lagos, Nigeria on SCD patients while unaffected patients were used as controls. It was found that the unaffected had better oral hygiene than those with SCD and this was not influenced by the socioeconomic class of the individuals. However there was no significant difference in

* Correspondence: E-mail: tored@nova.net.ng

the prevalence of dental caries between SCD patients and controls. Findings showed that dental abnormalities such as localized enamel hypoplasia, chronologic enamel hypoplasia, tetracycline staining and space problems such as crowding, generalized spacing and midline diastema were more prevalent among the SCD patients than the controls ($p<0.05$). There was a higher prevalence of maxillary protrusion and class II malocclusion in SCD subjects which enhanced a prognathic facial profile. Height, weight and head circumference were not significantly different between the two groups except at the age of 18 years when the SCD group weighed less than the controls ($p<0.05$). The mean mid upper arm circumference (MUA) was however significantly more apparent in the unaffected individuals than in the SCD group. Further study needs to be carried out to investigate if hemoglobin levels in these patients affect these parameters.

INTRODUCTION

Sickle Cell Disease (SCD) is an inherited hemoglobin disorder, which primarily affects the black race and their descendants. It arises as a result of the inheritance of a defective hemoglobin S caused by the substitution of amino acid valine for glutamic acid on one of the two ß polypeptide chains of the adult hemoglobin at position 6, as a result of mutation in the DNA molecule [1]. The gene for the abnormal Hb S in the erythrocyte is inherited according to Mendelian Laws [2]. Linus Pauling identified this Hb in 1949 as the abnormal Hb associated with Sickle Cell Anemia (SCA) [3]. The amino acids have different polarities and as a result, the HbS molecules on deoxygenation align in liquid crystals, called tactoids, which distort the red blood cells (RBCs) into the pathognomonic rigid sickle shape. This feature is also known as gelation.

On reoxygenation, the tactoids dissemble and the RBCs become once again discoid and flexible. Repeated sickling and unsickling however damages the red cell membrane such that the red cells cannot unsickle on reoxygenation. Sickling of the RBCs lead to increased mechanical fragility and reduced red cell survival time. They are thus prone to hemolysis and phagocytosis by the reticuloendothelial system. Consequently, hemolytic anemia and jaundice results from excess breakdown of red blood cells and accumulation of bilirubin in the blood. When the HbS is inherited from both parents and thus presents as the homozygous state, HbSS, the very severe symptoms of SCA occurs [4]. Crisis is usually precipitated by infections, dehydration, acidosis, exposure to cold, some forms of stress, rigorous exercise, emotional disorders and commonly in the tropical regions, malaria. Under these conditions, there is increased viscosity of blood, stasis and thrombosis in the small caliber terminal arteries, capillaries and veins. These in turn cause ischaemia, infarction, necrosis and fibrosis in soft tissues of various organs of the body and sclerosis of bone [2]. This phenomenon is a cyclic process.

The HbS in the heterozygous state is referred to as the Sickle Cell Trait, the term coined by Harin and Gillespie in 1927 [2]. In the heterozygote form with HbA (HbAS), sickling only occurs at extremes of hypoxia or acid pH because of the static interference of the ß-molecules in tactoid formation. Other variants of the abnormal hemoglobin are the HbC and Hb-ß-thalasemia. The combination of the HbS with these other variants produces HbSC or HbS-ß thal. The symptoms of SCD are less severe in these variants than in the homozygous HbSS state.

EPIDEMIOLOGY

SCD is common in Africa, the Mediterranean countries and India, and the descendants of people from these countries who have migrated to Europe and South, Central and North America and Bahrain [4,5].It has been described as a common community health problem in Tropical Africa [6]. It has a prevalence of 2% in Nigeria and Ghana [7,8]. In Nigeria it has an even distribution in all the geographical zones of the country. There is no gender difference and it cuts across social classes. The Sickle Cell Trait (HbAS) is reported in about 25% of southern Nigerians and 19-32.6% of Northern Nigerians. The estimated average is 25% [7]. In the USA, 8-10% of the Black population carry the HbAS gene, while 1:500 black children have the HbSS gene [3,9].

Organization statistics show that hemoglobinopathies are the commonest inherited disorders with over 200 million carriers and 200-300 thousand sufferers of the major hemoglobinopathies born annually. Sickling disorders constitute a significant proportion of this group. They are spreading into many ethnic groups due to intermarriage and racial mingling [10]. Experiments have confirmed the epidemiological evidence that sickle cell trait protects against *plasmodium falciparum* malaria, particularly in the 30-60 weeks age group [11], and that the sickle gene is encountered more in the malaria belt of the world.

SCA may be diagnosed in the 16th week of gestation but manifestations normally do not appear until the 6th month after birth.

The patho-physiology of HbSS presents acute and chronic problems referred to as Sickle Cell Crisis. Acute problems include painful vaso-occlusive crisis of bone and joints, especially the long bones and metacarpals/tarsals with overlying soft tissue involvement (the hand and foot syndrome), sequestration crisis, aplastic crisis and hyperhaemolytic crisis [12]. Symptoms may include accelerated breathing, abnormal heart rate, jaundice, fever and abdominal tenderness [13].

Painful crisis affects the entire body, including renal, cardiovascular, pulmonary and central nervous systems. Local vaso-occlusive phenomena leading to infarction and necrosis, chronic anemia and defects in the reticulo-endothelial systems predispose to infections in the SCA patients [14,15]. Osteoporotic marrow defects are also associated with the disease and may even be the only osseous manifestation [16].

ORAL HEALTH STATUS

Mucosal pallor, delayed eruption of the teeth, dental hypoplasia and radiographic changes in the tooth structure are the common reported oral findings associated with the disease [17].

Pallor of the gingivae, tongue and the buccal mucosa is expectedly common in SCD. This can be attributed to the chronic anemia frequently occurring in this group of patients. Pallor of the gingivae alone occurred in more than 50% of the SCD patients seen in some Nigerian subjects. Altemus and Okafor [6,18] have also reported this condition in literature. Delayed eruption of the canines was seen in a black male adolescent who also presented with rampant caries and discolored teeth [19].

Dental Abnormalities

SCD has been reported to have little effect on dental maturation because no significant difference in dental age was found between sickle cell and normal patients [20]. Also among sickle cell patients, there was no significant difference in chronologic and dental ages. Almost all dental anomalies were reportedly more common in Nigerian subjects with SCD [21]. Most significant was chronologic enamel hypoplasia. Its high prevalence is due to the frequent illnesses often experienced by children with SCD. The period of illness coincides with the time when amelogenesis takes place and therefore calcification of hard tissues is disturbed.

Enamel defects in the permanent dentition of SCD individuals have also been attributed to the products of hemolysis detected by the red fluorescence of porphyrin under ultraviolet light in a dark room [19].

Tetracycline staining, a common feature in the sicklers, occurred because it is still often used for childhood infections in some areas, most times, not on medical advice.

Fortunately, enamel hypoplasia and Tetracycline staining can be treated with the use of newer tooth-colored restorative materials for better esthetics. Midline diastema and interdental spacing were also found to be more prevalent in SCD. Hyperplasia of the marrow leading to expansion of the jaw bones, with consequent low tooth-arch ratio probably accounts for this finding in sicklers. If the diastema is not too large, it is a "desirable anomaly" in Nigeria. Most would prefer it to be left alone as it is seen as attractive.

Hypomineralization of dentine, interglobular dentine in the periapical areas, inclusion of peripulpal dentinal tubules, abrupt alteration of dentinogenesis, denticle-like calcified bodies in the pulp chamber and hypercementosis have been found by Soni [22]. Denticle-like hardened bodies as a result of calcification in the pulp suggest the evidence of blood vessel thrombosis [12]. These findings are however not pathognomonic for SCA but the sickling state has an effect on these changes.

There are controversies about the existence of radiographic changes in the maxilla and mandible. These are, increased radiolucency and coarse trabecular pattern of bone caused by a loss of fine trabeculae and an increase in the size of the marrow spaces caused by erythroblastic hyperplasia. The trabecular pattern is coarser and the lamina dura more prominent [23]. When this is found between the roots of teeth, there is a stepladder appearance [17]. The panoramic radiograph of an SCD patient showed bilateral multiple radioluscencies and decreased trabeculations in the mandible. [4].

Oral Hygiene and Periodontal Health

Oral hygiene of unaffected subjects has been reported to be better than in SCD patients [24]. This was confirmed in a study carried out in Nigeria [25], with females in both groups having lower scores, which indicated better oral hygiene than the males (Fig 1). It was attributed to the low level of care in sicklers by parents who were more preoccupied with the frequent crisis and hospitalizations experienced by the children. They did not pay enough attention to the oral hygiene, which they placed secondary to the main health problem. Some parents were even found to be less firm when enforcing discipline on children with SCD than other siblings. Unfortunately, poor oral hygiene can lead to oral infections such as periodontitis and osteomyelitis of the jaws, which can aggravate or precipitate crisis in SCD patients.

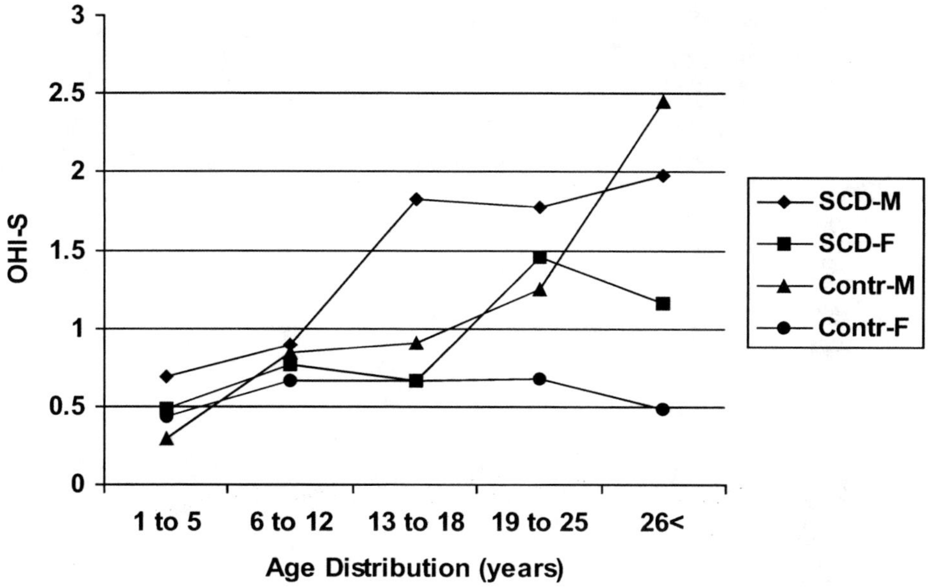

Fig. 1 Oral Hygiene Index Scores of Subjects by Age and Gender. Printed with permission from African Journal of Medicine and Medical Sciences June 2004 Volume 33 No 2

SCD has been thought to increase the severity of periodontal diseases. However, conflicting reports have been seen in the literature concerning the periodontal status of SCD patients. While Okoisor [24] observed poorer periodontal status in Nigerian SCD patients aged 0-6 years compared to normal ones of the same age group, some other workers did not find a significant difference in periodontal disease, although working with older age groups [26]. These findings were irrespective of socioeconomic classes.

Alveolar bone patterns were compared in sickle cell anemia adolescent patients and controls in Nigeria. The bone level as a percent of root length (BL/RL%) in the lower anterior region was found to be higher in the control group than in sickle cell patients, although the difference was not statistically significant [27]

Dental Caries

Some authors have reported no difference in dental caries experience between sicklers and the unaffected, while some reported a lower prevalence. The latter reported that most of the sicklers they examined thought sweets and sugary foods and drinks could add to their problems. Recent studies have shown no significant difference in dental caries experience among Nigerian individuals with SCD and controls [28]. Comparison of dental caries prevalence among socio-economic classes shows a significant difference among sicklers, which did not exist among the controls. These controversial reports are not unexpected because of the multi-factorial etiology of dental caries.

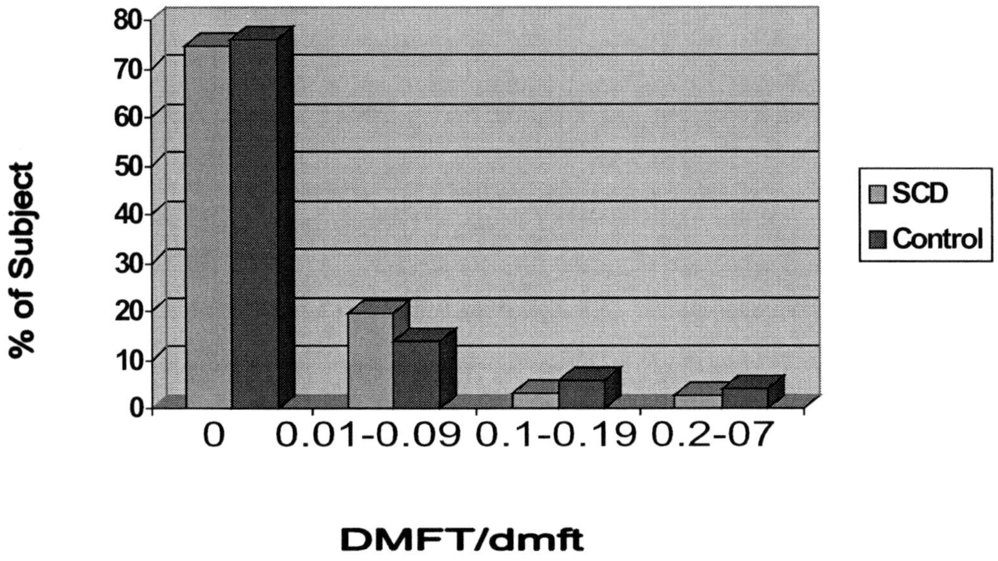

Fig. 2 Dental Caries Index (Decayed, Missing and Filled Teeth) of SCD Subjects and Controls. (Reprinted with permission from the *Nigerian Dental Journal* 2002;3:11-13)

ANTHROPOMETRIC FINDINGS

The bone marrow responds to the aplastic crisis by a compensatory hyperplasia; in the maxilla and mandible, it contributes to some malocclusions seen in SCD patients, which have been extensively reported in literature [29, 30]. The chronic hemolysis in SCA produces hyperplasia of the hemopoietic tissues in the bone marrow in an effort to replenish the numbers of circulating red blood cells.

It appears that gnathopathy in SCA patients is a combination of both maxillary prominence and a degree of mandibular retrognathism. However a lot of disparity have been seen in the clinical severity of the SC syndrome, even when all known factors appear to be equal [7]. Gnathopathy and overgrowth of the anterior part of the maxilla in the secondary dentition cause spacing and proclination of the incisor teeth [31, 32].

A recent hospital based study comparing 1- 45 year old SCD patients and controls in Lagos, Nigeria reported that a more protruded maxilla and a more retruded mandible were more prevalent in SCD subjects than controls [25]. These differences were quite significant (Table 1). Gnathopathy resulting from mid-facial overgrowth was first described by Konotey-Ahulu who noted an unusual enlargement of the maxilla with a peculiar progressive protrusion of the mid-face in sicklers [33]. This profile also would obviously affected their lip seal, which was found to be incompetent in a higher proportion of the SCD subjects compared with control groups.

Table 1: Facial Profile of SCD Subjects and Controls

Facial Profile	SCD (%)	Control (%)	TOTAL (%)
Normal	143 (77.3)	143 (94.7)	286 (85.1)
Maxillary prognathism	38 (20.5)	5 (3.3)	43 (12.8)
Mandibular prognathism	4 (2.2)	3 (2.0)	7 (2.1)
Total	185 (100.0)	151 (100.0)	336 (100.0)

Chi sq = 22.26
df = 2
$p < 0.05$

Cephalometric data of SCD patients and controls showed increased values of the ANB, M/M (maxillary /mandibular plane angle) and the LFHP (lower facial height proportion). These are indicative of a protrusive mid-face [34].

A protrusive maxilla or retruded mandible will cause incompetent lips and defective speech, which has been reported to be a significant complication of mid-face protrusion [30, 35]. It can also result in increased overbite and overjet which were found to be commoner among some Nigerian SCD patients (26-29%) compared with controls (6-8%) [25]. Class II malocclusion, a feature of a protruded maxilla and retruded mandible, was expectedly a significant finding in SCD subjects. Malocclusion of this type in sicklers has been reported extensively in the few literature available [6, 30, 34]. The malocclusion is however amenable to orthodontic treatment.

Affected individuals have also been found to present with, apart from the gnathopathy, frontal bossing, reduced weight, and low height-for-age and reduced skin-fold thickness. Children with SCA have been reported to be shorter, weighed less and were of thinner body build than the unaffected. Some other authors also found that adults with SCD, when compared with age-matched controls, exhibited longer limbs, a shorter trunk, narrower chests, pelvic and pectoral widths, and were thinner and taller [36]. Others have reported an average reduction in weight, height, sitting height, limb length, interacromial and intercristal diameters [37]. They have also shown increased antero-postero-lateral chest diameter ratio. Factors contributing to these changes in body shape are complex and include chronic ill health, a hyper-dynamic blood circulation and other ill-defined processes, which become operative by the age of four to six years [37]. Among some Nigerian children aged 1-18 years, there was no statistically significant difference in the overall height and weight values at <6 and 12 years between SCD patients and controls. However at the age of 18 years, mean weight of SCD children was significantly lower than that of controls (Fig.1, 2). There appears to be growth differences between SCD individuals and controls after the age of 5 years [38]. Such growth deficits have been reported in earlier studies to be more pronounced with increasing age [39]. Growth has been reported to proceed in a co-ordinated manner but that the mean height and weight significantly reduced with age [40]. It has been argued that most SCD individuals, irrespective of their social class were light in weight and that growth delays occur in both symptomatic and asymptomatic individuals [41]. This lag in skeletal maturation has been reported by many authors to occur primarily in older children [20, 42, 43]. This is especially so in a developing country such as Nigeria where class differences are closing up due to economic problems. There is also a delay in puberty, an average of 2.5 years in onset of menarche which is commensurate with delay in physical development. It has been suggested that during the pubertal growth spurt, the genotype difference between SCD and controls becomes greater but diminishes again when epiphyseal fusion terminates longitudinal bone growth in normal controls and the SCD population enters puberty. Hypersplenism may cause excessive bone marrow activity and cessation of growth.

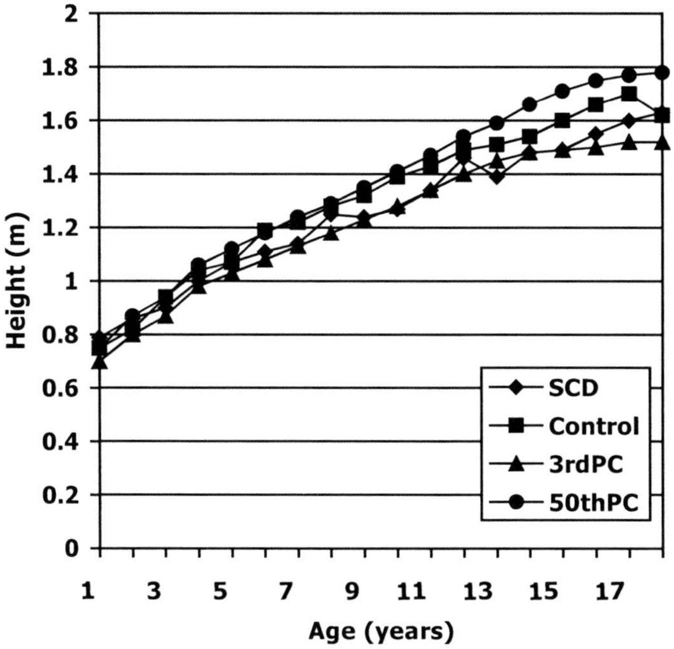

Fig. 3. Mean Height of SCD and Control Subjects compared with Anthropometric Reference Standard. (Reprinted with permission from the American Academy of Pediatric Dentistry, 211 E. Chicago Ave., Ste 700, Chicago, Il 60611-2663, phone 312-337-2169, fax312-337-6329, email aapdinfo@aapd.org, Web site:www.aapd.org)

SCD patients also demonstrated reduced mid upper arm (MUA) circumference compared with controls [38]. It has been attributed to the reduced skin-fold thickness caused by malnutrition and chronic illness [37]. The head circumference values were not significantly different between SCD patients and controls. Socio-economic class among SCD patients influences this latter parameter. This could be attributed to the varying degrees of nutritional deficiencies, which accompany frequent crisis in sicklers. The children suffer most from malaria, which further depletes red cell count and aggravates malnutrition. Therefore the importance of adequate nutrition cannot be over-emphasized in the management of patients with SCD. Where the affected children are properly nourished, adequate preventive care put in place and prompt medical care given, the deficiencies in these health parameters will be abolished.

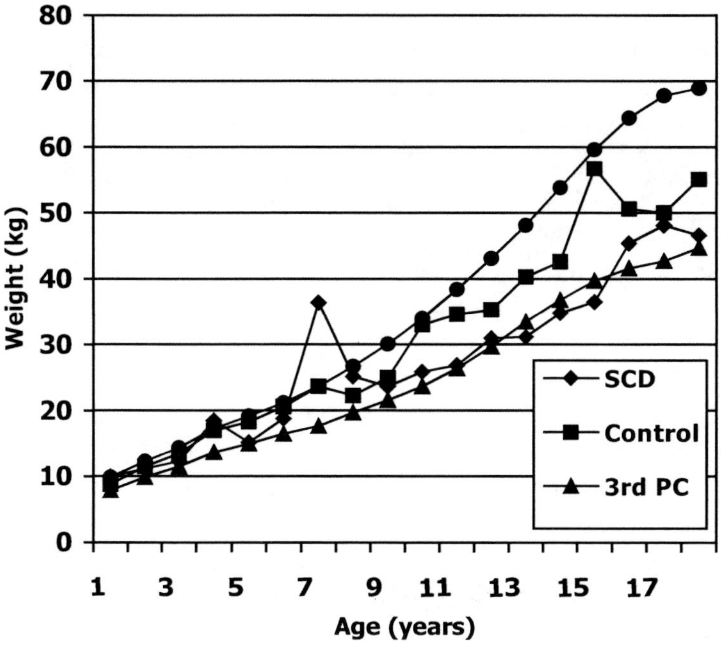

Fig. 4 Mean Weight of SCD and Control Subjects compared with Anthropometric Reference Standard. (Reprinted with permission from the American Academy of Pediatric Dentistry, 211 E. Chicago Ave., Ste 700, Chicago, Il 60611-2663, phone 312-337-2169, fax312-337-6329, email aapdinfo@aapd.org, Web site:www.aapd.org)

Dental Management

Sickle Cell Anemia remains a disorder with a high morbidity and mortality rate among patients living in Africa [44]. It has been noted that a number of factors such as climate and socio-economic circumstances may alter the clinical manifestations of SCD throughout the world [1]. Additional inherited factors may also modulate the clinical expression, by interacting with the sickle genotype to either ameliorate or aggravate the clinical picture. In Africa, the environmental factors such as infections (malaria, gastroenteritis), stress, fatigue, injury, air pollution and extremes of weather are of far greater importance in determining the clinical course and survival of individuals with sickle cell disease.

In earlier times, SCD accounted for the misconception of the 're-incarnate' child, which suffered from chronic ill-health after birth, failure to thrive and death before the age of 10 years. Clinical problems resulting from the crises make the patient susceptible to septicemia, meningitis and osteomyelitis. There is a recorded increased incidence of infection by Salmonella species, of which at least 77% were associated with osteomyelitis [1]. The increased susceptibility to infections has been associated with hyposplenism, following repeated splenic infarcts and fibrosis, dead tissue from infarction providing sites for colonization by bacteria, entry of pathogens through areas of micro-infarction in mucosal surfaces, defects of leucocyte function and cell mediated immunity, and hemolysis making iron available for bacterial metabolism [45, 46]. Treatment for malaria and other bacterial infections has interfered with this pattern [14].

Infectious states as well as surgical procedures invariably will require antibiotic coverage [47]. Most dental procedures produce some forms of bacteremia, therefore an antibiotic regimen should be commenced for the patient before and after treatment. If the patient has an acute infection such as an abscess, systemic antibiotics should be given instead of oral medications. However, despite advances in transfusion medicine, anti-infectious prophylaxis and new anti-sickling agents, the morbidity remains considerable and the course of the disease totally unpredictable [44].

The reduced liver and renal functions cause a reduced clearance of many drugs. Treatment should begin only after a thorough investigation has been performed on the patient's background [12]. Therefore a systematic screening of all systems and organs should be carried out before treatment of SCD patients. A good set of intra-oral radiographs must be taken to make a proper diagnosis [23]. As much as possible, treatment should never be initiated during a crisis except it is absolutely indicated, such as in emergency situations to reduce infection and discomfort [48]. Long and extensive procedures are fatiguing and should be avoided.

Local anesthetic is the preferred method of treating the patients when dental surgery is required, as it does not lower the oxygenation of blood. Lidocaine 2% with a vasoconstrictor is preferred if profound anesthesia is required, such as for extraction procedures. If general anesthesia is required, adequate hemoglobin level should be obtained 10-15 days before the operation. Optimum hemoglobin levels obtained for children after blood transfusions should be in the range of 10-12 g/dl [47].

Mental nerve paresthesia is an uncommon sequel of SCD which can occur before or after dental extraction as a result of the vaso-occlusive phenomenon. The dentist should be aware of this sign, document it and such patients undergoing any dental procedure should be warned of the problem in order to avoid litigation [4, 49].

Sickle Cell Disease may compromise the outcome of planned orthodontic treatment [50]. Treatment may initiate bacterial infections, so it should be strictly elective and if it must be carried out, monitored closely. Appliances should be designed to prevent discomfort and irritation of soft tissues.

Above all, preventive dental therapy is the ideal approach for treatment of the SCA patient [12]. It should be initiated as soon as the diagnosis of SCD is made. The goal of the dentist is to improve and maintain excellent oral health and to decrease the possibility of oral infections.

In the technologically advanced countries, the control of SCD depends on prenatal diagnosis by chorionic villus sampling, the identification of the S gene by the restriction enzyme MST II and the termination of affected pregnancies within the first trimester [1]. It is more practical to develop and implement a policy for the screening of all pregnant women by the solubility test followed by Hb electrophoresis on positive samples, and of all newborn infants of women carrying at least one S,C or ß thalassaemia gene by simple micro-column chromatography [51].

The role of the family is important in providing suitable support for the affected to build their self-confidence and enhance the quality of life. The primary role of the health professional is to assist the family to maintain the health of the members of the family born with SCD [10]. The functions of the clinics will be to educate the parents and the older patients, to maintain health and to provide a place where those in crisis may report and receive attention rapidly [10]. The patient and family can be educated by explaining the disease in comprehensible terms, and with the use of posters, booklets, handouts and films. A teamwork, constituting the physician, dental surgeon, the social worker and other health professionals should be encouraged in their management. The Sickle Cell Club in Lagos, Nigeria meets regularly with patients, parents, and health professionals where issues on improvement of their well being are discussed. Genetic counseling is carried out at health centers to discourage carriers from marrying each other. Some religious organizations even demand genotype reports as a pre-requisite to getting married in their denominations.

However, a thorough understanding and the knowledge of the disease had been advocated in order to treat the patient adequately and to instill a positive attitude in the patients and their parents towards maintaining good oral health [12].

CONCLUSIONS

1. There is a higher prevalence of dental abnormalities in people with sickle cell disease than unaffected people.
2. Oral hygiene is poor in people with sickle cell disease.
3. There was no significant difference in dental caries experience between people with sickle cell disease and controls.
4. Height and weight values were not significantly different between people with sickle cell disease and controls; growth deficits become noticeable with age.
5. Mid upper arm circumference was significantly lower in people with sickle cell disease than controls, while there was no difference in the head circumference.
6. Preventive oral health care through a teamwork approach is important so as to improve the quality of life.

REFERENCES

[1] Davies SC, Brozovic M. The presentation, management and prophylaxis of sickle cell Disease. *Blood Reviews* 1989; 3:29-44.

[2] Lagundoye S B. Radiological features of sickle cell Anaemia and related Haemoglobinopathies in Nigeria. *Afr J Med Sci* 1970; 1:315-342.

[3] Barnhart MI et al. *Sickle Cell.* 3rd Ed. Kalamazoo MI (The Upjohn Co) Scope Publication 1979.

[4] Ghassan D, Sammak, A A, Jowder M A, Ahmed Y. Mental Nerve Neuropathy in Sickle Cell Disease. Report of five cases. *The Saudi Dent J.* 1998; 10:123-127.

[5] Behbehani EMH, AL Ramzi AH, Victor DE, AL Waheidi EM. Orthopantomographic studies of the mandible in Sickle Cell Anaemia. *Dent News* 1996; 3:25-29.

[6] Okafor LA, Nornoo DC, Ojehanon PI, Aikhionbare O. Oral And Dental complications of Sickle Cell Disease in Nigerians. *The J. of Vasc Dis.* 1986; 37(9): 672-675.

[7] Akinyanju, O. O. A profile of Sickle Cell Disease in Nigeria. *Annals NY Ac Sc* 1989; 565: 126-136.

[8] 8. Konotey-.Ahulu FID. The Sickle Cell Diseases. Clinical Manifestations including the 'sickle crisis'. *Arch Intern Med* 1974; 133:611-619.

[9] Behrman RE, Vaughan VC eds. *Nelson Textbook of Pediatrics* 1987; Philadelphia. WB Saunders Co.

[10] Flemming AF. The Presentation, Management and Prevention of crisis In Sickle Cell Disease in Africa. *Blood Reviews* 1989; 3:18-28.

[11] Pasvol G, Weatherall DJ, Wilson RJM. Cellular mechanism for the protective effect of Haemoglobins against Plasmodium falciparum Malaria. *Nature* 1978; 274:701-703.

[12] Sams DR, Thornton JB, Amamoo PA. Managing the dental patient with Sickle Cell Anemia: a review of the Literature. *Ped Dent* 1990; 12:316-320.

[13] Rose LF, Kaye D. *Internal Medicine for Dentistry*. St. Louis; CV Mosby Co 1983.

[14] Onwubalili JK. Sickle Cell Disease and infection. *J Infect* 1983;7:2-20

[15] Steinberg MH, Rosenstock W, Coleman M. Effects of thalassemia and microcytosis on the hematologic and vaso-occlusive severity of sickle cell anemia. *Blood* 1984; 64:1353-1360.

[16] Jones JH, Mason DK. Diseases of the blood and blood forming organs. In: *Oral Manifestations of Systemic Diseases*. 2nd ed. Bailliere Tindall. 1990;666-667.

[17] Cox GM, Soni NN. Pathological effects of Sickle Cell Anemia on the pulp. *J Dent Child* 1984; 51:128-132.

[18] Altemus LA, Epps CW. Cephalofacial characteristics of North American Black Individuals with Sickle Cell Disease. *The Qt J Nat Dent Ass* 1974; 32:80-88.

[19] Richard PA. Pathophysiology of dental changes in sickle cell disease. A case report. *J Conn State Dent Ass* 1976;51:20-23.

[20] Sears RS, Nazif MM, Zullo T. The effects of sickle cell disease on dental and skeletal maturation. *J Dent Child* 1981; 48:275-277.

[21] Oredugba FA, Savage KO. Dental abnormalities in sickle cell disease- an ignored oral health problem. *Nig J Gen Pract* 2003;7:9-12.

[22] Soni NN. Micro- radiographic study of dental tissues in sickle cell disease. *Arch Oral Biol* 1966; 11:561-564.

[23] Smith DB, Gelbman JC, Dental management of the sickle cell anemia patient. *Clin Prev Dent* 1986;8:21-23.

[24] Okoisor FE. Oral health status and treatment needs of children with sickle cell anemia. *Nig Dent J* 1984; Suppl 1:39-45.

[25] Oredugba FA. Comparative oral health status of sickle cell disease subjects and controls in Lagos. *MPH Thesis* 2000.

[26] Arowojolu MO, Savage KO, Aken'ova Y. Periodontal disease in homozygous HbSS adolescent Nigerians. *Afr J Med Sc* 1996;25:261-264.

[27] Arowojolu MO, Savage KO. Alveolar bone patterns in Sickle cell anemia and non-sickle cell anemia adolescent Nigerians. A comparative study. *J Periodontol* 1997;68:225-228.

[28] Oredugba FA, Savage KO. Prevalence of dental caries in sickle cell disease: a comparative study from selected health institutions in Lagos. *Nig Dent J* 2002; 3:11-13.

[29] Shnorhokian HI, Chapman DC, Nazif MM, Zullo TG. Cephalometric Study of American black children with sickle cell disease. *J Dent Child* 1984;6:431-433.

[30] Brown DL, Sebes JI. Sickle cell gnathopathy: radiologic assessment. *Oral Surg* 1986;61:653-656.

[31] Serjeant GR, Serjeant BE. Management of sickle cell disease: lessons from the Jamaican cohort study. *Blood Reviews*. 1993;7:137-145.

[32] Shafer WG, Hine MK, Levy BM. *A textbook of Oral pathology. 4th ed.* Prism Books PVT Ltd. WB Saunders Company.1993;726-728.

[33] Konotey-Ahulu FID. Patterns of clinical hemoglobinopathy. *East Afr Med J* 1949; 46: 149-156.

[34] Adekile AD, Awofala S, Adepoju J. Gnathopathy in sickle cell anemia: cephalometric analysis. *Nig Med J* 1990;20:66-70.

[35] Grinnan AG. Roentgenographic bone changes in sickle cell erythroblastic anemia: report of nine cases. *Am J Roentgenol* 1935;34:297-309.

[36] Ashcroft MT, Serjeant GR. Body habitus of Jamaican adults with sickle cell anemia. *Southern Med J* 1972; 65:579-582.

[37] Stevens MCG, Hayes RJ, Serjeant GR. Body shape in young children with homozygous sickle cell disease. *Pediatr* 1983;71:610-614.

[38] Oredugba FA, Savage KO. Anthropometric findings in Nigerian children with sickle cell disease. *Pediatr Dent* 2002; 24:321-325.

[39] Oguntoye AP. Anthropometric status of sickle cell disease. *Community Health Dissertation. MBBS Degree*. University of Lagos. 1981.

[40] Stevens MCG, Mowde GH, Cupidore L, Jackson H, Hayes RJ, Serjeant GR. Pre-pubertal growth and skeletal maturation in sickle cell disease. *Pediatr* 1986; 78:124-132.

[41] Lesi FEA. Anthropometric status of sickle cell anaemia patients in Lagos, Nigeria. *Nig Med J* 1979;9:337-342.

[42] Ashcroft MT, Serjeant GR, Desai P. Heights, weights and skeletal ages of Jamaican adolescents with sickle cell anemia. *Arch Dis Child* 1972; 47:519-524.

[43] Serjeant GR, Ashcroft MT. Delayed skeletal maturation in sickle cell anemia in Jamaica. *Hopkins Med J* 1973; 132:95-102.

[44] Vermylen C, Cornu G. Bone marrow transplantation in sickle cell anaemia. *Blood Reviews* 1993; 7:1-3.

[45] Serjeant GR. *Sickle Cell Disease* 1985. Oxford University Press, Oxford.

[46] Attah Ed'B. The pathology of sickle cell disease. In: Flemming AF (ed) *Sickle Cell Disease: a Handbook for the General Clinician*. Churchill Livingstone, Edinburgh, 1982; 42-56.

[47] Rada RE, Bronny AT, Hasiakos PS. Sickle cell crisis precipitated by periodontal infection: report of two cases. *J Am Dent Ass* 1987;114:799-801.

[48] Smith HB, McDonald DK, Miller RI. Dental management of patients with sickle cell disorders. *J Am Dent Ass* 1987; 114:85-87.

[49] Konotey-Ahulu FID. Mental nerve neuropathy. A complication of sickle cell crisis. *Lancet* 1972; 2:388-389.

[50] Van Venrooy JR, Proffit WR. Orthodontic care of medically compromised patient: possibilities and limitations. *J Am Dent Ass* 1985; 111:262-266.

[51] Powars D, Schroeder WA, White L. Rapid diagnosis of sickle cell disease at birth by micro-column chromatography. *Pediatrics* 1975; 55:630-635.

INDEX

#

A

B

C

D

E

F

G

H

I

K

L

M

N

O

P

Q

R

S

T

U

V

W

X